PURIFICATION OF
INORGANIC AND ORGANIC MATERIALS

Techniques of Fractional Solidification

PURIFICATION OF INORGANIC AND ORGANIC MATERIALS

Techniques of Fractional Solidification

EDITED BY

Morris Zief

RESEARCH LABORATORIES

J. T. BAKER CHEMICAL COMPANY

PHILLIPSBURG, NEW JERSEY

1969

MARCEL DEKKER, INC., New York

PREFACE

In recent years chemists and physicists have centered their attention on the investigation of pure or ultrapure research materials, organic as well as inorganic. In the search for high purity three problems are interrelated—preparation, characterization, and containment. Along with the accelerated development of sophisticated methods in the area of trace analysis, the isolation of ultrapure materials has multiplied at a phenomenal rate. One of the most important preparative techniques is fractional solidification.

Fractional Solidification (edited by M. Zief and W. R. Wilcox) brought together for the first time the basic principles, apparatus, and applications of all types of solid-liquid processes. This volume brings together reliable methods, worked out by experienced investigators, for the preparation of pure materials. The choice of the methods reflects the interests of the editor. The methods were chosen for originality, reproducibility and adaptability to the problems normally encountered in the laboratory. The most useful methods available for zone melting, progressive freezing and column crystallization have been included from the fundamental and applied literature.

The most important methods for characterizing pure inorganic and organic chemicals are also covered. Excellent theoretical reviews of trace analysis have been published by Cali as well as Meinke and Scribner. Here we have been concerned mainly with the practical considerations for the non-specialist. A preparative method for an ultrapure material is meaningless unless adequate analytical characterization is available.

Container materials for ultrapure products have received scant attention in the literature. The pitfalls that must be avoided have been evaluated on the basis of the existing information available.

I am grateful for the assistance and encouragement provided by the J. T. Baker Chemical Company.

M.Z.

CONTRIBUTORS TO THIS VOLUME

E. L. Anderson, *Iron and Steel Industrial Corporation, Ltd., Pretoria, South Africa*

Edward M. Barrall, II, *Chevron Research Company, Richmond, California*

Walter Class, *Materials Research Corporation, Orangeburg, New York*

T. E. Cogswell, *Laramie Petroleum Research Center, Bureau of Mines, U. S. Department of the Interior, Laramie, Wyoming*

M. D. Danyi, *Department of Chemical and Metallurgical Engineering, University of Michigan, Ann Arbor, Michigan*

M. Delmas, *Department of Organic Chemistry, Marseille–Saint Jerome, Marseille, France*

John L. Dewey, *Reynolds Metals Company, Reduction Research Division, Sheffield, Alabama*

Daniel Ecklin, *Neuchâtel University, Neuchâtel, Switzerland*

D. H. Freeman, *National Bureau of Standards, Gaithersburg, Maryland*

C. L. Grant, *Engineering Experiment Station, University of New Hampshire, Durham, New Hampshire*

J. D. Henry, Jr.,* *Department of Chemical and Metallurgical Engineering, University of Michigan, Ann Arbor, Michigan*

M. T. Huckle, *Unilever Research Laboratory, Sharnbrook, Bedford, England*

Julian F. Johnson,† *Chevron Research Company, Richmond, California*

Hisomitsu Kaneko, *Department of Organic Synthesis, Faculty of Engineering, Kyshu University, Fukuoka, Japan*

Roy A. Keller, *Department of Chemistry, State University of New York, College at Fredonia, Fredonia, New York*

* *Present address:* Continental Oil Company, Ponca City, Oklahoma.
† *Present address:* Department of Chemistry, University of Connecticut, Storrs, Connecticut.

W. M. Smit, *Institute for Physical Chemistry, TNO, Zeist, The Netherlands*

K. E. Stine, *Beckman Instruments, Fullerton, California*

Keihei Ueno, *Department of Organic Synthesis, Faculty of Engineering, Kyshu University, Fukuoka, Japan*

W. F. Ulrich, *Beckman Instruments, Fullerton, California*

M. J. van Essen, *Institute for Physical Chemistry, TNO, Zeist, The Netherlands*

P. F. J. van der Most, *Institute for Physical Chemistry, TNO, Zeist, The Netherlands*

Roger W. Warren, *Research and Development Center, Westinghouse Electric Corporation, Pittsburgh, Pennsylvania*

J. C. Wilson, *Solid-State Division and Metals and Ceramics Division, Oak Ridge National Laboratory, Oak Ridge, Tennessee*

TABLE OF CONTENTS

Part II. PREPARATIVE METHODS

Contents of "Fractional Solidification"

PART I
ANALYTICAL METHODS

1 ANALYSIS OF ULTRAPURE MATERIALS

C. L. Grant

ENGINEERING EXPERIMENT STATION
UNIVERSITY OF NEW HAMPSHIRE
DURHAM, NEW HAMPSHIRE

1-1. INTRODUCTION

The continuing demand for materials of very high purity has necessarily been accompanied by a need for methods of detecting and measuring vanishingly low concentrations of impurities. This discussion will consider methods for estimating a variety of impurities from levels of approximately 100 parts per million by weight down to one or less parts per billion; only methods of measuring chemical composition will be considered. However, it should be recognized that structural imperfections can also exert a profound influence on the properties of materials (*1*). Consequently, this presentation does not cover all techniques that may be useful and/or necessary for complete characterization of a high-purity material.

The range of materials of interest includes both inorganic and organic substances. Typical inorganic materials are elements (especially metals), various compounds, and aqueous solutions. Typical organic compounds are crystalline materials as well as biologically active compounds. In this brief section, specific materials will be cited only as examples.

Perhaps the most frequent problem is the measurement of inorganic impurities in inorganic compounds. Both elements and compounds may be of interest, but the demand for information on the former predominates.

1

For organic materials, interest is about equally divided between impurity elements and compounds.

A firm answer to the question "which impurities are present?" can seldom be provided prior to the analysis, although the investigator often knows that certain impurities are more likely to be present than others. Still, the possibility of unsuspected contaminants being introduced during the "purification" process makes it imperative for the analyst to conduct both qualitative and quantitative determinations.

In addition to determining which impurities are present and in what amounts, it is often desirable to determine valence states, extent of chemical combination, and homogeneity on both a macro and a micro scale. For example, the impurities on the surface of a sample may be quite different from those in the bulk of the specimen. Bulk concentration gradients represent another type of heterogeneity.

1-2. SAMPLE SELECTION AND HANDLING

The chemical analyst must work closely with the materials scientist if meaningful results are expected. There is no portion of the total analytical system in which this is more true than for the sampling step. Aside from the more obvious examples of gross contamination through mishandling, many subtle possibilities exist for improper sample selection and preparation. In the realm of contamination, serious problems arise from dust in the laboratory environment, impurities in reagents, and impurities on laboratory apparatus the sample contacts. For liquid samples, containers can introduce either positive or negative errors in the measurement of trace impurities by (a) contributing contaminants through leaching or surface desorption and (b) by depleting concentrations through sorption. For solid samples, cutting and grinding tools invariably contribute contaminants. Excellent reviews on the subject of contamination during sampling and chemical pretreatment have been presented by Minczewski (2), Mizuike (3), and Thiers (4).

Another important aspect is the choice of sample. For a representative determination of bulk composition, a large sample is preferred. When cost and availability factors are not restrictive, samples of 1 g or more are common. If there are no serious problems associated with storing the sample as a solution, this technique affords a convenient means of obtaining aliquots for analysis, possibly by more than one method. Of course, this presupposes that a satisfactory dissolution method is available for solid samples. The notion of using more than one determinative procedure is particularly attractive because systematic errors are more readily found. This is especially true when the measurements depend on quite different principles. Although this approach increases the amount of analytical effort, far more reliable results are collected.

In contrast, a bulk composition analysis can be meaningless for many samples. When macro or micro heterogeneity data are needed, an entirely different approach to sampling is dictated. Because the analytical methods appropriate for such studies usually employ solid rather than liquid samples, and because small quantities of material are analyzed, reproducibility is generally poorer than for bulk analysis. This is true even when contamination due to handling is reduced by analyzing local areas *in situ*. This loss in reproducibility is a reflection of the combined effects of increased sample variability and less precise analytical measurements, rather than being solely due to the latter. Too often, this seemingly obvious fact is overlooked.

1-3. SELECTION OF A METHOD

Because of the large number of impurities and materials under investigation, no single method of chemical characterization is a panacea. It is often desirable or even imperative to use more than one method of determination of an impurity, particularly when development of new sample preparation procedures to meet the special requirements of an analysis is necessary. Even when the determinations are reasonably routine, a single method is often inadequate to generate all data pertinent to a given chemical characterization. For valuable materials, two or more methods will ensure the best possible results on all impurities; a compromise method may be only partially satisfactory for some or all of the impurities. Once again, close liaison will help to assure that the materials scientist receives adequate results.

Selection of methods for trace impurities is often partially dependent on the matrix, i.e., the major constituents of the sample. The magnitude of a signal for a given concentration of analyte may vary with the matrix. Suppose, for example, that we excited equal quantities of silicon and then sodium chloride in a dc arc for emission spectrographic analysis. If each sample contained 1 ppm of iron, the intensity of radiation from excited atoms of iron would be different because vaporization and excitation processes would vary in the two matrices. Consequently, it is necessary to use separate standards for each analysis in order to match both the chemical and physical properties of the samples. In some cases, components of the matrix may interfere so seriously that the direct determination of impurities is impossible.

To overcome such difficulties, trace impurities are often separated from the matrix prior to determination. In addition to the elimination of interferences, the enrichment of impurities attendant upon this process often produces considerable improvement in the quality of results. In fact, some determinations would be impossible without chemical preconcentration. Another advantage of separation is the possibility of converting impurities from several different matrices to a common matrix such as a solution containing metals as organic complexes.

Naturally, separation and preconcentration also have certain disadvantages. In addition to the added time and expenses, the most severe limitations are losses and/or gains of impurities during chemical manipulations. Errors of 100% or more are common. It is paradoxical that the lower the concentration of an impurity, the greater the need for preconcentration but the greater the probability of contamination or loss.

A wide variety of separation and preconcentration procedures are in use today. These include (a) wet and dry ashing, (b) volatilization of either impurities or matrix, (c) liquid–liquid extraction, (d) ion exchange, (e) precipitation, (f) electrochemical methods, and others.

1-4. SENSITIVITY AND LIMIT OF DETECTION

Sensitivity and limit of detection are probably the most important criteria in the selection of an analytical method for the measurement of trace impurities. In much of the literature, these two terms have been used interchangeably. Although there is still no universal acceptance of definitions for these terms, there is a growing tendency to recognize a distinction between them (5–9). In this discussion sensitivity is defined as the ability to discern a small change in concentration of analyte at some specified concentration (8). Most analytical methods that are useful at very low concentrations depend on the establishment of a calibration curve relating the magnitude of some measurable signal to quantity or concentration of analyte. As a consequence, sensitivity is directly correlated with the slope, dI/dC, of this curve. In addition, sensitivity is inversely related to the reproducibility of the signal. Thus, high sensitivity requires a large value of dI/dC and a small value of s, the standard deviation of the signal.

Limit of detection is the smallest quantity or concentration of analyte that can be detected "with certainty." Clearly, it depends on an ability to distinguish a difference in signal for a small increment of analyte in comparison to a blank signal. Based on these definitions, the limit of detection is inversely related to the sensitivity. The major difficulty here is obtaining a valid estimate for the standard deviation of the blank signal; the main consideration is the random fluctuation in blank signal, not the average value of the magnitude of the blank signal. Such fluctuations must include all possible variables in the total analytical system (reagents, sample preparation, and so on) rather than just the random electrical noise in the detection system.

The limit of detection also depends on the definition of "with certainty." It is widely accepted that a statistical definition must be used, but there is little agreement on the proper level of confidence. To assume that a single value for the confidence level is correct seems naïve. It is much more realistic to allow each investigator to choose a probability level that suits the requirements of the problem. Even for a given material, it is likely that quite different confidence levels would be appropriate for different impurities, depending on their influence on the properties of the material.

It is virtually impossible to tabulate meaningful detection limits for a given material. Most detection-limit data in the literature have been acquired from synthetic systems that were free of matrix elements. Such data seldom resemble what can be achieved with real samples, although the disparity varies greatly with matrix composition. The problem is further complicated by the lack of uniform definitions for calculating such results. In addition, tremendous variations exist in (a) the purity of different lots of reagents, (b) the cleanliness of laboratory atmospheres and apparatus, (c) the skill of analysts, (d) the extent to which the instrument used approached optimum performance, and (e) the actual quality of different models of a given type of instrument. Consequently, it is usually necessary to search the literature for information on the same or a similar problem, and to modify this information in accordance with the limitations imposed by particular circumstances.

Despite these difficulties, approximate general comparisons of detection limits have been reported, and they are useful as long as their limitations are kept in mind. Morrison and Skogerboe (7) have compared absolute detection limits (weight rather than concentration) for nine analytical methods. All of these techniques are useful for several elements down to 100 ng. Between 100 and 0.01 ng, solids mass spectroscopy and neutron-activation analysis can detect more elements than other techniques.

1-5. ACCURACY AND PRECISION

The accuracy of a method can be defined as "A quantitative measure of the variability associated with the relating of an analytical result with what is assumed to be the true value" (10). In a word, it expresses the reliability of a method. We must accept that the relative accuracy of methods will be poorer at very low concentrations than at higher concentrations. For example, a relative accuracy of $\pm 50\%$ may be quite satisfactory at a concentration of 10 ppb but totally unacceptable at a concentration of 0.1%.

Precision is defined as "The extent of agreement of a series of measurements with their average as frequently measured by the standard deviation. It is essential to express the conditions under which the data have been obtained" (10). Commonly, precision is expressed as the relative standard deviation (sometimes called coefficient of variation), i.e., the percentage ratio of the standard deviation to the mean of a series of measurements. If we accept that a realistic value for the precision of a method, applied to a given material, should include all steps from sampling to final estimation, the difficulty in making general statements for different methods becomes clear. Even if we omit the sampling step, there are many opportunities for variations between different laboratories using the same method.

Literature data on the precision of methods are useful as long as the scientist carefully notes which sources of variability are included in the precision estimates. For example, imagine that one investigator used a 1-g sample of a material. After several chemical manipulations, he obtained an aqueous solution of impurities that was relatively free of matrix elements. He then performed several replicate measurements on aliquots of this solution during a short time interval. The precision estimate from these replicate measurements was 1%. A second investigator employed a slightly modified analytical procedure and a completely different method of evaluating precision. He selected triplicate 1-g samples from five different batches of material expected to vary in impurity content over the usual range of interest. Each of these samples was carried through the complete pretreatment and measurement procedure. Precision was calculated by pooling the estimates of the standard deviation from the replicate samples of each batch of material (11). The precision estimate was 5%. In choosing between these two methods, many investigators would select the first method without reference to methods for obtaining precision estimates. In reality, no objective choice is available from the information presented. However, if ±5% was an acceptable precision for the total method, the second procedure should be selected because the comparable value for the first method could be much greater than 5%.

Some general comparative statements about precision are possible. Usually, methods that employ solutions for the final signal measurement give better precision than direct methods with solids. One reason for this difference is that larger samples are normally used for solution methods. Typical total relative standard deviations of 1–10% can be realized with solution methods, except when impurity concentrations approach the detection limit for the procedure. The total reproducibility of direct methods tends to be poorer (5–50%) because small samples are used and the sampling error becomes large. However, the advantage of solution techniques diminishes at or near the detection limit because of increased likelihood of contamination during pretreatment. This problem is at least minimized for direct methods. Further, direct methods offer information on sample homogeneity that is unavailable for procedures requiring large samples.

The precision of a method is often thought to be an estimate of accuracy. However, a method can easily yield very precise but highly inaccurate results if a systematic error is present. After systematic errors have been eliminated, the accuracy may become quite comparable to the precision if the latter includes all components of random error in the system.

Standards of known composition are normally used to calibrate analytical methods for measuring trace impurities. Such standards may be synthetic, or they may be materials that have been analyzed by several independent methods. Clearly, reliable standards for trace impurities are very difficult to prepare. Consequently, the variety and quantity of standards available are severely limited. Probably no other problem has been a greater deterrent to progress in this field.

A common misconception is that the ease of synthesizing solution standards obviates the need for a wide selection of original standards. Unfortunately, this approach overlooks all the systematic errors that can occur while converting the original sample to a solution. Furthermore, standards of the original material permit a much wider choice in the selection of a method.

1-6. SCOPE

The ability of a technique to determine a large number of elements is an important consideration. Although several methods provide data on several elements, optical-emission spectroscopy and spark-source mass spectroscopy are the premier methods for giving simultaneous information on a large number of elements. Consequently, these two methods are preferred for survey purposes. However, to achieve this breadth of coverage an appreciable compromise in precision and accuracy must be accepted, mainly because of the impossibility of finding optimum conditions for a large number of elements at the same time.

1-7. SPECIFICITY

Specificity refers to the extent to which the measured signal represents only the species being estimated. Many, if not most, methods are subject to interferences by either matrix elements or other impurities in the sample. Attempts to eliminate interferences by sample pretreatment are often successful, but can also introduce new interfering species. When separations are not feasible, theoretical or empirical corrections can frequently be applied. Undoubtedly the most serious aspect of interferences is lack of information about them. A competent analyst can usually eliminate an interference once he knows of its existence. All methods are subject to this difficulty to varying extents depending on the particular analytical problem.

1-8. MISCELLANEOUS CONSIDERATIONS

Factors such as (a) cost and availability of instruments, (b) time required for analysis, and (c) availability of competent analysts may be important determinants in selection of a method. Whether the samples are research samples, and therefore limited in number, or production samples in high volume will influence the choice. For trace analysis of valuable high-purity materials, these considerations should be secondary to the factors discussed earlier.

1-9. GENERAL COMMENTS ON METHODS

Only a few general remarks about specific methods will be offered because detailed information is presented in the ensuing chapters. Common methods for determining inorganic impurities in both inorganic and organic matrices are listed below:

1. *Nuclear methods.* Show very low limits of detection for several elements; are comparatively free of the reagent-blank problem; occasionally can be nondestructive.

2. *Optical-emission and X-ray spectroscopy.* Both applicable to solids, but optical-emission is destructive while X-ray is nondestructive; optical-emission gives moderately low detection limits, while X-ray is not as satisfactory in this regard; optical-emission gives a wide coverage of elements, but X-ray is good for some that are fairly unsatisfactory by optical-emission; electron-probe is a special form of X-ray for analyzing micron-size areas.

3. *Mass spectroscopy.* Spark-source gives very low detection limits; can be applied directly to solids and is useful to distinguish between surface and bulk impurities; broad coverage of elements.

4. *Flame emission and absorption.* Both are used for solutions in broad element coverage; they are complementary for optimum conditions, since one is better for some elements and vice versa; atomic fluorescence, an extension of these techniques, shows very low detection limits for some elements.

5. *Spectrophotometry and fluorometry.* For solutions and some solids; usually depend on chemical reactions to form complexes; lower detection limits for fluorometry than spectrophotometry; blanks sometimes are a problem.

6. *Electrochemical methods.* Various forms of polarography and coulometry are most common for trace analysis; very low detection limits in solution for some impurities.

7. *Thermal methods.* Not for very low detection limits, but very useful for studying chemical combinations of micro inclusions.

Some common methods for determining organic impurities are the following:

1. *Gas chromatography*. Applicable to liquids and gases, also to some solids when combined with pyrolysis; very low detection limits; often must be coupled with other techniques such as infrared absorption or mass spectroscopy to identify separated traces.

2. *Fluorometry*. Many organic species exhibit extremely low detection limits in solution; also useful for some solids.

3. *Mass spectroscopy*. Low detection limits; spectra are often very complex and difficult to interpret; a very useful adjunct to gas chromatography.

4. *Electrochemical methods*. Both polarography and coulometry are useful for dissolved organic species that are reactive.

5. *Thermal methods*. Useful to study phase changes and related properties; good for fairly small samples.

The discussion in this chapter is an attempt to describe the major considerations necessary to an intelligent choice of methods. Careful study of the whole problem should precede this selection process.

REFERENCES

1. N. B. Hannay, in *Trace Characterization—Chemical and Physical* (W. W. Meinke and B. F. Scribner, eds.), Natl. Bur. Std. (U. S.) Monograph 100, 1967, p. 5.

2. J. Minczewski, *Ibid.*, p. 385.

3. A. Mizuike, in *Trace Analysis: Physical Methods* (G. H. Morrison, ed.), Wiley-Interscience, New York, 1965, p. 103.

4. R. E. Thiers, in *Trace Analysis* (J. H. Yoe and H. J. Koch, Jr., eds.), Wiley, New York, 1957, p. 637.

5. J. Mandel and R. D. Stiehler, *J. Res. Natl. Bur. Std.,* **53**, 155 (1954).

6. R. D. Stiehler and J. Mandel, *Anal. Chem.,* **29**, 17A (1957).

7. G. H. Morrison and R. K. Skogerboe, in *Trace Analysis: Physical Methods* (G. H. Morrison, ed.), Wiley-Interscience, New York, 1965, p. 1.

8. R. K. Skogerboe, A. T. Heybey, and G. H. Morrison, *Anal. Chem.,* **38**, 1821 (1966).

9. H. Kaiser, in *Trace Characterization—Chemical and Physical* (W. W. Meinke and B. F. Scribner, eds.), *Natl. Bur. Std. (U. S.) Monograph 100,* 1967, p. 149.

10. American Society for Testing Materials, *Methods for Emission Spectrochemical Analysis,* 4th ed., ASTM, Philadelphia, Pa., 1964, p. 220.

11. W. J. Youden, *Statistical Methods for Chemists*, Wiley, New York, 1951.

2 | OPTICAL-EMISSION SPECTROCHEMICAL ANALYSIS—ARC, SPARK, AND FLAME

C. L. Grant

ENGINEERING EXPERIMENT STATION
UNIVERSITY OF NEW HAMPSHIRE
DURHAM, NEW HAMPSHIRE

2-1. INTRODUCTION

Probably no other analytical method has been used more extensively than optical-emission spectroscopy for the detection and estimation of impurities in high-purity materials. Several reasons account for this popularity. The characteristic line spectra emitted in flames, arcs, sparks, and other sources are highly specific for each element and therefore provide qualitative and quantitative determination of trace impurities. This is not to imply that the method is free of ambiguities, for such is far from the truth. However, an experienced spectroscopist can normally detect and resolve such difficulties.

As a survey method, no other analytical technique is capable of providing so much information for a given amount of effort. As a result of the relatively minimal amount of sample pretreatment required by most samples, contamination levels are held at tolerable levels. A wide variety of sample types and forms can be readily accommodated. Furthermore, approximately seventy elements can be determined in amounts as low as 10 ng, and lower in ideal cases. Photographic recording provides a permanent record available at a later date for information not originally required when the analysis was performed.

Of course, no method is a panacea. It should be recognized that the suitability of optical-emission spectrochemical analysis depends on the requirements of a particular analysis. A general survey method can never be optimized for all elements. Consequently, such survey methods provide only moderately good precision, and the detection limits for various elements may be far from optimum because of compromises required in the procedure for exciting the samples and detecting the radiation. Survey methods also suffer from a lack of adequate standards. Consequently, quantitative analysis is generally less precise and accurate as the number of elements to be determined is increased. Still, the precision and accuracy are usually adequate for survey work. For more specific problems, the use of photoelectric recording and/or other refinements usually provide sufficiently precise and accurate data at the trace-element level.

Optical-emission spectrochemical analysis has moderately good detection capability for extremely small samples and very good capability for large samples. When the sample is plentiful, a large spectrograph with high resolution is required, whereas a small spectrograph with very high speed is necessary for optimum performance with micro samples.

Flame photometry is usually considered as a separate subject, primarily because different instrumentation is employed when a flame is the source. The reason for this difference is that the lower temperatures of flames compared to arcs or sparks provide a simpler spectrum. High-energy lines are not excited in most flames. Therefore, a much simpler monochromator can be used for resolution of the emitted radiation. Nonetheless, the fundamental principles underlying both techniques are the same. With the advent of increasingly hotter flame sources, the line of demarcation between these techniques is no longer sharp.

2-2. BASIC PRINCIPLES

Since the principles of optical-emission spectroscopy have been discussed in several texts (1–7), only the fundamentals will be presented here. In 1944 Churchill (8) stated that "because of the almost unlimited number of combinations and permutations of electrical, optical, chemical, and physical variables possible in a spectrochemical analysis, and because of the interdependence of these variables on each other, there is no optimum value for any one of the variables except in relation to all of the others." In view of this limitation, many of the generalities described in the following paragraphs would have to be modified in applying them to specific situations.

Atomic line spectra are produced when a large amount of energy is added to atoms in the "ground state." The introduction of this energy results in some electrons moving from their normal energy levels to higher energy levels. In this form, the atom is said to be "excited." When the electrons return to their normal energy levels, they release energy stepwise in the form of light. Since each step accounts for a definite amount of energy, the light produced has a specific frequency associated with each step. Because the atomic structure for each element is different, the frequencies of spectral lines produced for each element are also different and therefore serve as a fingerprint for that element.

The number of spectral lines produced for any element is a function of the atomic structure; elements having comparatively few electrons produce comparatively simple spectra (alkalies and alkaline earth metals). In contrast, an element such as uranium produces thousands of discrete lines of widely varying wavelengths. Clearly, the analytical problems associated with elements that produce spectra with thousands of lines are much more severe than for elements with simpler spectra. Spectral interference (incomplete resolution of lines of similar wavelengths) can present difficulties, and limits of detection are generally poorer because the lines are less intense.

Analysis by optical-emission spectroscopy involves four main steps: (a) vaporization and excitation, (b) resolution of emitted radiation into constituent wavelengths, (c) recording spectral lines, and (d) interpretation.

A. Vaporization and Excitation

The energy required to excite lines originating from electron transitions in the neutral atom (often called arc lines) of most elements commonly studied by this technique ranges between 1 and 10 eV. To excite lines originating from electron transitions in ions (often called spark lines) the energy must be greater than the ionization potentials of the neutral atoms, which range from 3.89 eV for cesium to 24.48 eV for helium. Meggers (9) pointed out that none of the elements commonly determined have ionization potentials greater than about 10 eV. This relatively low energy requirement permits different sources of excitation to be used successfully.

In flame sources, the vaporization step is largely thermal. When a solution of a metal salt is aspirated into a flame in the form of minute droplets, the solvent evaporates and deposits small particles of salt residue. Decomposition and vaporization of these salt particles produce a vapor containing atoms and molecules. The atoms are then excited by inelastic collisions with high-velocity molecules liberated by chemical reaction between the fuel gases.

Many types of flames have been used. Among the most common ones are air–acetylene, oxy–hydrogen, and more recently, nitrous-oxide–acetylene. Flame temperatures between 2000 and 4800°K have been observed for various flame combinations. Since the flame must decompose the compounds into gaseous atoms or molecules, flame temperature is of great importance. In most early work, low-temperature flames were employed. For this reason the flame has traditionally been considered suitable only for easily vaporized and excited elements such as the alkalies and alkaline earths. However, Fassel *et al.* (*10, 11*) showed that many elements that tend to form stable oxides in normal stoichiometric flames could be dissociated to produce analytically useful atomic populations in a fuel-rich oxygen–acetylene flame. Recently, Pickett and Koirtyohann (*12*) have reported the successful use of the nitrous-oxide–acetylene flame for the emission determination of many elements previously considered to be too refractory for analysis by this method. Elements such as aluminum, molybdenum, titanium, tungsten, and zirconium have been detected at concentrations of 1 ppm or less in solution. This breakthrough, coupled with the comparative simplicity of spectra excited by a flame source and the inherent reproducibility of the flame for quantitative work, suggests a bright future in the field of trace analysis.

Traditionally, the dc arc has been considered the most sensitive source for trace element analyses by emission spectroscopy. One reason for this high sensitivity lies in the fact that comparatively large samples (100 mg or even more in some cases) can be employed with dc arc excitation. In addition, the electrode is heated very rapidly, thus very efficiently vaporizing the sample. Consequently, the density of emitting atoms in the analytical gap is greater than for most methods of excitation. The major drawback of this source is the oft repeated statement that it suffers from a lack of precision. Although it is true that the relative standard deviation of many determinations in the dc arc may be ±25–50%, it is also true that such precision is often adequate for trace-element survey analyses. For more specific problems, the precision can normally be appreciably improved.

Particulate samples, such as powders, drillings, and the like, are normally placed in the crater of a supporting graphite or carbon electrode. Two typical electrode shapes are shown in Fig. 2-1(a) and (b). The selection of carbon and graphite as electrode materials is based on the fact that they are electrically conductive, readily obtained in high purity, and easily machined; the carbon vapor produced does not depress the excitation characteristics of the arc, since the ionization potential of carbon is greater than that of most elements determined by this method.

A large variety of electrode shapes provides certain desirable charac-

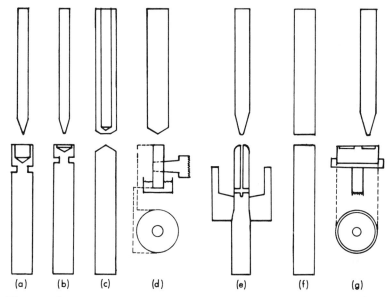

Fig. 2-1. Cross-sectional diagrams of a few common electrode combinations.

teristics for various types of sample matrices. Many of these electrode shapes are discussed by Mitteldorf (13). Although the majority of electrodes are made of graphite, carbon attains higher temperatures because its crystal structure makes it a poorer conductor of both heat and electricity. The main disadvantage of carbon is that it is more difficult to machine because of hardness and brittleness.

One of the major causes of the poor precision of the dc arc is the tendency of the arc to wander in a nonrandom manner. Since the crater containing the sample is analogous to a small distillation vessel, any fixation of the arc at one or a few spots on the anode results in temperature gradients that promote selective volatilization of the sample. Many techniques have been used to control this instability. Electrode geometry and current control are important factors that should be optimized for a particular matrix. Another technique in stabilizing the discharge is the use of a "spectroscopic buffer." In addition to providing steadier and more reproducible arc burns, these buffers, usually compounds containing elements having low ionization potentials, reduce the effective excitation temperature of the arc and increase the population of neutral atoms. Enhancement of spectral lines originating from these atoms results.

Another important development in the control of dc arcs was the Stallwood Jet (14, 15). In this device a sheath of gas is blown up and around the electrode pair, thereby reducing diffusion of air into the analytical gap. Gas mixtures such as argon–oxygen eliminate the troublesome cyanogen bands that interfere with large areas of the spectrum. The flowing gas also serves to reduce arc wandering and selective volatilization. Inert gases such as argon or helium often provide large gains in sensitivity for certain elements (*16, 17*).

Sometimes it is desirable to take advantage of selective volatilization. By promoting the volatilization of certain elements during a specific time period of the discharge, and opening the shutter to the spectrograph only during this period, the line-to-background ratio for those elements is significantly improved. Compounds are often added to induce chemical reactions which promote or reduce selective volatilization. Perhaps the best example is the carrier-distillation method first described by Scribner and Mullin (*18*). A comparatively large sample (100 mg) is mixed with a carrier such as gallium oxide or silver chloride and then packed into a deep-cratered electrode (Fig. 2-2). A special tool is used to place a vent hole in the center of the sample to permit a smooth evolution of volatile gases after the arc is struck. The electrode geometry is especially chosen to reduce heat loss from the sample-containing anode. For matrix materials, such as uranium, that are capable of flooding the spectrum with lines, great enhancement of sensitivity can be realized for the impurity elements by keeping the refractory matrix in the electrode while the impurities are transported into the excitation zone with the carrier.

Another dc-arc technique for trace analysis is the "cathode layer" (the sample is placed in the cathode rather than in the anode). Strock (*19*) reported sensitivity increases by a factor of 100 for some elements in certain matrices when only the light from an area 1 to 2 mm high and directly adjacent to the cathode tip was admitted to the spectrograph. The enhancement is greatest for elements of low ionization potentials. It is generally thought that only small samples (1–5 mg) can be used for this technique. However, Mitteldorf (*20*) has questioned the necessity of restricting sample size in view of the success achieved in the analysis of high-purity graphite and carbon electrodes by this method.

The high-voltage spark is generally considered to provide improved precision but less sensitivity; it is usually employed where precision is the more important characteristic of the analysis. Improved precision with a spark discharge is largely attributable to the constant reignition of the discharge, thereby improving the random sampling of the surface being analyzed. The poorer sensitivity compared to a dc arc discharge is largely caused by the fact that the electrodes remain relatively cool and considerably less sample is consumed. However, this also offers the advantage that metal specimens can be used as self-electrodes, a useful con-

Fig. 2-2. Electrodes for the carrier distillation method (sample and vent hole shown).

venience for comparing surface composition with bulk composition. An excellent review of the characteristics of spark discharges was recently published (*21*).

B. Resolution of Emitted Radiation

Many successful arrangements employing prisms or gratings have been developed for resolving emitted light into its component wavelengths. For a thorough treatment of this subject, the reader is referred to the text by Sawyer (*7*). Only a few points of special interest for trace and micro analysis will be considered here.

One of the most important properties of a spectrograph is adequate dispersion, usually expressed as the reciprocal linear dispersion in Å/mm. According to Mitchell (*22*), "it is in general not the elements to be determined, but the source to be used and the composition of the material to be examined, insofar as its major constituents are concerned, which decide the instrument to be used." As the number of lines produced by the major components increases, the reciprocal linear dispersion must decrease so that lines from the matrix material will not interfere with analytically important lines.

Sensitivity is directly related to dispersion. Line-to-background ratio is most often the factor limiting sensitivity. Ths rato increases as the reciprocal linear dispersion decreases because the same amount of background is spread over a larger area while the line remains unaffected. Jarrell (23) emphasized that this increase in sensitivity occurs only up to the critical dispersion at which the slit and line widths are equal. Further reduction in the reciprocal linear dispersion actually decreases line-to-background ratio. Figures 2-3 and 2-4 illustrate these relationships.

A second factor of particular interest is speed, which we can approximately define as light yield. Mitteldorf (24) pointed out that dispersion is the most critical factor governing sensitivity in bulk samples but speed is most important for microsamples. Thus, we normally accept the poor optical speed (typically $f/30$) of a large spectrograph where sample size is unlimited; for the analysis of microsamples we normally employ smaller instruments to achieve high speed (typically $f/10$).

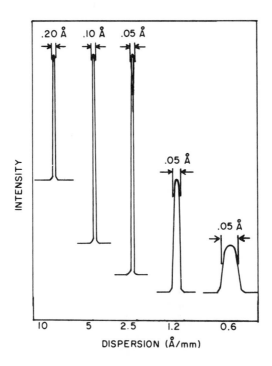

Fig. 2-3. Variations of spectral-line and background intensities with dispersion, for a slit width of 20 μ. (Courtesy Jarrell–Ash Company.)

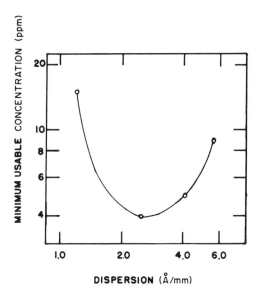

Fig. 2-4. Sensitivity-dispersion relationship for the determination of cadmium in zinc. (Courtesy Jarrell–Ash Company.)

C. Recording Spectral Lines

Spectral lines are normally recorded either photographically on films and plates or photoelectrically. For photographic detection, a wide variety of emulsions have been developed to cover various wavelength regions with different speed and resolving power. For survey analyses, emulsions having moderate contrast but rather high speed are best. For quantitative analysis, however, an emulsion of high contrast is usually preferred to improve the precision of intensity measurement.

Direct photoelectric recording of spectral intensities is considerably more precise than photographic recording and is therefore often the method of choice for quantitative work. Inasmuch as direct readers lack the flexibility required for a survey instrument, it is unlikely that photographic recording will become obsolete in the immediate future.

D. Interpretation

In qualitative analysis, spectral lines emitted by an excited sample are generally photographed. When only a few specific elements are sought, their lines are usually identified by comparison with spectra of the pure elements photographed in juxtaposition. For a general qualitative analysis, it may be necessary to determine the wavelengths of lines by precisely measuring the distances that separate them from lines of known wavelength. A detailed knowledge of possible spectral interferences is essential to unambiguous qualitative analysis of complex spectra.

Quantitative analysis is based on the fact that the intensity of a spectral line of an element is a function of the amount of that element in the source. To obtain a relative measure of intensity, photographic densities can be measured by a densitometer or microphotometer. These values are converted to relative intensities by means of an emulsion-calibration curve relating these two variables. Strock (25) indicated some of the difficulties in this procedure and emphasized that photographic intensities are only relative measures of light-source intensities. Nonetheless, reliable quantitative work can be performed photographically. Direct-reading instruments with photoelectric detectors eliminate many errors inherent in photographic procedures.

Apparently, quantitative analysis should involve only the construction of an analytical calibration curve relating the intensity of a line to the known amount of the element responsible for that line in a series of standards. However, because of the multitude of factors that affect the total amount of light emitted by a given weight of an element, it has been necessary in most applications to employ the principle of internal standardization first introduced by Gerlach (26) in 1925. In this procedure, concentration of the element to be determined is measured in terms of the ratio of the intensity of the analysis line to the intensity of a "homologous" line of another element present in fixed concentration in all samples and standards. Uncontrollable fluctuations that affect the intensities of both lines to the same extent should not affect the intensity ratio between them. Unfortunately, complete success has never been attained in efforts to find line pairs whose intensity ratios are insensitive to changes in chemical and physical composition of the sample. If possible, all lines selected should be free from self-reversal. In most cases, they must be free of interference by lines of other elements, although satisfactory corrections can occasionally be applied. Obviously, compromises are necessary in general-purpose methods. Despite some limitations, the internal-standard principle placed quantitative analysis on a firm foundation.

A successful quantitative analysis depends on the availability of standard samples for calibration. The lack of primary standards for many materials is therefore a problem of utmost concern. The use of secondary standards that have been analyzed by other methods is sometimes satisfactory, although the likelihood of serious bias exists if samples have been analyzed by only one laboratory. When several laboratories participate in a standardization program, there is seldom good agreement in analytical data, particularly for trace elements. This is particularly true for powders, which are apt to be heterogeneous. Consequently, standards are often synthesized from high-purity chemicals in individual laboratories. In this connection, solution methods have the advantage of homogeneity; powder standards are likely to fractionate on standing because of differences in particle size, and density and because of electrostatic effects.

After a satisfactory method has been developed, close control must be maintained over calibration curves, which are subject to shifts caused by environmental and other factors. It is common practice in many laboratories to expose one or more standards along with samples each time a set of analyses is made. Another approach involves the use of statistical quality-control procedures.

2-3. A TYPICAL METHOD

Let us attempt to summarize the information presented in the previous sections by considering the steps necessary to conduct a typical analysis. For this purpose, assume that we plan to use a dc arc for the qualitative and subsequent quantitative determination of elements A, B, and C in some solid matrix Z. Let us further imagine that the matrix Z is a powder of such a composition that a moderately complex spectrum will result.

Our first requirement is to ensure that the spectrograph provides sufficient resolving power and adequate speed for the detection and estimation of elements A, B, and C in Z. This means that we must be able to locate sensitive lines of A, B, and C free from interferences by lines of the matrix elements. Further, we must be able to detect A, B, and C down to concentration levels important in the analysis.

If little or nothing is known about the sample, the powder is mixed with graphite and packed into an electrode that serves as the anode. The sample will then be vaporized and excited in such a manner as to assure complete vaporization of elements A, B, and C, and the spectrum will be recorded photographically. If a master plate with labeled lines for elements A, B, and C has not been previously prepared, we might possibly record spectra of the pure elements A, B, and C in juxtaposition to the sample. After developing the photographic plate, lines of the desired elements would be looked for and, if detected, would serve as a confirmation of the presence of these elements in the sample.

For quantitative analysis, we must assume that prior work has established a proper method. Most likely, such a method requires mixing weighed portions of sample and some buffer–internal-standard mixture. The buffer provides good burning characteristics of the discharge, and the internal standard has lines suitable for taking care of uncontrollable fluctuations. In addition to preparing the sample, we must have available a series of standards containing the elements A, B, and C in varying, known concentrations. These standards must be mixed with the buffer–internal-standard mixture in the same ratio as the sample to be analyzed. Both the sample and the standards are excited in the same manner and recorded on the same photographic plate. After careful development of the photographic plate, the analytical lines for elements A, B, and C and the internal-standard lines are labeled and their densities measured. The densities are converted to intensities with an emulsion-calibration curve. The intensity ratios of analytical lines for A, B, and C relative to the selected internal-standard lines are calculated and plotted on log-log paper versus the respective concentrations of A, B, and C in the standards. The intensity ratios for the unknown concentrations in the sample are then read from the appropriate calibration curves.

For the analysis of large numbers of samples, direct-reading spectrometers are generally used to reduce the effort required on the part of the analyst. For example, many large direct-readers have been connected directly to computers that automatically plot calibration curves and interpolate results for unknowns. Concentration results for many elements are printed in a matter of minutes for each sample. To justify such equipment, however, a large volume of similar samples must be analyzed.

2-4. SOME PRACTICAL CONSIDERATIONS

A. Detection Limits

Some specific procedures necessary to achieve improved detection limits have beeen discussed by DeKalb et al. (27). In addition, several tabulations of comparative detection limits with different techniques have been published (27, 28). It should be remembered, however, that most of these detection limits are reported for ideal situations in which there is no matrix interference or other limiting characteristic. Furthermore, such limits of detection do not represent concentrations that can be determined with quantitative precision and accuracy comparable to that expected for higher concentrations. In general, the detection limits in emission spectrochemical analysis are competitive with almost any other analytical technique.

Aside from instrumental improvements in line-to-background ratio, detection limits can also be improved by sample preparation and excitation techniques. Manipulative procedures that provide enrichment of the analyte have been widely used. Naturally, the admonition to avoid contamination becomes increasingly strong as the extent of chemical pretreatment increases. Excellent reviews of techniques such as volatilization, liquid–liquid extraction, ion exchange, precipitation, and electrochemical methods have been presented by Minczewski (29) and Mizuike (30).

B. Analysis of Solutions

Occasionally, samples to be analyzed for trace impurities are already in the form of solutions. Although most samples are solids, conversion to solutions is advantageous in order to destroy any past history of the sample (segregation or physical characteristics) that might influence the vaporization characteristics in an excitation source. Another advantage of solutions is the ease of preparing synthetic standards. In addition, many of the enrichment procedures such as solvent extraction and ion exchange yield the enriched analyte in the form of a solution. Consequently, much research has been conducted on methods for analyzing solutions by emission spectroscopy.

Solution methods can be classified in two general categories: true solution and solution residue. With flame excitation, solutions offer the most convenient form of introducing the sample into the discharge. For dc-arc analysis, solutions are added to crater electrodes and evaporated to a residue prior to analysis. This technique has never been widely used. The spark discharge, however, has been used for both true-solution and solution-residue methods.

In the porous-cup technique developed by Feldman (*31*) a solution slowly percolates through the porous bottom of a hollow electrode [Fig. 2-1(c)]. After the liquid sample has been placed in the top electrode, a spark discharge is initiated that porosifies the floor of the sample-containing electrode; the sample slowly seeps through onto the bottom of the electrode. Here the discharge vaporizes and excites the residue to produce the emission spectrum.

Another very versatile true-solution method involves the use of a rotating graphite disk that dips into the solution to be analyzed and transports fresh solution on its periphery into the spark excitation zone [Fig. 2-1(d)]. This method was popularized by Applied Research Laboratories, Glendale, California (*32*). One advantage of this method in comparison to the porous cup is that a wider variety of source conditions can be employed without overheating.

Flickinger, Polley, and Galletta (*33*) described a method in which the solution is held in a polyethylene vial cap fitted tightly around a center-post electrode. The solution feeds through a small hole in the outer electrode wall and bathes the center post, which conducts it to the analytical gap by capillary action. A modification of this technique in which the electrode has a small hole drilled in the top for conducting the solution was described by Zink (*34*) [Fig. 2-1(e)].

A discussion of true-solution methods should also include the plasma jet, sometimes called the gas-stabilized dc arc (*35, 36*). In this procedure the solution is aspirated into a chamber by an inert gas under pressure and then swept through a small orifice into a dc arc discharge. When the gas flow is increased through the orifice, the electrical conductivity of the jet rises, resulting in a high temperature at the core of the discharge. The particular advantage of this discharge, in addition to providing excellent sensitivity, is the stability. Precision values are much improved over a conventional dc arc. A commercial version of this device has been described (37).

For very small samples, solution methods may be impractical because of the volume required for analysis. In such situations, residues from the evaporation of these solutions can be analyzed. Several methods of dc-arc excitation are amenable to the analysis of solution residues. However, the best-known solution residue method is probably the copper-spark technique of Fred, Nachtrieb, and Tomkins (38). A hydrochloric acid solution containing a very small amount of sample (<0.2 mg) is applied to the end of a high-purity copper rod and dried. The sample is then subjected to spark excitation. Very low limits of detection have been obtained with this procedure (27). Of course, copper cannot be determined; and solvents that react with copper cannot be used. In an attempt to circumvent this limitation, Pickett and Hankins (39) used graphite electrodes treated with paraffin dissolved in toluene [Fig. 2-1(f)]; but this coating was not impervious to the perchloric acid solutions they wished to use. Morris and Pink (40) achieved detection limits in the low millimicrogram range for several elements evaporated from aqueous solutions containing little or no acid by treating graphite electrodes with Apiezon-N grease dissolved in ether. This method has been referred to as the graphite-spark technique. Another variation of this technique is the rotating "platrode" developed by Rozsa and Zeeb (41) wherein a graphite disk is substituted as the bottom electrode so that solution volumes up to 0.5 ml can be evaporated [Fig. 2-1(g)].

C. Precision and Accuracy

Any discussion of the precision and accuracy of spectrochemical methods in general is doomed to failure because of the tremendous variations to be expected with different procedures and different types of samples. If we remember that the precision and accuracy should include the sample preparation steps as well as the actual spectrochemical analysis and if we assume that reliable standards are available, then it is probably reasonable to "guesstimate" a best possible relative precision and accuracy of ±5% for trace determinations. Under less than optimum conditions, the precision and accuracy will be poorer. It is critically important to match the methodology to the requirements of the analysis at hand.

REFERENCES

1. L. H. Ahrens and S. R. Taylor, *Spectrochemical Analysis,* Addison-Wesley, Reading, Mass., 1961.

2. G. L. Clark, ed., *Encyclopedia of Spectroscopy,* Reinhold, New York, 1960.

3. G. R. Harrison, R. C. Lord, and J. R. Loofbourow, *Practical Spectroscopy,* Prentice-Hall, New York, 1948.

4. C. E. Harvey, *Spectrochemical Procedures,* Applied Research Laboratories, Glendale, Calif., 1950.

5. G. H. Morrison, ed., *Trace Analysis,* Wiley-Interscience, New York, 1965.

6. N. H. Nachtrieb, *Principles and Practice of Spectrochemical Analysis,* McGraw-Hill, New York, 1950.

7. R. A. Sawyer, *Experimental Spectroscopy,* 3rd ed. Dover, New York, 1963.

8. J. R. Churchill, *Ind. Eng. Chem. (Anal. Ed.),* 16, 653 (1944).

9. W. F. Meggers, *J. Opt. Soc. Amer.,* 31, 39 (1941).

10. V. A. Fassel, R. H. Curry, and R. N. Kniseley, *Spectrochim. Acta,* 18, 1127 (1962).

11. V. A. Fassel and V. G. Mossotti, *Anal. Chem.,* 35, 252 (1963).

12. E. E. Pickett and S. R. Koirtyohann, *Spectrochim. Acta,* 23B, 235 (1968).

13. A. J. Mitteldorf, *The Spex Speaker* (Spex Industries, Inc.), II, No. 3 (1957) and X, No. 1 (1965).

14. B. J. Stallwood, *J. Opt. Soc. Amer.,* 44, 171 (1954).

15. A. J. Mitteldorf, W. H. Champs, E. C. Snooks, and D. M. Shaw, *The Spex Speaker,* (Spex Industries, Inc.), VII, No. 3 (1962).

16. R. L. Rupp, G. L. Klecak, and G. H. Morrison, *Anal. Chem.,* 32, 931 (1960).

17. G. H. Morrison, R. L. Rupp, and G. L. Klecak, *Ibid.,* 32, 933 (1960).

18. B. F. Scribner and H. R. Mullin, *J. Res. Natl. Bur. Std.,* 37, 379 (1946).

19. L. W. Strock, *Spectrum Analysis with the Carbon Arc Cathode Layer,* Adam Hilger, London, 1936.

20. A. J. Mitteldorf, *The Spex Speaker* (Spex Industries, Inc.), VI, No. 1 (1961).

21. J. P. Walters and H. V. Malmstadt, *Anal. Chem.,* 37, 1484 (1965).

22. R. L. Mitchell, *Commonwealth Bur. Soil Sci. (Gt. Brit.) Tech. Commun.* 44, (1948).

23. R. F. Jarrell, in *Encyclopedia of Spectroscopy* (G. L. Clark, ed.), Reinhold, New York, 1960, p. 243.

24. A. J. Mitteldorf, *ibid.,* p. 308.

25. L. W. Strock, *Spectrochim. Acta,* 1, 117 (1939).

26. W. Gerlach, *Z. Anorg. Allgem. Chem.,* 142, 383 (1925).

27. E. L. DeKalb, R. N. Kniseley, and V. A. Fassel, *Ann. N. Y. Acad. Sci.,* 137, 235 (1966).

28. G. H. Morrison and R. K. Skogerboe, in *Trace Analysis* (G. H. Morrison, ed.), Wiley-Interscience, New York, 1965, p. 1.

29. J. Minczewski, in *Trace Characterization—Chemical and Physical* (W. W. Meinke and B. F. Scribner, eds.), Natl. Bur. Std. (U. S.) Monograph 100, p. 385 (1967).

30. A. Mizuike, in *Trace Analysis* (G. H. Morrison, ed.), Wiley-Interscience, New York, 1965, p. 103.

31. C. Feldman, *Anal. Chem.,* 21, 1041 (1949).

32. Applied Research Laboratories, Inc., Glendale, Calif., *Spectrographer's News Letter,* 2, No. 9 (1948).

33. L. C. Flickinger, E. W. Polley, and F. A. Galletta, Pittsburgh Conference on Analytical Chemistry and Applied Spectroscopy (1958).

34. T. H. Zink, *Appl. Spectry.,* 13, 94 (1959).
35. M. Margoshes and B. F. Scribner, *Spectrochim. Acta,* 15, 138 (1959).
36. L. E. Owen, *Appl. Spectry.,* 15, 150 (1961).
37. A. J. Mitteldorf and D. O. Landon, *The Spex Speaker* (Spex Industries, Inc.), VIII, No. 1 (1963).
38. M. Fred, N. H. Nachtrieb, and F. S. Tomkins, *J. Opt. Soc. Amer.,* 37, 279 (1947).
39. E. E. Pickett and B. E. Hankins, *Proc. Am. Assoc. Spectrographers,* Chicago (1953).
40. J. M. Morris and F. X. Pink, in "Symposium on Spectrochemical Analysis for Trace Elements," ASTM Special Tech. Publ. No. 221, p. 39 (1957).
41. J. T. Rozsa and L. E. Zeeb, *Petrol. Processing* 8, 1708 (1953).

3

SPARK-SOURCE MASS SPECTROGRAPHY

P. R. Kennicott

GENERAL ELECTRIC COMPANY
SCHENECTADY, NEW YORK

3-1. INTRODUCTION

The spark-source mass spectrograph has become the preferred technique for the analysis of trace elements in solids below the limits of emission spectroscopy. Its advantages are its high sensitivity and its ability to determine nearly all elements with essentially equal sensitivity. In this section we will give a very brief sketch of the history of the technique and an equally brief introduction into the design philosophy of the instrument, and then dwell on the principal problems of the technique today. We will then indicate the present-day capabilities of the technique and will predict what may lie in the future.

The beginnings of the spark-source mass spectrograph go back to a paper by Dempster (*1*) in 1936 in which he discussed three possible ion sources that would be suitable for the mass-spectroscopic examinations of solids. These were the vibrating dc source, the pulsed dc source, and the rf spark source. A paper by Shaw and Rall (*2*) in 1947 discussed a spark-source mass spectrograph quite similar to those in use today, but little application work was reported. A paper by Gorman, Jones, and Hipple (*3*) in 1951 discussed a mass spectrometer that used an rf spark source and electrical ratio detecting. Its sensitivity was insufficient for trace applications. Two papers (*4, 5*) from the Bell Telephone Laboratories by Hannay and Ahearn in 1954 mark the beginning of the rf spark-source mass spectrograph as applied to trace analysis. Five years later, papers appeared from two commercial firms, Associated Electrical In-

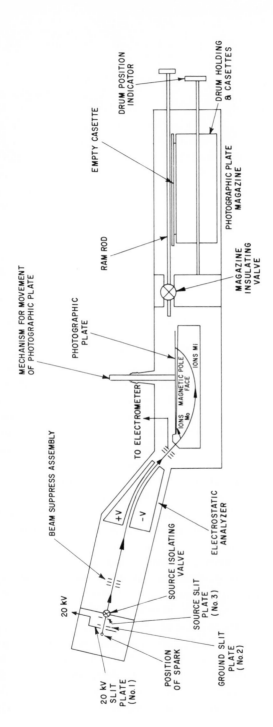

Fig. 3-1. Mattauch–Herzog mass spectrograph.

dustries (6) and Consolidated Electrodynamics Corporation (7), describing the AEI MS7 and the CEC 21-110. At present, instruments are also available from Nuclide Associates, Varian, and JEOL.

Since the description of the Bell Telephone instrument and the commercial instruments, relatively few changes have been made in the basic instrumentation of the rf spark-source technique. Figure 3-1 shows a sketch of a typical rf spark-source instrument. As in any mass spectrometer, three items are required: the source, the mass analyzer, and the detector. In this case, since we are dealing with solids, and wish to ionize each of the elemental constituents of the solid with as nearly equal efficiency as possible, an rf spark is selected for the ion source. The source consists of two electrodes of the material to be analyzed, between which a 1-MHz rf voltage of from 10 to 100 kV is impressed. This voltage is pulsed with a repetition rate from 10 to 10,000 cycles and pulse width from 5 to 200 μsec. The discharge produced by this voltage serves to both volatilize and ionize the sample.

It is a characteristic of the spark source that the total ion production varies rather widely with respect to time. In addition, the energy of ions produced by the source may vary by as much as 3000 volts. These two characteristics dictate the design of the remainder of the instrument. In order to accommodate the wide energy fluctuation, a mass analyzer that focuses in velocity as well as energy is required; to accommodate the varying ion intensities an integrating detector is required. The analyzer selected is the Mattauch–Herzog geometry (8). The locus of the foci of the various masses for this analyzer is, to the first order, a plane located at the exit of the magnetic analyzer. This makes a photographic plate an attractive detector. The plate not only is an effective integrator but also permits the simultaneous collection of the entire spectrum. In order to determine the total exposure to which the plate has been subjected, an electrometer amplifier is fed by a monitor placed between the electrostatic and magnetic analyzers. The monitor thus samples the total ion beam before mass analysis.

By means of the total exposure as measured by the monitor, the sensitivity of the plate can be determined. Thus, the amount of any trace impurity may be measured as in emission spectroscopy. The identity of the impurity is determined from its position on the plate.

The spectrum of an element consists of lines due to each of its isotopes. If the concentration is high, multicharged ions will produce lines in the spectrum at $\frac{1}{2}$, $\frac{1}{3}$, . . . of the actual mass. Lines due to Si^{+7} have been observed from a silicon matrix. Occasionally, molecular ions are also observed. Despite these complications, the relative simplicity contributes to the extreme sensitivity of the technique.

3-2. SAMPLING

The problem of sampling is really several subproblems. Sources of surface contamination are of prime importance. Among the approaches to this problem are cleaning the sample by chemical etching, mechanical means, thermal etching, argon-ion etching, and presparking in the instrument.

Chemical cleaning must be used with care because the reagents employed may contain impurities that are deposited on the sample. The alkali metals are particularly troublesome in this respect. The author has found electronic-grade reagents necessary for cleaning samples; in fact, the distillation of these reagents in Teflon ware before use has appeared attractive. Mechanical cleaning, i.e., the machining of the sample in a lathe with a diamond-pointed tool, seems to be an excellent technique in those cases where the machinability of the sample will permit such a procedure.

Some samples can be cleaned by heating to a high temperature. Since interesting impurities may be preferentially volatilized by this process, this restriction removes much of the general applicability of thermal etching. With some instruments it is possible to perform the thermal etch by electron bombardment in the source. Argon ion etching, a more generally applicable technique, has also been carried out in the instrument source in some cases. It avoids heating and contamination problems.

A somewhat better cleaning technique is pre-sparking in the source. This technique has become routine in many laboratories. One simply sparks as much of the surface of the electrodes as possible prior to the actual analysis of the sample. A reasonable amount of sparking is that necessary to give an exposure of 100 nC, if the ions produced by the sparking are actually measured by the monitor.

The use of rotating electrodes shows some promise in solving this contamination problem (9, 10). If the electrodes were of cylindrical cross sections and could be rotated about the cylinder axes, it would be much easier to remove the surface of the electrodes by presparking, since the rotational symmetry of the electrodes would permit all parts of the surface to be treated alike. The major difficulty in presparking is the runout of the bearings used to support the electrodes inside the vacuum system. It appears that a runout of less than 1 mil will be required (11). If this problem can be overcome, rotating electrodes may offer an extremely convenient way of removing surface contamination from the sample.

A second problem involved with sampling is homogeneity. Because the spark-source technique rarely consumes over 100 mg, this sample may not represent the average composition. Usually spark-source mass-spectrograph results look very poor when compared in precision with techniques sampling more material. One of the solutions is the consumption of more sample in the analysis. A paper by Brown, Swift, and Vossen (*12*) describes a system that will allow the ion beam to be switched on and off with a varying duty cycle. The idea is to consume more material while actually sampling the ion beam over the same effective period of time as before.

A more radical solution to the problem is the chemical homogenization of the sample exemplified by the fusion technique reported by Nicholls *et al.* (*13*). They found fluxes for fusing samples; the fluxes do not interfere with the analysis of impurities (precision within 5%). It should be pointed out that this is a rather special solution but one that should not be ignored when applicable.

In general, chemical manipulation of the sample should be avoided because of the likelihood of contamination. With some samples, however, it is necessary to remove a major constituent while leaving behind the impurities. Examples are water solutions and organic materials.

The first of these preconcentration techniques is the water analysis reported by Ahearn (*14*). The liquid sample was placed by means of a dropper on the end of a clean silicon electrode and allowed to evaporate. This procedure could be repeated several times if necessary in order to obtain a sufficient concentration of material. After the deposit was in place, the electrodes were mounted in the source and the surface layer was sparked in the usual manner.

A new preconcentration technique is the cold-oxygen-plasma asher (*15*), which removes organic material. An oxygen plasma, generated in an rf cavity over the sample, reacts with the carbon and the hydrogen in the sample, thereby removing carbon dioxide and water products and leaving the inorganic elements behind as oxides. With this technique the sample can be kept below 150°C.

A paper by Paulsen and Alvarez (*16*) describes an electrical preconcentration technique; control of these electrical techniques will offer a useful preconcentration scheme. The small amount of material sampled allows one to investigate sample inhomogeneity or surface contamination. One is often faced with the problem of analyzing only a selected portion of a sample, as, for example, when comparing one portion of a sample with another portion. The most straightforward method involves successive short exposures, which gradually consume the electrodes and thus sample different portions of them. Glavin and Lyubchenko (*17*) report an example of such a technique in the distribution of impurities through a GaAs junction. They mounted the sample so that, as the ends of the electrodes were sparked, the region from which the material was sampled progressed through the junction. The author has found the technique feasible with a similar sample. Micrometer screws on the electrode manipulators are useful in indicating sample consumption.

Several workers have experimented with a source in the form of a pointed electrode that is sparked against a plane surface. If the surface and point are stationary with respect to each other, the technique becomes a microvolume sampling method, while if the surface moves with respect to the point, the technique samples a surface layer. Hickham and Sweeney (*18*) have reported experiments in which the plane surface is rotated by a small motor. When the speed of rotation is fast enough so that individual cycles of the rf supply occur on different portions of the surface, it is possible to sample material from extremely thin layers of the plane's surface. They have reported craters due to individual rf cycles of the order of 2000 Å deep.

Another aspect of the sampling problem is the type of source. Dc discharges have been extensively investigated by Franzen, Schuy, and Hintenberger (*19*), and by Honig, Glass, and Woolston (*20*). Perhaps the simplest dc discharge is the vibrating arc. In this source, an arc is initiated by breaking electrical contact between the electrodes. A slightly more complicated arrangement for a dc discharge is to keep the electrodes stationary and to initiate a discharge with a high-voltage trigger pulse. The dc supply is maintained across the electrodes as before. The impedance of the supply can be adjusted to attain the desired discharge time. Finally, it is possible to go one step farther and remove the low-voltage supply. Only the trigger pulse is used to produce the discharge. In this latter case, the discharge is no longer properly regarded as an arc. The advantages of these dc discharges are that the spark is more easily maintained, the production of ions is often higher than that of the rf spark, the energy distribution of ions produced by the discharge is much narrower (100 volts instead of the 3000 volts for the rf source), and material is preferentially sampled from one electrode. A possible disadvantage is that material is transported from one electrode to another. Another disadvantage of the arc source is the character of the spectrum.

The laser suggests itself as a possible alternative to the spark or discharge type of ion source. Lasers have afforded somewhat mixed results. Honig and Woolston (*21*) report using a conventional ruby laser to excite the sample. When an electrical bias on the sample delivered only positive ions produced by the laser discharge at the spectrograph slit, they found that the spectrum approximated that expected from a thermally excited sample in equilibrium at 5000°K. Ion production was low. If the sample bias was reversed so that electrons produced by the laser discharge was accelerated in the direction of the slit, much higher ion production was observed, and the character of the spectrum was that of a long pulse arc.

A number of papers describing the use of lasers in mass spectrometers have appeared (22–26); the future will see more applications of the laser. The laser has an advantage over other sources in that one can select in advance the area of the sample upon which the analysis is to be made.

3-3. INSTRUMENTAL CONTAMINATION

The most troublesome source of instrumental contamination is the atmosphere in which the sparking takes place. Typical constituents of this atmosphere are hydrogen, nitrogen, oxygen, carbon monoxide, carbon dioxide, and various hydrocarbons. Hydrocarbons are troublesome because they appear at a wide number of masses and, in principle, interfere with lines due to elemental impurities at these masses. Fortunately, the relatively high resolution of the Mattauch–Herzog geometry usually separates these lines into doublets. If automatic plate interpretation is employed, however, elimination of the hydrocarbon components of these doublets is desirable. By making a number of changes in the source vacuum system, the author has been able to reduce the hydrocarbon background in his instrument. It was necessary to replace the oil-diffusion pump by an ion pump and to insert a molecular-sieve trap between the roughing pump and the source. In addition, the source is etched by introducing 50 μ of argon and turning on the rf supply for a period of 10 min after each bakeout. Hydrocarbons have been reduced by a factor of 100.

A more troublesome source of atmospheric contamination comes from the oxygen, water, and carbon monoxide in the source. These gases all contribute to lines at masses 12 and 16 and thus interfere with analyses of carbon and oxygen in the sample. Two sources of these gases are the walls of the source and the sample itself. Baking the source is the most effective means of removing these gases from the walls of the source and the surface of the samples; but only an efficient pumping system can cope with the production of gas from the interior of the sample during sparking (27).

A measure of the effectiveness of the removal of the interfering gases is the apparent blank for oxygen, nitrogen, and carbon in a GaAs sample extremely low in these impurities. By giving the source a good bake, the author has measured oxygen at 2 ppm, nitrogen at 1 ppm, and carbon at 0.1 ppm in GaAs. In 1965, Harrington, Skogerboe, and Morrison (28) presented a paper describing the use of cryosorption panels inside the source, where they could pump the gas extremely efficiently. Because of the increased efficiency, their blanks should be significantly below the author's.

Another source of instrument contamination is memory from previous samples. Material is scattered on the inside of the source by the rf spark. If another matrix is introduced into the sample, lines due to the old matrix will be observed on the plate for some time. There are two possible solutions to this problem. Interchangeable liners on the inside of the source may be used for each material, or the work may be scheduled in such a way that a heavy layer of the current matrix may be built up to cover any exposed areas of old matrices. Neither of these schemes is completely effective, but a better solution has not been reported.

3-4. REPRODUCIBILITY

Probably the most important factor in reproducibility is the vacuum within the instrument. A poor vacuum in the source will lead to contamination, but a poor vacuum anywhere in the instrument will scatter ions from the beam and result in charge-transfer lines on the plate. These lines are produced by ions that change their charge state during the passage through the instrument because of collisions with gas molecules. When delivered, the author's instrument had a vacuum specification of 2×10^{-8} Torr in the analyzer. It has actually maintained a vacuum of less than 5×10^{-9} Torr. When the vacuum rises above this level, a distinct deterioration in the reproducibility of analyses is noticed. A similar observation was made in the paper by Harrington, Skogerboe, and Morrison (28).

Poor reproducibility as a result of poor vacuum is probably unnecessary in today's commercial instruments. A problem that still exists is the accurate measurement of the total charge. The beam chopping of Brown, Swift, and Vossen (12) may aid in the solution of this problem. By lowering the duty cycle, it produces an ion beam having a lower average current. This should permit more uniform exposures and thus more accurate measurements of charge. The beam-chopping system helps during sparking also by allowing extremely short exposures to be made without changing the spark parameters.

The author has found additional measures useful in achieving reproducibility. In order to maintain the spark at the same point in the ion optics during an analysis, it is useful to use a telescope with cross hairs at the desired location to observe the spark. The author has also found that maintaining a constant spark gap improves reproducibility. The size of the gap can be estimated by observing the current in the spark circuit. A current transformer is used to obtain the current, and the output is displayed on an oscilloscope synchronized with the spark pulse. The appearance of the display is the rf waveform, on which are superimposed the spikes of the discharge. The position within the pulse of the first appearance of the spikes depends on the spark gap. Thus, the operator merely watches the display and adjusts the gap to keep the position of the first spike constant and thereby maintains a constant gap.

Another aspect of reproducibility is the photoplate and its handling. Since the emulsion must be made as thin as possible, the technique places the most stringent requirements on the photographic technique. Temperatures must be maintained constant in the developing chemicals. Time must be carefully controlled in the developing process. The activity and agitation of the developer must be carefully controlled.

Background fog on the photoplate is a source of poor reproducibility. Two types of fog may be distinguished: a uniform fog over the entire plate due to the emulsion, and a fog concentrated in the region of strong lines in the spectrum. This latter fog is due to charge build-up on the plate, which scatters ions from the beam, and to secondary ions scattered from the plate on bombardment by the primary beam. Anything that will reduce this background while maintaining the desired information regarding the lines will be an advantage. Among the possibilities are the removal of a portion of the plate from the beam (29, 30), the internal-image developer reported by the author (31), and gelatin-free plates (32, 33).

3-5. PLATE INTERPRETATION

The problem of plate interpretation falls into two parts: more rapid interpretation of the plate, perhaps by less experienced personnel, and more accurate interpretation of the plate. Conzemius (34) improved qualitative analysis with a computer program that permits interpretation by relatively inexperienced personnel. The computer takes information on the intensity of each line on the plate and offers an interpretation in terms of a self-consistent analysis. The resulting analysis is not 100% correct, but an experienced worker can quickly spot and correct the mistakes the computer has made.

In quantitative analysis of the plates, an exciting development has been the increased use of automatic systems of plate interpretation. The advantages of automation are the greater rapidity of analysis, the ability to use more of the information on the plate, and the ability to make the resulting analysis self-consistent for all of the input data, thus producing greater precision in the resulting analysis. The author has found an improvement of at least a factor of 10 in the amount of time devoted to the examining of plates, and has noticed an improvement in precision from $\pm40\%$ to $\pm15\%$ using an automatic system (35). The large number of plate-interpretation schemes leads one to believe that the choice is still being made on a matter of personal preference rather than on a technical basis.

3-6. STANDARDIZATION

The final problem to be examined is that of standardizing the technique. When numbers are produced from the plate-interpretation scheme, the mass spectrographer is likely to regard these numbers as the values of the concentrations of the various impurities in the sample. This interpretation is not correct. The mass spectrographer is probably spoiled somewhat by the fact that these numbers are within a factor of 3 of the correct numbers, but he should remember that it is necessary to standardize any analytical technique. Gorman, Jones, and Hipple in their paper (3) define the relative-sensitivity coefficient, i.e., the efficiency with which one ion is produced with respect to another. A set of these coefficients is equivalent to standardization of the technique. Two attempts have been reported to calculate these relative-sensitivity coefficients. Such a calculation, if made practical, would be a significant advance. In the meantime, however, a better approach to the standardization problem is to use a homogeneous standard that is well characterized and for which accurate analyses are available. Recently, the National Bureau of Standards has started a program (36) to produce such standards for the mass spectrograph.

Before leaving the problem of standardization, it should be pointed out that a large amount of work can be done on the basis of relative analyses that does not require standardization. If one is studying the improvement of a material subjected to various purification schemes or if one wishes to compare two samples of the same material, accurate relative analyses are perfectly satisfactory. Indeed, in the author's own work over the past four years, he has yet to standardize any matrix used in the instrument.

3-7. FUTURE DEVELOPMENTS

At the present time the mass-spectrograph technique is capable of providing analyses of electrically conducting samples with a sensitivity of 1 to 3 ppb for most elements. The exceptions are carbon, oxygen, nitrogen, and those elements that may interfere with lines from other elements. The precision of an analysis will be from 10 to 20%; accuracy without standardization will be within a factor of 3. Powders and insulators can usually be handled in a straightforward way if compounding with graphite or a metal powder can be tolerated. Analyses of small areas of the sample can be made, but with some difficulty. Inhomogeneity and contamination are still problems, although one sees hope of a solution.

In the future, sources will be developed that will facilitate the sampling of selected areas of the sample. The current work in source vacuum will hopefully reduce the blank for carbon, nitrogen, and oxygen. There is even a possibility that baking the source can be eliminated with consequent higher throughput of samples. Changes in the monitor amplifier may improve the reproducibility of the technique. The present multitude of plate-interpretation schemes may be reduced to one or two. Finally, we expect the availability of standards to assist in the standardization of the technique in the parts-per-billion range.

This chapter has attempted to present a brief description of the spark-source mass-spectrograph technique and its current problems. Although these problems do not prevent the method from providing useful trace analyses, they do provide a stimulating challenge for workers in the field. Thus, new developments will continue to keep the technique in a state of flux. A newcomer to the field will find personal contact the most useful source of information. At the present time the conferences sponsored by A. S. T. M. Committee E14 are the principal medium for information exchange. Finally, the book by Ahearn (*37*) will be found to be a useful source of information and literature references.

REFERENCES

1. A. J. Dempster, *Rev. Sci. Instr.,* **7**, 46 (1936).

2. A. E. Shaw and W. Rall, *Rev. Sci. Instr.,* **18**, 278 (1947).

3. J. G. Gorman, E. J. Jones, and J. A. Hipple, *Anal. Chem.,* **23**, 438 (1951).

4. N. B. Hannay, *Rev. Sci. Instr.,* **25**, 644 (1954).

5. N. B. Hannay and A. J. Ahearn, *Anal. Chem.,* **26**, 1056 (1954).

6. R. D. Craig, G. A. Errock, and J. D. Waldron in *Advances in Mass Spectrometry* (J. D. Waldron, ed.), Pergamon, New York, 1959, p. 136.

7. C. R. Robinson, G. D. Perkins, and N. W. Bell, Eastern Analytical Symposium, New York, 1959.

8. R. Herzog, *Z. Physik,* **89**, 447 (1934); J. Mattauch and R. Herzog, *ibid.,* p. 786; J. Mattauch, *Phys. Rev.,* **50**, 617 (1936).

9. F. Aulinger, *Proc. Ann. MS7 Mass Spectrometer European Users Conf., 6th, Manchester, 1966.*

10. E. R. Blosser and W. M. Henry, Report to U. S. Navy, Bureau of Naval Weapons, Contract NOw 65-0365-c, p. 22 (1966).

11. E. R. Blosser, private communication.

12. R. Brown, P. Swift, and P. G. T. Vossen, 15th Ann. Conf. on Mass Spectrometry and Allied Topics, Denver, 1967, Paper 56.

13. G. D. Nicholls, A. L. Graham, E. Williams, and M. Wood, *Anal. Chem.,* **39**, 584 (1967).

14. A. J. Ahearn, *J. Appl. Phys.,* **32**, 1197 (1961); P. Chastagner, 12th Ann. Conf. on Mass Spectrometry and Allied Topics, Montreal, 1965, Paper 55.

15. R. Bersin, *LTA-600 Low Temperature Dry Asher Technical Applications Guide,* Tracerlab, Richmond, Calif., 1965.

16. P. J. Paulsen and R. Alvarez, 15th Ann. Conf. on Spectrometry and Allied Topics, Denver, 1967, Paper 57.

17. G. G. Glavin and V. I. Lyubchenko, *Soviet Phys. Solid State (English Transl.),* **7**, 409 (1965).

18. W. M. Hickam and G. G. Sweeney in *Mass Spectrometric Analysis of Solids* (A. J. Ahearn, ed.), Elsevier, New York, 1966.

19. J. Franzen, K. D. Schuy, and H. Hintenberger, 12th Ann. Conf. on Mass Spectrometry and Allied Topics, Montreal, 1964, Paper 39.

20. R. E. Honig, S. S. Glass, and J. R. Woolston, *Proc. Intern. Conf. on Ionization Phenomena in Gases, 6th, Paris, 1963,* Vol. 2, pp. 209–216.

21. R. E. Honig and J. R. Woolston, *Appl. Phys. Letters,* **2**, 138 (1963).

22. J. Berkowitz and W. A. Chupka, *J. Chem. Phys.* **40**, 2735 (1964).
23. A. S. Gilmour, Jr. and F. A. Giori, 13th Ann. Conf. on Mass Spectrometry and Allied Topics, St. Louis, 1965, Paper 60.
24. F. J. Vastola, A. J. Pirone, and B. E. Knox, 14th Ann. Conf. on Mass Spectrometry and Allied Topics, Dallas, 1966, Paper 24.
25. E. Bernal, L. P. Levine, and J. F. Ready, *Rev. Sci. Instr.*, **37**, 938 (1966).
26. N. C. Fenner and N. R. Daly, *ibid.*, p. 1068.
27. A. J. Socha and R. K. Willardson, 14th Ann. Conf. on Mass Spectrometry and Allied Topics, Dallas, 1966, Paper 37.
28. W. L. Harrington, R. K. Skogerboe, and G. H. Morrison, *Anal. Chem.*, **37**, 1480 (1965).
29. A. J. Ahearn and D. L. Malm, *Appl. Spectry.*, **20**, 411 (1966).
30. H. Mai, *J. Sci. Instr.*, **42**, 339 (1965).
31. P. R. Kennicott, 13th Ann. Conf. on Mass Spectrometry and Allied Topics, St. Louis, 1965, Paper 34.
32. M. H. Hunt, 14th Ann. Conf. on Mass Spectrometry and Allied Topics, Dallas, 1966, Paper 58.
33. R. E. Honig, J. R. Woolston, and D. A. Kramer, 14th Ann. Conf. on Mass Spectrometry and Allied Topics, Dallas, 1966, Paper 99.
34. R. J. Conzemius, private communication.
35. P. R. Kennicott, 14th Ann. Conf. on Mass Spectrometry and Allied Topics, Dallas, 1966, Paper 61.
36. National Bureau of Standards (U.S.), *OSRM Bull. 6.*
37. A. J. Ahearn, *Mass Spectrometric Analysis of Solids,* Elsevier, New York, 1966.

4 ATOMIC-ABSORPTION SPECTROSCOPY

J. W. Robinson

LOUISIANA STATE UNIVERSITY
BATON ROUGE, LOUISIANA

4-1. INTRODUCTION

Atomic absorption spectroscopy is concerned with the measurement of radiant energy absorbed by atoms of various elements. Each element in the atomic state absorbs only radiation of characteristic and well-defined wavelengths. In the process of absorption, the atom becomes excited. This is the reverse physical process to that involved in flame photometry or emission spectrography.

This relationship (Fig. 4-1) leads to the principle that all experimental variables that affect the total atom population affect the emission and absorption signal in a similar fashion. All variables that affect the number of excited atoms in that population affect emission intensity; all variables that affect the number of unexcited atoms in that population affect only the atomic-absorption signal. This principle should always be remembered when developing new analytical procedures based on atomic-absorption spectroscopy.

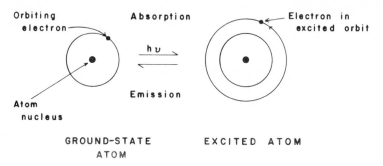

Fig. 4-1. Relationship between absorption and emission.

4-2. ANALYTICAL POTENTIAL

The method is useful for the determination of metals in a wide variety of samples. The sensitivity of the procedure varies from one metal to the next, but is generally in the part-per-million range. Interferences arise from the predominant anion present (chemical interference) and from changes in the matrix or solvent of the sample. However, the method generally suffers from fewer analytical interferences than most other analytical procedures used for the same type of analysis. Direct absorption interferences by other metals present in the sample are virtually non-existent because atoms of different elements do not absorb at the same wavelength. It is therefore capable of providing accurate and precise answers when the analysis is performed properly.

At the present time, no atomic-absorption procedures have been developed for the determination of the nonmetallic elements such as the halides, oxygen nitrogen, and so on. The reason is based on the fact that their resonance absorption lines are in the vacuum ultraviolet. Special equipment would be necessary to work in this part of the spectrum. Such equipment would be expensive and difficult to use. In conventional atomic-absorption spectroscopy the sample is atomized by injection into a flame. This technique limits the sample type that can be handled to liquids. As a consequence, solid samples and gas samples must be converted to liquids before they can be analyzed. This step may involve dissolving or trapping the sample in a suitable solvent.

4-3. EQUIPMENT

In practice, the sample is aspirated into a flame. The flame reduces the components of the sample to atoms. Radiation of the correct wavelength is passed through the flame, and the amount of radiation absorbed by atoms of the sample is measured. The composition of the sample is deduced from the degree of absorption. A schematic diagram of the equipment is shown in Fig. 4-2.

A. Source

The radiation source used is a hollow cathode (1). The absorption lines of atoms are very narrow ($\approx$0.02 Å). Radiation sources of continuous wavelength such as hydrogen lamps are unsuitable for use because the amount of radiation absorbed by the sample from such a source is very small compared to the amount of radiation emitted by the source even over a narrow waveband such as 30 Å. As a result there would be a severe loss in sensitivity. However, hollow cathodes emit very narrow lines, and those that are absorbed by the sample can be strongly absorbed even at modest sample concentration. It is conventional, therefore, to use hollow cathodes as the radiation source. The resonance line absorbed must be that of the element being determined. It is thus necessary to use a hollow cathode made of the same element as that being determined. This necessitates changing the hollow cathode when it is necessary to determine a different element.

B. Monochromator

The function of the monochromator is to select radiation of the correct wavelength and prevent radiation of other wavelengths from falling on the detector. The most common monochromators used are gratings, although quartz prisms can be used. The gratings are usually useful over the wavelength range 2000 to 8000 Å.

C. Detector

Photomultipliers are used almost exclusively in commercial instruments as radiation detectors. The detector measures the intensity of radiation

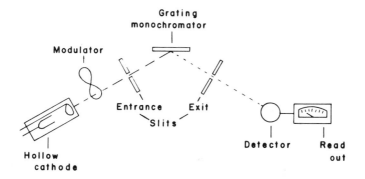

Fig. 4-2. Schematic diagram of atomic-absorption spectrometer.

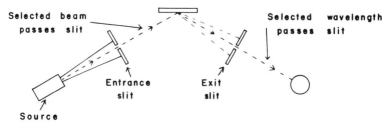

Fig. 4-3. Function of the slits.

from the source, with and without absorption by the sample. The degree of absorption by the sample can be calculated from the difference.

D. Optical Slit System

Two slits are included in the optical system: an entrance slit and an exit slit. The entrance slit serves to obtain a narrow, parallel beam of light from the source. Other radiation is physically blocked out by the walls of the slit. The exit slit is used to select radiation of the correct wavelength after it emerges from the monochromator. Other radiation is blocked out and not allowed to continue down the light path. The function of the slits is illustrated in Fig. 4-3.

E. Modulation

The wavelength at which atoms are absorbed is usually the "resonance wavelength." It denotes a transition from the ground state to the first excited state of the atom. Unfortunately, the atom in a flame also *emits* radiation at this same wavelength in most cases. This is particularly so if the resonance wavelength is below 3000 Å, because radiation can be intense in this region.

This emission could create a problem in measuring the degree of absorption by the sample. For example, examine the following circumstances:

Intensity of radiation from lamp	Intensity of radiation after absorption by sample	Emission intensity by sample
100 units	50 units	20 units

The "observed" absorption would be $100 - (50 + 20)$ units = 30 units. The true absorption was $100 - 50$ units = 50 units.

The flame emission can thus be a serious source of error. It can be overcome by using an ac light source and a detector tuned to the same frequency. Under these circumstances, the detector "sees" the ac light from the source and can measure any absorption of that light; but it does not "see" the dc light from the flame. The flame emission is therefore not measured by the detector, and the source of error is eliminated.

4-4. ANALYTICAL PARAMETER TO BE CONTROLLED
FOR QUANTITATIVE ANALYSIS

The principal analytical application of atomic-absorption spectroscopy is for the *quantitative* determination of metals in narrow compounds. It is not useful as a *qualitative* tool because each element must be examined separately, using a different hollow cathode for each metal. This is a tedious process and can be performed much more efficiently by other methods, such as emission spectrography.

In order to obtain reproducible quantitative results, certain variables in the analytical process must be controlled.

The degree of absorption is described by the relationship

$$\int K\nu \, d\nu = \frac{\pi e^2}{mc} Nf \qquad (4-1)$$

where

$\int K\nu \, d\nu$ = total amount of light absorbed at frequency ν

e = charge of the electron

m = mass of the electron

c = speed of light

N = number of atoms in the light path

f = oscillator strength of the absorption line

It can be seen that for a given absorption line

$$\int K\nu \, d\nu = \text{const} \times N \qquad (4-2)$$

Hence, the degree of absorption is dependent on the number of atoms in the light path. This number, N, is proportional to the number of atoms in the sample and therefore to the concentration of that element in the sample. Hence, the absorption is proportional to the concentration of the element in the sample.

The conversion of atoms existing in the sample as molecules to free atoms is a very inefficient process. A valid arithmetic calculation of N, and therefore the concentration of the element in the sample, cannot be made. Variables such as the efficiency of atomization negate the calculation. The relationship between absorption and concentration is therefore usually determined experimentally by using a calibration curve.

A. Preparation of Calibration Curves

A series of solutions of the sample element are prepared. The concentration of each solution is predetermined by weighing known amounts of a salt of the metal into a known volume of solution.

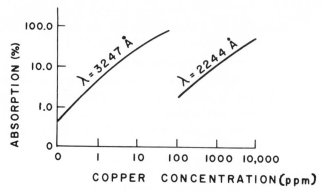

Fig. 4-4. Calibration curves for copper determination.

The atomic-absorption spectrometer is set at the desired resonance wavelength for the metal, and each solution is introduced successively into the flame atomizer. The absorbance is measured for each solution and the relationship is then plotted. The plot constitutes a "calibration curve." Typical calibration curves are shown in Fig. 4-4. The curves indicate the relationship between absorbance and concentration. Hence, we can conclude that

$$\int K\nu\, d\nu \text{ (total absorption)} = \text{const} \times N$$
$$= \text{const}' \times \text{concentration of metal in sample} \qquad (4\text{-}3)$$

When a sample of unknown concentration is to be analyzed, it is introduced into the atomizer and the absorbance measured. From the calibration curve, the concentration corresponding to the measured absorbance is measured; the analysis of the original sample can be determined directly.

B. Interferences

Equation (4-3) shows that there is a relationship between absorbance and concentration, provided that N is proportional to concentration. Any variable that affects the relationship between N and concentration is a source of interference to the method. The most important variables are as follows.

C. Flame Composition

The fuel and oxidant used in the atomizing flame must be the same for the standard and the sample. The flame directly controls the efficiency of producing neutral atoms from the sample after introduction into the flame.

It is also important to keep the type and *ratio* of fuel to oxidant constant for all measurements.

D. Solvent

Organic solvents generally vaporize and burn in flames more easily than aqueous samples. This directly affects the efficiency of producing atoms from the sample. Further, different organic solvents react differently because of variation in viscosity, surface tension, and stability between them. It is therefore important that the solvent used for the calibration curve be the same as that used for the sample.

E. Chemical Interference

In aqueous solutions, the predominant anion determines the chemical form of the sample element prior to decomposition by the flame. For example, calcium chloride is broken down more easily than calcium phosphate. Therefore, calcium solutions that are predominantly phosphate will not decompose in the flame as easily as if the predominant anion was chloride. Calibration curves should therefore be prepared from solution with the same predominant anions as the samples to be analyzed.

F. Flame Position

Atoms are produced rapidly in the reaction zone of the flame. They tend to become oxidized to molecules in the upper portions of the flame. Such molecules do not absorb at atomic-resonance lines. It is therefore important to take all measurements with the optical beam passing through the same part of the flame in all cases.

4-5. ANALYTICAL PROCEDURES

A detailed account of analytical procedures that have been developed for many elements of the periodic table is given elsewhere (*2, 3*). In all methods the sample must be converted to the liquid phase. Many liquid samples, such as water, biological fluids, beverages, and so on, can be analyzed directly. However, gaseous and solid samples must be dissolved or extracted prior to analysis.

After the sample is converted to the liquid state, it is then aspirated into the burner of a commercial atomic-absorption spectrophotometer. The degree of absorption by the sample is observed directly on a dial or recorder. The sample analysis is then calculated by using a calibration curve prepared as indicated in Section 4-4.A. The procedure is relatively simple and requires a minimum of training.

The sensitivity limits for a number of elements are shown below. As a rule of thumb, the quantitative analytical range is usually between 10 and

100 times the sensitivity limits. For example, if the sensitivity limits of an element are 0.1 ppm, the quantitative analytical range should be between 1.0 and 10.0 ppm.

The range can frequently be extended downward by using solvent-extraction techniques, or upward by choosing a different absorption line (2).

4-6. ANALYTICAL SENSITIVITIES OF THE VARIOUS ELEMENTS

Sensitivity is here defined as that concentration of the element which leads to the absorption of 1% of the resonant radiation passing through the atomizer. Reported sensitivities and the corresponding wavelengths are given in Table 4-1. These sensitivities are reported by different workers

TABLE 4-1

Element	Wavelength ($\mathring{A}$)	Sensitivity (ppm)	Element	Wavelength ($\mathring{A}$)	Sensitivity (ppm)
Al	3092	2.0	Mg	2852	0.02
Sb	2175	0.5	Mn	2798	0.01
As	1937	3.0	Hg	2357	10.0
Ba	5536	5.0	Mo	3133	0.5
Be	2349	0.2	Ni	2320	0.2
Bi	2231	1.0	Pd	2474	1.0
B	2497	250	Pt	2148	2.0
Cd	2288	0.04	K	7665	0.1
Ca	4227	0.1	Rb	7800	0.2
Cs	8521	0.15	Se	1961	0.5
Cr	3579	0.15	Ag	3281	0.1
Co	2407	0.5	Na	5890	0.03
Cu	3247	0.1	Sr	4607	0.05
Ga	2944	∼4.	Tl	2767	1.0
Au	2428	0.1	Sn	2863	5.0
Fe	2483	0.3	Ti	3653	12.0
Pb	2170	0.5	V	3184	∼7.
Li	6708	0.07	Zn	2138	0.05

in the field and may vary somewhat with equipment and experimental conditions.

REFERENCES

1. A. Walsh, *Spectrochim. Acta,* **7**, 108 (1955).
2. J. W. Robinson, *Atomic Absorption Spectroscopy,* Dekker, New York, 1966.
3. Jarrell Ash Company, *Atomic Absorption Methods Manual,* Waltham, Mass., 1967.

5 | INFRARED SPECTROPHOTOMETRY

K. E. Stine and W. F. Ulrich

BECKMAN INSTRUMENTS
FULLERTON, CALIFORNIA

5-1. INTRODUCTION

Although infrared spectrophotometry has proven to be a widely used and powerful analytical technique, its acceptance in the realm of trace analysis has been slow. To a large extent the earlier limitations in instrument performance have been greatly improved in recent years. Consequently more attention is being given to the use of infrared procedures for detecting impurities down to the parts-per-million level. Where applicable, infrared can provide advantages in speed and specificity over other methods. Also, the test sample usually can be reclaimed intact after examination and used for other studies.

The discussion here reviews aspects of instrumentation and technique significant in trace measurements. Several applications are described to illustrate its usefulness with different types of samples.

5-2. EXPERIMENTAL PROCEDURES

A. Transparent-Matrix Samples

The simplest trace analyses are those involving highly transparent matrices. In these cases it is usually sufficient to make measurements in the conventional manner but with thicker than normal samples. For example, gases can be analyzed in cells with path lengths of 10 meters or more, liquids and solids with 10–100- and 10–20-cm paths, respectively. The success of this approach depends upon the absence of absorption by major components at the analytical wavelength.

In order to increase sensitivity even further, ordinate scale expansion can be used to advantage. This simply involves electronic expansion of signal so that it is more readable above the background signal. However, inasmuch as the noise level is increased by the same amount, the use of scale expansion depends upon operating conditions that yield low noise. Many of the research-type spectrophotometers are now equipped with scale-expansion capabilities and sufficient control of operating parameters to give proper signal-to-noise conditions.

B. Opaque-Matrix Samples

If only transparent samples could be analyzed, the utility of infrared methods for trace analysis would be seriously limited. Fortunately, development of high-energy double-beam spectrophotometers has extended the capability of the technique, and measurements can be made even when components other than the analyte absorb at the analytical wavelength. Differential techniques are useful in these cases.

Differential analysis essentially involves use of suitable materials in the reference beam of the spectrophotometer such that interfering absorption is cancelled. This is illustrated in Fig. 5-1, which depicts spectra of two similar transformer oils. As seen in Fig. 5-1(a), the uncompensated spectra are very similar, although spectrum 2 exhibits several additional weak bands. However, these are difficult to detect and measure. By placing sample 1 in the reference path and measuring sample 2 against it, all absorption bands common to the two are effectively cancelled and only the differences are recorded. These are shown in the top curve of Fig. 5-1(b). By means of scale expansion, the weak difference bands can be intensified to increase both readability and sensitivity as shown in the other curves.

Reliable results can be assured in differential analysis only if the operator understands the pitfalls that might exist. Therefore a brief review of these seems appropriate. More complete discussions are given by Potts (1).

In the detector system of any double-beam optical-null instrument, any difference in the intensity of the alternating sample and reference beams appears as an ac signal. The strength of such a signal is proportional to the difference in intensities. When the beams are of equal intensity, no ac signal is observed. An optical wedge, or comb, placed in the reference beam responds to any imbalance between the two beams and moves in or out of the reference beam according to the direction of the imbalance. The

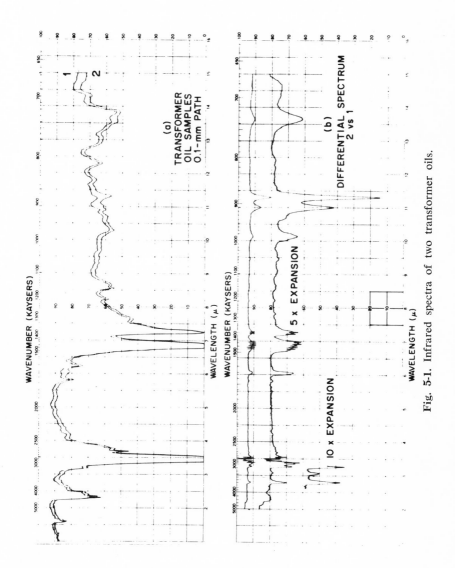

Fig. 5-1. Infrared spectra of two transformer oils.

null position of the comb indicates the transmittance of the sample, and this information is fed electronically to the recorder.

Since the signal supplied to the recording system is also directly dependent upon the reference-beam energy, the pen response and the permissible scanning speed are also directly influenced by the reference-beam energy. When radiation is removed from the reference beam, either by atmospheric absorptions or by reference-solvent or sample absorptions, the instrument may be found to lack response because too much radiation has been removed. The more energy removed from the reference beam, the poorer the pen response will become, since the signals supplied to the comb and pen servo systems become less adequate to drive them.

In those regions where lower than normal energy exists, several choices are available for counterbalancing these energy losses: (a) The low-energy regions may simply be accepted with a corresponding reduction in scanning speed; (b) The amplifier gain may be increased and/or the period reduced; or (c) The slits may be widened to regain lost energy.

In actual practice, some combination of the above will probably be most helpful. However, a reduction in scanning speed will frequently result in inordinately long scan times; a decreased period and/or increased gain is useful only to the extent that noise can be tolerated. Widening of the slits is especially advantageous and, probably, most practical, since the energy increases as the square of the slit width. Although some resolution will be lost, the resolution of high-resolution–grating instruments is still adequate, even at wide slits, for the majority of liquid and solid work.

Of course, where no energy exists in the reference beam (e.g., totally opaque solvent bands), nothing can be done to restore pen response. In such regions, any pen tracings are meaningless and should be disregarded.

Aside from instrumental considerations, it is important also to consider sample thickness. For highest sensitivity it is beneficial to utilize the maximum path lengths that still transmit about 30 to 40% of the radiation in the regions of interest. It has beeen shown that thicker samples reduce energy to such an extent that precision is seriously impaired.

As a final point, it should be remembered that differential analysis involves measurement of very small differences. Therefore it is essential that sample and reference materials be carefully prepared and handled. Even minor temperature differences between the two can produce abnormal signals.

C. Separation Procedures

In many cases direct application of infrared procedures is impractical. However, coupling infrared measurements with separation techniques often provides a practical method for detecting small impurities in very complex samples. Of particular use in this regard has been the combined use of infrared with gas (2), thin-layer, and paper chromatography. Similarly, quantitative infrared determination of trace impurities in solids at the 0.01% level have been achieved after fractional crystallization of the sample (3).

5-3. APPLICATIONS

A. Gases

Infrared spectrophotometry still provides important advantages for determining impurities in gases, in spite of the advances made in gas chromatography and mass spectrometry. In general, infrared methods are relatively simple and rapid; they can be adapted to continuous operation; and, above all, they offer high specificity to the analysis. A review of instrumental factors, technique, and detection limits has been given by Ulrich (4).

Most trace applications for gas samples involve the infrared-inactive gases such as hydrogen, oxygen, nitrogen, and helium. Extremely long path lengths are practical in these cases. Applications include determination of trace constituents in the atmosphere, in breathing oxygen, and in liquid gases used in missiles. As an example, infrared procedures have been developed for the analysis of breathing oxygen at the following levels: CO_2, 10.0 ppm; methane, 25 ppm; ethane, 2.0 ppm; acetylene, 0.05 ppm; ethylene, 0.2 ppm; and N_2O, 1.0 ppm.

In some instances the impurities have intense absorption bands and relatively short-path cells are adequate. Rand (5) used cells of 1 to 5 cm in length to determine components in semiconductor epitaxial-process gas streams. Hydrogen streams containing $SiCl_4$, $GeCl_4$, $SiBr_4$, and $GeBr_4$ were monitored successfully at low concentration levels.

B. Liquids

Numerous trace-analysis applications can be cited for liquid samples. The spectra in Fig. 5-1 represents one area of interest, namely the detection of impurities or additives in oils. Sloane (6) described a differential method for determining additives in lubricating oils quantitative in the 0.05–0.25% range; a phenol additive was detected at the 5-ppm level.

In some cases the sample matrix is reasonably transparent at the analytical wavelength and cell paths as long as 10 cm can be utilized. An example is the analysis of residual hydrocarbon oils in missile-systems wash solvent (7). Since complete freedom from hydrocarbons is essential in preventing explosions, all components must be thoroughly washed. Usually a halogenated hydrocarbon such as carbon tetrachloride or Freon-

TF* is employed. The wash solvent is reused until it is contaminated beyond a specified level. Fortunately these solvents are highly transparent in the 3.5-μ region where normal hydrocarbons have their strongest bands. Measurement at this wavelength with 10-cm cells gives sufficient sensitivity to detect as little as 1 ppm hexane. Since some solvent absorption may be present, the differential technique is usually employed for the lower-level measurements.

C. Solids

Infrared spectrophotometric determinations of trace amounts of impurities in solids by direct measurements are relatively rare. The desirable conditions of high transparency for long path lengths of the major constituent are seldom realized in the solid state. Path lengths much over a millimeter are very unusual because of the usual presence of strong, and frequently interfering, bands of the major component. Consequently, impurities generally have detection limits of only about 1 mole %. Differential techniques, which can be of great value for liquid-phase work, are not as readily adapted to the solid state because of the obvious difficulties associated with obtaining reproducible equivalent path lengths in both sample and reference specimens.

In addition, quantitative work in the solid state is further complicated by a number of solid-state effects. Scattering effects (1), often evidenced by a gradually decreasing I_0 baseline in going from longer to shorter wavelengths, may cause severe energy losses, in some cases equivalent to those losses caused by true absorption bands. A peculiar type of scattering caused by the rapid change in refractive index in the vicinity of an absorption band may produce an asymmetrical band distortion known as the Christensen effect (8, 9, 10). This type of distortion generally appears as a relatively high transmission level on the short-wavelength side of an absorption band, which gradually tails off on the long-wavelength side. In addition to distorting the I_0 baseline badly, such distortions can produce frequency shifts as large as 50 cm^{-1} (9). Finally, it is well known that polymorphic forms of the same compound can produce significantly different spectra; consequently great care must be exercised when examining samples of this type.

Because of these difficulties, solution techniques are commonly preferred whenever possible. Since normal solution techniques can result in a substantial dilution of the impurity as well as the major component, some type of simple selective extraction or fractional crystallization procedure (3) may be required. In a few cases, however, where the matrix

* DuPont trade mark.

material is reasonably transparent, trace impurities can satisfactorily be determined directly in the solid state. Two such cases are discussed below, one involving semiconductors and the other, surface chemistry.

A semiconductor material with excellent electrical properties can be manufactured by vacuum depositing a very thin layer of a lightly doped semiconductor material, e.g., silicon, germanium, or silicon dioxide, on a heavily doped layer of the same material. The former is referred to as the epitaxial layer and the latter as the substrate. A knowledge of the types and levels of impurities, as well as the layer thickness, is essential because of their pronounced effects on the electrical properties.

Thickness measurements have been accomplished in the past either by weighing the wafer before and after vacuum deposition or by a lapping and staining method with visual observation of the film–substrate interface.

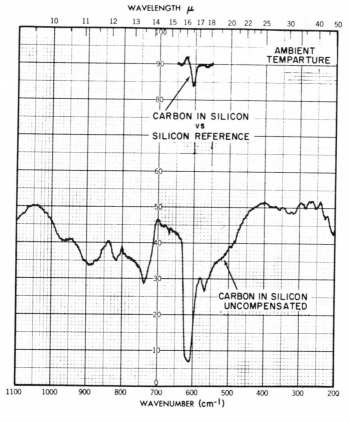

Fig. 5-2. Infrared spectra of silicon containing 300 ppb carbon: (a) compensated with pure silicon as a reference; (b) uncompensated.

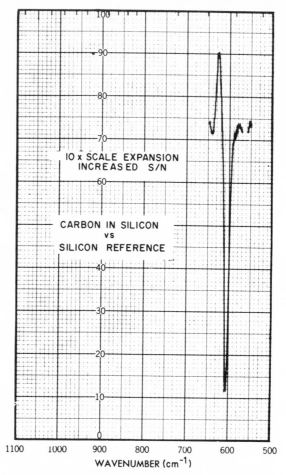

Fig. 5-3. The trace of Fig. 2(a) at 10× scale expansion.

Neither method was wholly satisfactory, and the latter destructive technique was entirely too expensive.

The infrared-reflectance method proposed by Spitzer and Tanenbaum (*11*) has proven to be an accurate, rapid, nondestructive technique for measuring silicon and germanium film thicknesses (*12, 13*). The use of a double-beam recording visible–ultraviolet spectrophotometer to determine the thickness of oxides on silicon from the reflection spectrum has been described by Corl and Wimpfheimer (*14*).

Infrared spectroscopy has been used rather extensively in the study of silicon impurities (*15*). Osafune *et al.* (*16*) used infrared techniques to determine phosphorus in doped SiO_2 layers grown on silicon substrates.

Oxygen in silicon and carbon in silicon were investigated at the 1–30 ppm level by Kaiser and Keck (17) and Newman and Willis (18). Baker (19) has shown detection limits of 200 ppb for oxygen and carbon by differential techniques, and 0.5 ppb for arsenic, boron, and phosphorus at liquid-nitrogen temperatures.

The spectrum of pure silicon exhibits several lattice-absorption bands throughout the 1100–500 cm^{-1} region of sufficient intensity to obscure any weak absorption bands due to impurities. An example of these intense spectral interferences is illustrated by the lower curve in Fig. 5-2, obtained from a 2-mm-thick sample of silicon containing approximately 300 ppb carbon as an impurity. In this case, the extremely strong silicon lattice band at 610 cm^{-1} limits the sample thickness to about 2 mm, since greater thicknesses would seriously limit the spectrophotometer energy.

The 607 cm^{-1} band due to the presence of substitutional carbon in silicon, located almost exactly under the silicon lattice band at 610 cm^{-1}, was only recently discovered (19). The upper curve of Fig. 5-2 shows a differential scan of two silicon samples, one containing 300 ppb carbon, the other pure silicon as the reference. Figure 5-3 presents the differential spectrum at $10\times$ scale expansion and an increased signal-to-noise ratio. Differential techniques are essential here for low-level impurity detection.

Differential techniques are not necessary for the common doping elements, arsenic, phosphorus, and boron, since their absorptions occur beyond 500 cm^{-1}, where silicon itself is reasonably transparent.

Infrared techniques supply direct evidence on the nature of chemisorbed layers (20), which are generally present in relatively small amounts. This technique typically employs high-surface-area solids, e.g., silica gel, alumina, or dispersed metals on which the substance of interest has been chemisorbed. When placed in the beam of an infrared spectrophotometer, the chemisorbed species can be examined directly and the results interpreted by analogy to spectra of conventional compounds. The sensitivity and energy limitations imposed by the supporting matrix, which is highly absorbing and scattering, frequently require many of the techniques usually associated with trace analysis, e.g., differential spectra, scale expansion, and so on. Chemisorbed species such as carbon monoxide, acetylene, water, carbon dioxide, and acetic acid have been studied extensively by these techniques.

5-4. CONCLUSIONS

The examples given here illustrate the application of infrared procedures for trace analysis, but by no means represent all possible uses. It is seen that the advent of high-energy infrared spectrophotometers and the use of differential techniques have extended the scope of infrared capabilities to many new areas, including the analysis of relatively opaque substances. With proper selection of operating parameters and appropriate technique, impurities down to and even below the parts-per-million level can be measured.

REFERENCES

1. W. J. Potts, Jr., *Chemical Infrared Spectroscopy,* Wiley, New York, 1963.
2. J. E. Stewart, R. O. Brace, T. Johns, and W. F. Ulrich, *Nature,* **186,** 628 (1960).
3. C. C. Bard, T. J. Porro, and H. L. Rees, *Anal. Chem.,* **27,** 12 (1955).
4. W. F. Ulrich, in *Analysis Instrumentation 1963* (L. Fowler, R. D. Eanes, and T. J. Kehoe, eds.), Plenum, New York, 1963, pp. 209–218.
5. M. J. Rand, *Anal. Chem.,* **36,** 1112 (1964).
6. H. J. Sloane, 12th Pittsburgh Conference on Analytical Chemistry and Applied Spectroscopy, February (1961).
7. H. J. Sloane, *Beckman Analyzer,* **3,** No. 4, 11 (1962).
8. A. H. Pfund, *Phys. Rev.,* **36,** 71 (1930).
9. G. Duyckaerts, *Analyst,* **84,** 201 (1959).
10. H. J. Sloane, *Beckman Analyzer,* **1,** No. 4, 16 (1960).
11. W. G. Spitzer and M. Tanenbaum, *J. Appl. Phys.,* **32,** 744 (1961).
12. M. P. Albert and J. F. Combs, *J. Electrochem. Soc.,* **109,** 709 (1962).
13. H. J. Sloane, *Beckman Application Data Sheet IR-8077,* Beckman Instruments, Inc., Fullerton, Calif.
14. E. A. Corl and H. Wimpfheimer, *Solid-State Electron.,* **7,** 755 (1964).
15. R. Newman, *Phys. Rev.,* **103,** 103 (1956).
16. H. Osafune, Y. Matukura, S. Tanaka, and Y. Miura, Electrochemical Society Meeting, Buffalo, N. Y., October, 1965, Paper 110.
17. W. Kaiser and P. H. Keck, *J. Appl. Phys.,* **28,** 882 (1957).
18. R. C. Newman and J. B. Willis, *J. Phys. Chem. Solids,* **26,** 373 (1965).
19. J. A. Baker, to be published.
20. R. P. Eischens, *Science,* **146,** 486 (1964).

6

GAS–LIQUID CHROMATOGRAPHY*

Roy A. Keller

DEPARTMENT OF CHEMISTRY
STATE UNIVERSITY OF NEW YORK
COLLEGE AT FREDONIA
FREDONIA, NEW YORK

6-1. INTRODUCTION

Gas–liquid chromatography, GLC, is a separation technique based on the differential migration of components in a mixture from a narrow initial zone. Figure 6-1 is a schematic diagram for an idealized gas chromatograph. Since extensive theoretical treatments of GLC are available (*1–6*), discussion here is concerned mainly with the practical problems encountered in the important subdivisions pictured in the figure.

6-2. CARRIER GAS

A flowing stream of gas, the carrier, is supplied from a cylinder. Its identity largely depends upon the detector selected, e.g., helium for thermal-conductivity cells. The quality of the final chromatogram can depend upon its purity, e.g., with flame ionization the noise level of the final record can be reduced by catalytic oxidation of trace combustible materials in the carrier and absorption of the water and carbon dioxide. After

* The author is indebted to the National Institute of Health, R01 GM14250, and the National Science Foundation, GP 4643, for the support of his research, of which this article is a by-product.

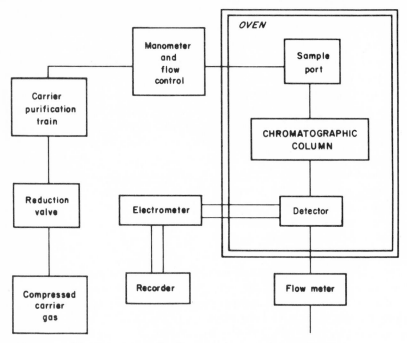

Fig. 6-1. Schematic diagram of a gas chromatograph.

suitable pressure reduction, it is passed through a constant-flow valving system and led to the sample-injection port.

A. The Sample-Injection Port

A liquid sample mixture is introduced into the gas stream by means of a hypodermic syringe. The needle passes through a self-sealing septum into a heated chamber, where the sample is rapidly vaporized in the carrier stream. Gas-tight syringes are available for gas samples, and all-metal syringes that can be heated in an oven can be used to produce molten samples of solids. Syringes and sample-port configurations are available whereby the sample can be led to the column packing and injected directly onto the columns (on-column injection). This minimizes the initial zone size and avoids chemical alteration in the sample chamber, but requires that sample injection be at the column temperature. Gas sampling loops are available where, by means of a suitable valve, the carrier stream can be diverted through a bypass loop to sweep a gaseous sample onto the column. It is common practice to provide the sample chamber with its own heating unit and temperature control. Sample chambers are not innocent attachments and can be an insidious source of error: e.g., (a) the sample undergoes decomposition or reaction catalyzed by the chamber material, (b) the inner surface of the chamber adsorbs sample components that may be slowly bled off later into the column or be displaced by the components of a subsequent sample to give a spurious peak, (c) pyrolysis products accumulate that are catalytic or adsorptive. These eccentricities are particularly bothersome in trace analysis. It is advisable in trace analysis to monitor the behavior of the chromatograph by use of one or more standards of established behavior and to randomize the order of their injection and the time periods between injections to detect such effects. Glass-lined chambers with replaceable liners are available. The Hamilton inlet (7) is one of the better-designed sample ports. Special attention must be paid to large samples, in which the heat of vaporization may cool the port and reduce the rate of vaporization.

The collection and storage of representative samples prior to GLC requires a word of caution. Sampling is fundamental in trace analysis, and a sufficient warning of the difficulty is provided by air pollution (8), from which the sampling or storage container can adsorb the trace constituents of interest. Kaiser (2) also emphasizes that appreciable equipment costs and operator time can be cast away by inattention to sampling.

B. The Chromatographic Column

The mixture now passes into the column, where the components exchange between an immobile phase and the mobile gas phase. While in the gas phase, the molecules move with the carrier velocity v, whereas their velocity in the immobile phase is zero. The immobile phase may consist of particles of some solid adsorptive agent, e.g., charcoal, alumina, silica gel, and so on, and solute molecules are fixed directly to it by secondary valence forces. This is gas–solid chromatography, GSC. Alternately, the particles of a nonadsorptive solid may be coated with a nonvolatile liquid in which the solute molecules may dissolve. This is gas–liquid chromatography, GLC. A dynamic exchange exists between solute molecules in the moving gas and the fixed solute molecules. At the front of the solute zone, the downstream limit, gas containing solute molecules enters a region of the column where the immobile phase is devoid of solute; in this nonequilibrium situation a net deposition of solute onto the stationary phase occurs. At the tail of the zone, the upstream limit, carrier devoid of solute contacts solute-laden immobile phase; a net transfer of solute into the carrier takes place. At some point within the zone, the rates of condensation and vaporization are equal. This dynamic equilibrium is commonly taken as a point of thermodynamic equilibrium; it represents the behavior of an average molecule. How fast the average molecule migrates through the column depends upon the amount of time it spends in the immobile phase, a function of the affinity of the solute for the stationary phase, relative to the amount of time spent in the moving gas. If R is the fraction of any time period that an average molecule spends in the mobile phase, then it travels down the column with velocity $u_i = R_i v$, where the subscript denotes a particular solute species. Logically, if R is small, the solute has a relatively great affinity for the immobile phase and its concentration in this phase is greater than in the mobile. The retention parameter R as a time average may be equated to the population average as given by the concentration; i.e., R is the fraction of all of the molecules in the mobile phase. Viewed in this latter fashion, the time honored derivation of R_i (3) yields

$$R_i = \frac{1}{1 + \alpha_i(A_s/A_m)} \qquad (6\text{-}1)$$

where

α_i = the partition coefficient, the ratio of the concentration of the solute in the stationary phase, c_{is}, to that in the mobile phase, c_{im}, i.e., c_{is}/c_{im}

A_s = amount of stationary phase per unit length of column

A_m = amount of mobile phase per unit length of column

A more detailed discussion of Eq. (6-1) defines the retention volume, the volume of gas that precedes the average molecule through the column, as the parameter of importance (3). It depends only upon the affinity of the solutes for the immobile phase and the temperature as reflected by the partition coefficient. The observed retention volume can be altered by the amount of retentive phase on the column either by changing the amount per unit length of column, i.e., the liquid load, or by changing the column length. Solute separation, as exhibited by differences in retention time or volume of the components of the mixture, is a factor of first importance. The separated solutes now leave the column exit as individual puffs of vapor.

The second factor vital to separations is the extent of the column over which the solute zones extend. Ideally, the concentration of the solute as a function of time, carrier volume, or column length, is a Gaussian error curve. Asymmetry of the concentration profile (tailing in the great majority of situations) always exists to some degree because peak shape also depends upon sample injection (ideally, a sharp pulse or δ-function) and kinetic effects. The broadness of these peaks is of concern. One may have peak maxima well separated, but the peaks are so broad they overlap or

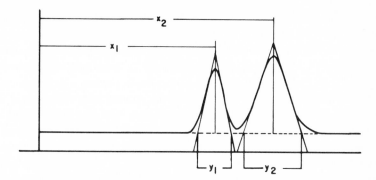

Fig. 6-2. Method of calculating the plate height from a gas-chromatographic trace.

are so flattened that the concentration of solute in the vapor is reduced below the minimum amount the detector can sense and are missed completely. If the peaks are sharp and appear as spikes on the record, then complete resolution can be achieved even if the peaks show small differences in retention volume.

Peak broadness is measured by the height equivalent to a theoretical plate, H. Figure 6-2 shows how this is determined.

$$N = 16(x/y)^2 \qquad (6\text{-}2)$$

where N is the total number of plates in the column and

$$H = L/N \qquad (6\text{-}3)$$

In a chromatographic sense, plate height is a measure of spread of the solute zone. The net plate height is the sum of molecular, eddy, and chromatodiffusion effects.

Molecular diffusion from a region of high concentration into regions of lower concentration, from the center of the solute zone to its borders, is a result of molecular thermal motion and always occurs. The greater the residence time in the column, the greater the extent of spreading. Thus molecular diffusion varies inversely as the carrier velocity.

Eddy diffusion is the term given to random processes in a column. The velocity of gas flowing through a tube is not uniform; i.e., the gas near the wall has a linear velocity less than that along the axis of the tube. If two molecules start at the same initial position but, by chance, one consistently spends more of its time in the slow-flow stream near the wall while the other consistently elects the fast-flow streams near the center, then in the same period of time the two are separated even though they are identical chemically. In a packed column, these tubes are the channels between particles of the packing. These channels vary in size and thus in the average gas velocity within them; some are faster than others. They meet at junction points. Two identical molecules may start their journey at the same point in the column but one may, again by chance, consistently elect fast channels while the other finds its way through the slower streams.

Chromatodiffusion describes movement of solute in the liquid film. Molecules trapped in the liquid film must find their way to the liquid–gas interface before they can enter the gas phase. The liquid film on the particles may show a very nonuniform structure as it fills capillary pores, spreads out over smooth regions, and "puddles" at contact points between particles. Some molecules may find themselves entrapped within a pore, and time is consumed while they find their way to the surface. Meanwhile, more fortunate companions have moved on down the column. This leads to separation of identical molecules and further band spreading.

The net plate height is velocity dependent. There is some velocity that gives a minimum plate height. Below it, the band broadens because molecular diffusion dominates; above it the band broadens because eddy diffusion and chromatodiffusion dominate. For analytical purposes columns should be operated at this optimum velocity, which can be determined from a few determinations of plate height vs carrier velocity.

This discussion presumes band broadening to be a column phenomenon. This is not true. The sample-injection port, ancillary plumbing, detector, and read-out system all make their own contributions. Sternberg (9) has established the guidelines on this subject.

It is appropriate at this point to define the problem of trace analysis, because it dictates the choice of column and detector. *In trace analysis, one particular component is present in an overwhelmingly greater proportion than any other* (as a result the ratio of the corresponding peak heights is very much different from unity). Bennett et al. (10) defined a trace component as one present to the extent of 1 to 200 ppm; i.e., the major component has a concentration about 10^6 times that of the trace. The problem of trace analysis is the problem of this disparity of concentration. It leads to two difficulties: (1) The amount of the major component either overloads the column, i.e., exceeds the capacity of the immobile phase so that equilibrium between solute in the gas phase and in the immobile phase cannot exist, and/or produces a solute zone so broad that it swamps out the peaks of the minor constituents. (2) A sample that can be tolerated by the column contains such a small amount of the trace that it is missed by the detector. The maximum permissable sample volume has been shown to be

$$v_p = 0.5(V_R/\sqrt{N}) \qquad (6\text{-}4)$$

where v_p is the vapor-phase volume of the sample (*11–13*). Slight overloading may be beneficial if it increases the sensitivity without degrading resolution.

An excellent review, in English translation, which every interested reader should consult, is that by Vigdergauz, Afanas'ev, and Gol'bert (*14*).

C. Column Types

Halász, Hartmann, and Heine (*15*) first summarized the various column configurations that have been employed.

1. Packed Columns

a. Macrocolumns

In macrocolumns the internal diameter of the column tubing is either ¼ or ⅛ in.; the latter is becoming conventional.

(*1*) *Conventional Packed Columns (CP)*. The conventional packed column is packed with an inert support coated with a liquid. Support studies is a chapter in its own right; the review by Ottenstein (*16*) is required reading on this subject. The support should be strong, of uniform particle size, and deactivated (silanized) so it does not participate in retention, which can lead to nonlinear retention isotherms and tailing or virtually irreversible adsorption of solutes, which is particularly worrisome in trace analysis. The ratio of column diameter to particle diameter should be from 5 to 50 (*9*) (30–60 mesh for ¼-in. columns and 80–100 mesh for ⅛-in. columns). Popular column lengths are from 4 to 8 ft.

The total number of plates and peak separation can be increased by using longer columns. This also leads to broader and flatter peaks. Resolution increases by $L^{1/2}$. The minimum particle size and the maximum length of column is set by the driving pressure required for optimum carrier velocity.

Resolution is improved by low liquid loads; e.g., a 32% liquid load of Carbowax 400 on a firebrick support did not completely separate the members of a mixture of four ketones in 1 min. Resolution of the mixture was achieved in 30 sec with a 1% load at 50°. Low liquid loads allow a series of solutes to be resolved in the same period of time as a higher load, but at a lower temperature; the latter allows greater exploitation of solute–solvent intermolecular forces; i.e., the partition coefficients differ by greater amounts. Low-load columns have been reviewed by Karger and Cooke (*17*). However, the sample size must also be reduced to parallel the reduced column capacity. This may reduce the concentration of the trace component below the sensitivity of the detector.

(2) *Glass-Bead Columns* (*B*).   Glass-bead columns have their origin
in the desire to avoid support surface activity and support porosity; they
reduce the operating temperature. Liquid loads and hence sample size
must be reduced. Support activity for diatomaceous-earth supports has
ceased to be a major problem with the introduction of deactivation with
silanizing agents. Guiochon (*18*) points out that chromatographic behavior on a 1% liquid-load diatomaceous-earth support is roughly equivalent to glass beads with a 0.25% liquid load. For the present state of
the art, glass beads show no marked advantage over conventional packed
columns; the reduced sample size argues against them.

(3) *Porous-Layer Bead Columns* (*PLB*).   In porous-layer bead columns glass beads are modified by (a) etching or coating with diatomaceous
earth to increase the liquid load; (b) coating with an adsorbent to exploit
adsorptive forces (GSC); (c) coating with an adsorbent and a liquid to
take advantage of a combination of liquid–solid retention for particularly
difficult separations. Small sample sizes are still a disadvantage. These
columns have not found general application.

b. Packed Capillary Columns

In an imaginative violation of the tube-to-particle diameter ratio stated
earlier, Halász loosely filled a normal-diameter glass tube with particles
and drew out the heat-softened glass to form a capillary (0.3 mm I.D.)
packed with particles of 0.10 to 0.15 mm in diameter (tube diameter/
particle diameter of 2 to 5). Plate heights are large, but a large gas
permeability allows construction of long columns. The high temperature
used in construction restricts the nature of the packing material. Sample
capacities are small; analysis time is fast; resolution is excellent. The
author knows of no application to trace analysis, but sample sizes seem
borderline. These columns have been reviewed by Halász and Heine (*19*).

2. Open-Tubular Columns

In open-tubular columns tube diameters are normally in the capillary
range, e.g., 0.2 mm I.D., although larger diameters have been investigated
(1.5 mm). The walls of the tube are coated with the partitioner. Large
column permeability allows long columns having a large number of theoretical plates with tremendous resolving power. The dramatic difference in
configuration of the column makes the details of the contributions to plate
height quite different; only the major qualitative ideas of molecular, eddy,
and chromatodiffusion remain (*6*).

a. Conventional Open-Tubular Columns (COT)

The wall of the conventional open-tubular column is coated with a thin
layer of liquid. The choice of liquid is restricted by the necessity that it

coat the wall. A 300-ft column 0.01 mm in I.D. contained 12,000 theoretical plates. The ultimate was perhaps a mile-long nylon capillary with
one million plates. Sample capacity is very small, i.e., 10^{-2} to 10^{-3} μl per
component. This requires a stream splitter as the injection port, which
vents some 90% of the normal sample to the atmosphere and admits the
remainder to the column. The price for high resolution is the small sample,
which requires a highly sensitive detector. Presently this seems to be a
severe limitation in trace analysis. This column is second to the classical
packed column in popularity. The monograph by Ettre (20) is the best
summary of these columns.

b. Porous-Layer Open-Tubular Columns (PLOT)

In porous-layer open-tubular columns the walls of the tube are coated
with adsorbent to increase the capacity for the liquid partitioner; this
allows use of a larger sample while retaining the column permeability and
much of the resolution of the conventional open-tubular coumn. These
columns overlap the small-diameter, low-liquid-load, conventional packed
column. Although sample sizes are small, they have great potential in
trace analysis, and the author expects to see more reports of their use as
they become available. Ettre, Purcell, and Billeb (21) have compared
conventional packed columns and porous-layer open-tubular columns.

Table 6-1, adapted from Guiochon (18), shows approximate values for

TABLE 6-1

Comparison of Column Types[a]

Column type	H_{min} (cm)	V_{opt} (cm/sec)	Sample size (μl)
Classical packed	0.06–0.2	5–20	10–1000
Glass bead	0.1–0.3	10–20	1–100
Porous-layer bead	—	—	1–100
Packed capillary	0.05–0.2	10–40	1–50
Conventional open-tubular	0.04–0.2	10–100	0.1–50
Porous-layer open-tubular	0.06–0.2	20–160	1–50

[a] Vigdergauz, Afanas'ev, and Gol'bert (14) give an important and more extensive
table of sample sizes and accompanying sensitivities.

the minimum plate height, H_{min}, which are not very different for the
different columns. The number of plates that may be achieved practically
depends upon the permeability. Open tubular columns, conventional and
support-coated, and packed capillaries are superior in this respect, but
the sample size is limited. Classical packed columns have limited length

and afford the slowest separation. The optimum velocity, V_{opt}, is that which yields H_{min}. Sample sizes are the most difficult to quote. Those listed do not acknowledge the total liquid in the column, the tube diameter, the number of components in the mixture, or its physical state. Because overloading refers to a single component, a mixture of fifty components allows a total larger sample if concentrations are nearly equal. In trace analysis the sample size is the lower limit of the ranges indicated, since one component predominates. Thus, if the conventional open tubular columns has a limit of 0.01 to 0.1 μl for a single component, this is the limit for a trace sample; the trace is reduced to 10^{-7} to 10^{-8} μl, a challenge for the detector.

6-3. DETECTORS

The second most vital component of the gas chromatograph is the detector, which has the responsibility of discovering the solute vapor in the effluent gas stream at the terminus of the column. Detectors may be nonspecific or universal, i.e., capable of sensing any substance in the carrier gas that is different from the carrier. Specific detectors show a different response to different chemical species. Inasmuch as the recent review by Svojanovský et al. (22) on trace analysis emphasizes the role of the detector, only the briefest discussion will be given here.

A. Thermal-Conductivity Cell

The thermal-conductivity cell is a nonspecific, nondestructive (solutes are not destroyed during sensing) detector that registers the difference in thermal conductivity between pure carrier gas in a reference chamber and a solution of solute in the carrier in a sample chamber. It has been very popular with classical packed columns. Improved design has brought it into the range of support-coated open-tubular columns. The sensitivity can be as good as 1 part solute in 10^5 parts carrier. The minimum detectable quantity is 10^{-9} g/sec (22).

B. Flame-Ionization Detector

The flame-ionization detector is a specific destructive detector. The effluent stream is mixed with hydrogen and oxygen or air in a jet and burned; ions produced by certain solutes are collected on charged electrodes. It will not sense the inert gases, oxygen, nitrogen, carbon disulfide, carbonyl sulfide, hydrogen sulfide, sulfur dioxide, nitrous oxide, nitric oxide, nitrogen dioxide, ammonia, carbon monoxide, carbon dioxide, water, silicon tetrachloride, trichlorosilane, silicon tetrafluoride, and so on, which reduces its usefulness in air-pollution studies. Because of this selectivity, complete solute resolution is often not necessary, since the detector may not see one component of a poorly resolved pair, e.g., ethanol and water. The minimum detectable quantity is 10^{-12} g/sec (22). It is by far the most promising detector for trace analysis and can be used with all column types. A wire containing a sodium salt placed in the flame enhances the response to compounds containing halogens [sensitivity 10 to 20 times greater (22)] and phosphorous [sensitivity 600 times greater (22)], which makes it very useful for some pesticide analysis. Aue and Ertingshausen (23) converted alcohols, phenols, amines, anilines, and thiophenols to their diethylphosphate derivatives and determined them semiquantitatively in the 1–10 pg range (original compounds before derivatization). The detector sensitivity claimed was 10^4 in excess of the carbonaceous background.

C. Radiation-Induced-Ionization Detectors

The beta-ray-ionization detector acts by the production of ions from solute molecules in a stream of electrons from Sr^{90}, which are collected in a region of electrical potential. The sensitivity is about that of a good thermal-conductivity cell.

The argon detector, an outgrowth of the beta-ray detector, uses argon as the carrier gas. The effluent stream is exposed to the beta rays from Sr^{90} or Kr^{85}. This radiation produces Ar^+ ions and electrons, which are accelerated in an electric field. These electrons collide with other argon atoms to produce excited metastable argon atoms; more than one excited argon can be produced by a single electron. Collision of these metastable atoms with solute molecules of lower ionization potential produces ions, which increase the conductivity of the gas. The argon detector is reported to be 17 to 100 times more sensitive than flame ionization. The minimum detectable amount is about 10^{-13} g/sec (22). It also has great promise in trace analysis. It will not detect solute species having ionization potentials greater than the excitation potential of argon (11.7 eV), e.g., hydrogen, nitrogen, oxygen, carbon monoxide, carbon dioxide, water, and the fluorocarbons; it gives a feeble response to other molecules, e.g., methane, and ethane. It will see some solutes not detected by flame ionization, e.g., hydrogen sulfide, nitric oxide, nitrogen dioxide, and ammonia. Some of these are important in air-pollution studies.

The electron-capture detector is very similar to the argon detector. The cell geometry is modified to sense the effect of the electron capture by solute species entering the electron stream. It is highly specific to molecules of high electron affinity, e.g., oxygen and the halogens. It can be adjusted so that weakly electron-capturing compounds, e.g., hydrocarbons, give no response at all, so that halogen-containing solutes can be selectively seen when in an incompletely resolved mixture of hydrocarbons. On this account it is often used in combination with flame-ionization detectors. The minimum detectable amount of carbon tetrachloride is 3×10^{-14} g/sec (22). Ross and Sievers (24) used this detector for the ultratrace analysis of toxic beryllium (4×10^{-13} g), after conversion to the volatile trifluoroacetylacetonates. Albert (25) compared this detector with the flame ionization detector for the volatile chelates of Cr(III), Al(III), and Cu(II). Gas chromatography of trace-metal analysis of the volatile chelates has also been studied by Brandt and Heveran (26) and Fernando, Freiser, and Wise (27). Juvet and Zado (28) have reviewed the gas chromatography of metals and Moshier and Sievers' (29) monograph contains a number of references to trace analysis. Application to pesticide analysis (0.1–0.25 ppm) in crops, soils, and tissues is given by Reynolds (30). The detector has proved useful for lead alkyls (31).

The electron-mobility detector uses an alternating current to collect the electrons of the beta rays. These electrons undergo elastic collisions with the argon carrier molecules and are not completely collected in an electrostatic field applied for a brief period. Their random motion is decreased in the presence of a solute and they are collected far more easily. The minimum detectable amount is 10^{-9}–10^{-11} (carbon dioxide) g/sec (22).

Karmen (31a) has reviewed ionization detectors and Coulson (31b) has summarized electrolytic conductivity detectors.

Winefordner and Glenn (32) have reviewed nonionization detectors. Among these are microwave-emission (limit of detection, 10^{-4}–10^{-11} g), rapid-scanning infrared [see also Ulrich, Gallaway, and Johns (33)], ultraviolet-absorption, dielectric-constant, semiconductive thin-film, contact-potential, ultrasonic, and electrolytic detectors. Caruso, Bramer, and Hoak (34) have discussed use of rapid-scan infrared spectrophotometers and mass spectrometers to identify compounds separated in the semiquantitative determination of trace organic compounds in water. Eustache, Guillemin, and Auricourt (35) combined gas chromatography with mass spectrometry for the determination of trace impurities in acrylonitrile [cf. (35a)].

Selection of a detector does not rest only on the sensitivity. Other pertinent factors are the following: (a) *Stability.* Short-term noise or irregular random oscillation of the signal to the recorder or electronic integrator may mask peaks. The signal-to-noise ratio becomes important. Long-term stability or drift may contribute difficulties. (b) *Speed of response.* How rapidly does the signal respond to solute entering or leaving the detector? (c) *Universality of response.* This is particularly important in quantitative work. No detector will show exactly the same response to the same amount of different solutes in the detection chamber. The variation from detector to detector is from no response to some solutes for specific detectors to minor but still important differences for universal detectors. (d) *Linearity of response.* The signal is not a linear function of solute concentration or amount in the sensing chamber. These matters also depend upon the associated electronics and the final read-out system, e.g., strip recorder or electronic integrator and printer. One of the most critical and appropriate discussions of these factors is that of Kaiser (2).

Lewin, Conner, and Königsbacher (36) suggested a detectability index (%) to evaluate any instrumental technique used in trace analysis. It is defined as:

$$\text{Detectability index (\%)} = \frac{S_N + \Delta S_T + 2\delta S_B}{S_X} \times 100 \qquad (6\text{-}5)$$

where

S_X = fraction of the output signal corresponding to the desired response of the unknown

S_N = fraction of the output signal corresponding to unavoidable noise

ΔS_T = error in the output signal due to "drift" characteristic of the instrument

S_B = background signal

The index should represent these combined influences.

A method of calibration, vital in quantitative work, depending upon prepared mixtures of known composition containing trace quantities has been given by Novák (37).

Janák's (22) group lists four factors important in gas chromatographic trace analysis: (a) the detector, (b) the sample size, (c) the position of the trace component in the chromatographic spectrum, i.e., the retention volume, and (d) the efficiency of the chromatographic separation. These are all interconnected. Efficiency and resolution depend upon the type of column in terms of plate height and the total number of plates on the column. Conventional open-tubular columns are best in this respect, but the reduced column capacity reduces the sample size and the trace may be missed. In special cases where the detector is extremely sensitive, e.g., electrolytic conductivity for halogens, the column may still be utilized. Classical packed columns employ larger samples, but there is a possible loss of resolution because of the fewer plates. Unless the analysis is specialized so that a particularly sensitive detector can be used, support-coated open-tubular columns and classical packed columns are the best general selections. With the latter, reduced liquid load can improve resolution but reduces sample capacity.

Temperature programming is a technique whereby solutes representing a wide range of volatilities are resolved by increasing the column temperature throughout the separation. Essentially, the solutes depart from the inlet end at different temperatures depending upon their affinity for

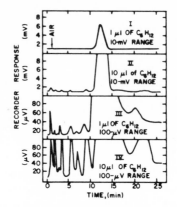

Fig. 6-3. Chromatograms of cyclohexane at 10-mV and 100-μV full-scale sensitivity ranges (*10*). (Courtesy of *Analytical Chemistry*.)

the immobile phase (*38*). A more profound and detailed treatment has been given by Harris and Habgood (*39*) and Hollingshead, Habgood, and Harris (*40*) have demonstrated its use in trace analysis with large samples. Marcali (*41*) applied temperature programming to the separation of fluorocarbons.

6-4. SELECTION OF THE LIQUID PARTITIONER

Figure 6-3 shows the trace of cyclohexane with two different sample loads and two sensitivity ranges. Note that the peak of the major component is broad and tails in profiles III and IV; the last peak, although its maximum is quite different from that of the major component, is nonetheless imperfectly resolved because of this tail. This is also demonstrated in Fig. 6-4. *In trace analysis best results are obtained in terms of peak overlap if the trace components precede the major component.* There must therefore be a judicious choice of the partitioner.

An increasingly popular method for tabulating retentive properties of liquid phases is Kovat's retention index, defined as

$$I(A) = 100 \frac{\log V_g(A) - \log V_g(P_n)}{\log V_g(P_{n+1}) - \log V_g(P)_n} + 100n \qquad (6\text{-}6)$$

where

$I(A)$ = retention index of solute A
$V_g(A)$ = specific retention volume of solute A
$V_g(P_n)$ = specific retention volume of an n-alkane of n carbons
$V_g(P_{n+1})$ = specific retention volume of a n-alkane of $(n + 1)$ carbons

The n-alkanes are such that they bracket A in order of emergence from the column. In this scheme $I(\text{methane}) = 100$, $I(\text{ethane}) = 200$, and so on. If solute A has $I(A) = 320$ for a particular partitioner, then it will elute between n-propane and n-butane. A survey of tabulated retention indices may quickly decide the choice of liquid. Kovats (42) has summarized his work with these indices. Kaiser (43) presents much of his retention data in its terms. The best compilation of index values is that of McReynolds (44). The index requires that the compound of interest has been chromatographed on a number of liquids. If this has not been done, the problem becomes more difficult. Kovats gives some rules for predicting index values for untried compounds from experimental values of tested compounds when structural differences between the two are not too great or for predicting behavior of a compound on an untested immobile phase. Schomburg (45) also comments on this problem. If this attack proves unfruitful, Bayer's (46) selectivity coefficient is useful in selecting liquids that show a difference in retention of homologous series of different functional groups. Relative retention volumes are ratios of the retention volume of the solute of interest to that of some reference substance. They may also serve as a guide to partitioner selection; A.S.T.M. has collected and organized many of these (47).

Water has always been a challenge because of its inherent tendency to tail. New hope for the separation of water and other highly polar solutes is offered by microporous polymer beads. The papers by Hollis and Hayes (48, 50) and Hollis (49) describe results obtained with these materials.

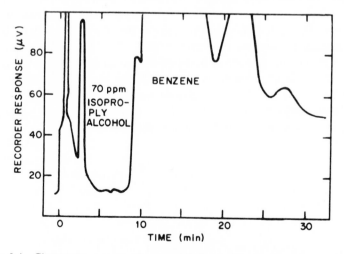

Fig. 6-4. Chromatogram of 70 ppm of isopropyl alcohol in benzene (10). (Courtesy of *Analytical Chemistry*.)

Cieplinski and Spencer (*51*) report their potential for determining trace amounts of water in organic compounds and traces of organics in water. Great promise is also shown by porous silica beads (*52*).

6-5. TECHNIQUES OF TRACE ANALYSIS

Three fairly standard general techniques of trace analysis are in common use: (a) concentration of trace components by some preliminary step, (b) removal of the interfering major component, and (c) chromatography of the unmodified sample. Very often the first two techniques appear in combination.

Trapping procedures essentially increase the amount of the trace to a level that can be dealt with by a common analytical column. Novák, Vasak, and Janák (*53, 54*) presented theoretical and practical considerations of gas chromatographic enrichment of trace quantities for subsequent gas chromatographic analysis. Experimental utilization of these principles was applied to analysis of industrial atmospheres. Brenner and Ettre (*55*) concentrated trace impurities in large sample volumes by using a condenser column packed with a suitable adsorbent, e.g., silica gel, which adsorbed traces at low temperature and desorbed them rapidly into the carrier gas at an elevated temperature. The main component was unadsorbed or only slightly adsorbed and thus eliminated. Lysyj (*56*) used a combination of activated charcoal at liquid-nitrogen temperature and a molecular sieve to resolve *o*-,*p*-hydrogen and determine trace gases in hydrogen in the parts per billion range. Markosov, Zaichenko, and Lityaeva (*57*) determined 0.001% CO in ethylene from a 0.1- to 0.5-liter sample by preconcentration on activated charcoal. Umsted and Williams (*58*) used a trap of Porapak, a microporous polymer, to trap chlorinated hydrocarbons.

The trap may be an adsorbent, an adsorbent in combination with a low-temperature bath, or a low-temperature bath alone. Durrett (*59*) stripped methylethyl ketone from waxes and lubricating oils with helium at 220°C and trapped them on firebrick at −50°C. Durand (*60*) trapped the carbon dioxide from the combustion of trace carbon in metals at liquid-oxygen temperature for subsequent quantitative gas chromatography. Self (*61*) reports a cold trap used in conjunction with capillary columns. Riddle (*62*) employed steam distillation as a preconcentration step.

Such concentration steps can serve three purposes. First, the sensitivity of the analysis may be increased: e.g., Bellar, Brown, and Sigsby (*63*) extended the analysis of olefins and paraffins in the atmosphere to the parts-per-billion range. Farrington *et al.* (*64*) used three traps and a freeze-out system to determine hydrocarbons and oxygenated compounds in the presence of large amounts of water in polluted atmospheres at a few parts per 100 million. Second, the trap can be used to eliminate the major component. The traces are condensed and concentrated for conventional gas chromatography while the major constituent is passed on and vented to the atmosphere (*65, 66*). Mikkelson (*67*) used a concentration column, a trap, and an analyzing column to determine traces at the 10-ppb level for impurities in vinyl chloride. Third, the trap may be used to fix the major component and pass on the traces to the analytical column. Kilner and Ratcliff (*68*) used a precolumn of calcium sulfate to remove water in the determination of dissolved permanent gases. Scott and Phillips (*69*) freed *n*-heptane from the alkenes with a precolumn of alumina modified with silver nitrate, and Prevot and Cobeza (*70*) determined residual solvents in oils by retaining the oil on a precolumn. A precolumn or trap can be used to separate compound classes both of which are then analyzed on the same or different columns (*71–73*).

REFERENCES

1. J. C. Giddings and R. A. Keller, eds., *Advances in Chromatography,* Vols. 1–7, Dekker, New York, 1966–1968; *Ibid,* Vol. 8, in press.

2. R. Kaiser, *Chromatographie in der Gasphase—IV: Quantitativ Auswertung,* Bibliographisches Institut, Mannheim, 1965.

3. R. A. Keller and J. C. Giddings, in *Chromatography,* 2nd ed. (E. Heftmann, ed.), Reinhold, New York, 1967.

4. A. B. Littlewood, *Gas Chromatography,* Academic, New York, 1962.

5. M. Lederer, ed., *Chromatographic Reviews,* Vol. 8, Elsevier, Amsterdam, 1966.

6. J. C. Giddings, *Dynamics of Chromatography—Part I: Principles and Theory,* Dekker, New York, 1965.

7. Hamilton Company, Whittier, Calif., *Catalog H-65.*

8. A. Altshuler, in *Advances in Chromatography,* Vol. 5 (J. C. Giddings and R. A. Keller, eds.), Dekker, New York, 1968, p. 229.

9. J. C. Sternberg, in *Advances in Chromatography,* Vol. 2 (J. C. Giddings and R. A. Keller, eds.), Dekker, New York, 1966, p. 205.

10. C. E. Bennett, S. dal Nogare, L. W. Safranski, and C. D. Lewis, *Anal. Chem.,* **30**, 898 (1958).

11. J. J. van Deemter, F. J. Zuiderweg, and A. Klinkenberg, *Chem. Eng. Sci.,* **5**, 271 (1956).

12. A. Klinkenberg, in *Gas Chromatography–1960* (R. P. W. Scott, ed.), Butterworth, London, 1960, p. 182.

13. G. W. A. Rijnders, in *Advances in Chromatography,* Vol. 3 (J. C. Giddings and R. A. Keller, eds.), Dekker, New York, 1966, p. 215.

14. M. S. Vigdergauz, M. I. Afanas'ev, and K. A. Gol'bert, *Russ. Chem. Rev.,* **32**, 330 (1963).

15. I. Halász, K. Hartmann, and E. Heine, in *Gas Chromatography–1964* (A. Goldup, ed.), Institute of Petroleum, London, 1965, p. 38.

16. D. M. Ottenstein, in *Advances in Chromatography,* Vol. 3 (J. C. Giddings and R. A. Keller, eds.), Dekker, New York, 1966, p. 137.

17. B. L. Karger and W. D. Cooke, in *Advances in Chromatography,* Vol. 1 (J. C. Giddings and R. A. Keller, eds.), Dekker, New York, 1966, p. 309.

18. G. Guiochon, in *Advances in Chromatography,* Vol. 8 (J. C. Giddings and R. A. Keller, eds.), Dekker, New York, in press.
19. I. Halász and E. Heine, in *Advances in Chromatography,* Vol. 4 (J. C. Giddings and R. A. Keller, eds.), Dekker, New York, 1967, p. 207.
20. L. S. Ettre, *Open-Tubular Columns in Gas Chromatography,* Plenum, New York, 1965.
21. L. S. Ettre, J. E. Purcell, and K. Billeb, in *Separation Techniques in Chemistry and Biochemistry* (R. A. Keller, ed.), Dekker, 1967, p. 229.
22. V. Svojanovsky, M. Krejčí, K. Tesařík, and J. Janák, in *Chromatographic Reviews,* Vol. 8 (M. Lederer, ed.), Elsevier, Amsterdam, 1966, p. 90.
23. W. A. Aue and G. Ertingshausen, 154th Meeting, American Chemical Society, Chicago, September 1967.
24. W. D. Ross and R. E. Sievers, in *Gas Chromatography—1966* (A. B. Littlewood, ed.), Institute of Petroleum, London, 1967, p. 272.
25. D. K. Albert, *Anal. Chem.,* 36, 2034 (1964).
26. W. W. Brandt and J. E. Heveran, 142nd Meeting, American Chemical Society, Atlantic City, N. J., September, 1962.
27. Q. Fernando, H. Freiser, and E. N. Wise, *Anal. Chem.,* 35, 1994 (1963).
28. R. S. Juvet, Jr. and F. Zado, in *Advances in Chromatography,* Vol. 1 (J. C. Giddings and R. A. Keller, eds.), Dekker, New York, 1966, p. 249.
29. R. W. Moshier and R. E. Sievers, *Gas Chromatography of Metal Chelates,* Pergamon, New York, 1965.
30. J. G. Reynolds, *Chem. Ind. (London),* 1962, 729 (1962).
31. R. E. Laramy, L. D. Lively, and G. Perkins, Jr., Pittsburgh Conference on Analytical Chemistry and Applied Spectroscopy, Pittsburgh, Pa., March, 1962.
31a. A. Karmen, in *Advances in Chromatography,* Vol. 2 (J. C. Giddings and R. A. Keller, eds.), Dekker, New York, 1966, p. 293.
31b. D. M. Coulson, in *Advances in Chromatography,* Vol. 3 (J. C. Giddings and R. A. Keller, eds.), Dekker, New York, 1966, p. 197.
32. J. D. Winefordner and T. H. Glenn, in *Advances in Chromatography,* Vol. 5 (J. C. Giddings and R. A. Keller, eds.), Dekker, 1968, p. 263.
33. W. F. Ulrich, W. S. Gallaway, and T. Johns, Pittsburgh Conference on Analytical Chemistry and Applied Spectroscopy, Pittsburgh, Pa., March, 1960.
34. S. C. Caruso, H. C. Bramer, and R. D. Hoak, 152nd Meeting, American Chemical Society, New York, September, 1966.
35. H. Eustache, C. L. Guillemin, and F. Auricourt, *Bull. Soc. Chim. France,* 1965, 1386.
35a. W. H. McFadden, in *Advances in Chromatography,* Vol. 4 (J. C. Giddings and R. A. Keller, eds.), Dekker, New York, 1967, p. 265; W. H. McFadden, in *Separation Techniques in Chemistry and Biochemistry* (R. A. Keller, ed.), Dekker, New York, 1967, p. 263.
36. S. Z. Lewin, J. Conner, and K. Königsbacher, 138th Meeting, American Chemical Society, New York, September, 1960.
37. J. Novák, *Chem. Listy,* 54, 1189 (1960).
38. J. C. Giddings, *J. Chem. Ed.,* 39, 569 (1962).
39. W. E. Harris and H. W. Habgood, *Programmed Temperature Gas Chromatography,* Wiley, New York, 1966.
40. L. W. Hollingshead, H. W. Habgood, and W. E. Harris, *Can. J. Chem.,* 43, 1560 (1965).

41. K. Marcali, Pittsburgh Conference on Analytical Chemistry and Applied Spectroscopy, Pittsburgh, Pa., March, 1960.
42. E. sz. Kovats in *Advances in Chromatography,* Vol. 1 (J. C. Giddings and R. A. Keller, eds.), Dekker, New York, 1966, p. 229.
43. R. Kaiser, *Gas Chromatography: Vol. 3, Tables for Gas Chromatography,* Butterworth, London, 1963.
44. W. O. McReynolds, *Gas Chromatographic Retention Data,* Preston Technical Abstracts, Evanston, Ill., 1966.
45. G. Schomburg, in *Advances in Chromatography,* Vol. 6 (J. C. Giddings and R. A. Keller, eds.), Dekker, New York, 1968, p. 211.
46. E. Bayer, *Gas Chromatography,* Elsevier, Amsterdam, 1961, p. 29.
47. American Society for Testing Materials, *Compilation of Gas Chromatographic Data,* A.S.T.M. Special Technical Publication AMD 25A, Philadelphia, Pa., 1967.
48. O. L. Hollis and W. V. Hayes, in *Gas Chromatography—1966* (A. B. Littlewood, ed.), Institute of Petroleum, London, 1967, p. 57.
49. O. L. Hollis, *Anal. Chem.,* 38, 309 (1966).
50. O. L. Hollis and W. V. Hayes, *J. Gas Chromatog.,* 4, 235 (1966).
51. E. W. Cieplinski and S. F. Spencer, Pittsburgh Conference on Analytical Chemistry and Applied Spectroscopy, Pittsburgh, Pa., March, 1967.
52. C. L. Guillemin, M. LePage, and A. J. deVries, *Anal. Chem.,* 39, 940 (1967).
53. J. Novák, V. Vasak, and J. Janák, *Gas Chromatography—1965,* East German Academy of Sciences, Berlin, 1965, p. 353.
54. J. Novák, V. Vasak, and J. Janák, *Anal. Chem.,* 37, 660 (1965).
55. N. Brenner and L. S. Ettre, *Anal. Chem.,* 31, 1815 (1959).
56. I. Lysyj in *Gas Chromatography* (L. Fowler, ed.), Academic, New York, 1963, p. 149.
57. P. I. Markosov, V. N. Zaichenko, and Z. A. Lityaeva, *Ind. Lab. (USSR), (English Trans.),* 27, 288 (1961).
58. M. E. Umsted and F. W. Williams, Pittsburgh Conference on Analytical Chemistry and Applied Spectroscopy, Pittsburgh, Pa., March, 1967.
59. L. R. Durrett, *Anal. Chem.,* 31, 1824 (1959).
60. J. C. Durand, T. Chaudron, and J. Montuelle, *Bull. Soc. Chim. France,* 1965, 3109.
61. R. Self, *Nature,* 189, 223 (1961).
62. V. M. Riddle, *Anal. Chem.,* 35, 853 (1963).
63. T. A. Bellar, M. F. Brown, and J. E. Sigsby, Jr., *Anal. Chem.,* 35, 1924 (1963).
64. P. S. Farrington, R. L. Pecsok, R. L. Meeker, and T. J. Olson, *Anal. Chem.,* 31, 1512 (1959).
65. A. A. Carlstrom, C. F. Spencer, and J. F. Johnson, *Anal. Chem.,* 32, 1056 (1960).
66. V. J. Jahnsen, *Anal. Chem.,* 39, 141 (1967).
67. L. Mikkelsen, Pittsburgh Conference on Analytical Chemistry and Applied Spectroscopy, Pittsburgh, Pa., March 1960.
68. A. A. Kilner and G. A. Ratcliff, *Anal. Chem.,* 36, 1615 (1964).
69. C. G. Scott and C. S. G. Phillips, *Nature,* 199, 66 (1963).
70. A. Prevot and F. Cobeza, *Rev. Franc. Corps Gras,* 7, 34 (1960).
71. G. Heuschkel, J. Wolny, and S. Skoczowski, *Erdoel Kohle,* 13, 98 (1960).
72. J. Janák and M. Rusek, *Collection Czech. Chem. Commun.,* 20, 923 (1955).
73. F. T. Eggertsen and S. Groennings, 139th Meeting, American Chemical Society, St. Louis, Mo., March, 1961.

DIFFERENTIAL THERMAL ANALYSIS AND DIFFERENTIAL SCANNING CALORIMETRY

*Edward M. Barrall, II, and Julian F. Johnson**

CHEVRON RESEARCH COMPANY
RICHMOND, CALIFORNIA

Recent developments in the well-established fields of differential thermal analysis (DTA) and differential scanning calorimetry (DSC) have now placed precise thermometry and calorimetry within the technical and time limitations of most modern laboratories. Although DTA and DSC are nonequilibrium methods, which cannot afford the ultimate precision and accuracy of classical techniques, data directly applicable to purity measurements can be obtained with a minimum expenditure of time and effort. For very pure materials that attain equilibrium rapidly and exhibit first-order phase transformations, the present authors have found that DSC and DTA yield results surpassed only by the very best classical methods.

It is the purpose of this chapter to discuss DTA and DSC in the limited framework of purity determinations. All considerations not directly applicable have been omitted in favor of careful directions for actual measurements. Only the minimum amount of theory necessary for application of these techniques is considered. For further information concerning theory and broader applications, the reader is referred to three excellent recent books and the kinetics paper of Reed *et al.* (*1, 2, 3, 4*).

7-1. DIFFERENTIAL THERMAL ANALYSIS

Differential thermal analysis compares the temperature difference between an active sample and an inert reference to temperature or time. Gen-

* *Present address:* Dept. of Chemistry, University of Connecticut, Storrs, Connecticut.

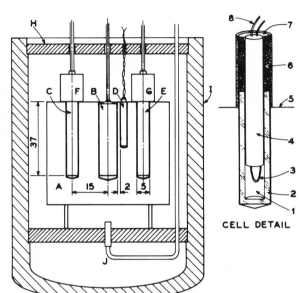

Fig. 7-1. Centrally mounted thermocouple cell design (5): A, aluminum block (50 mm × 50 mm); B, 500-W cartridge heater; C, sample cell; D, control thermocouple well; E, reference cell; F, G, sample and reference thermocouples; H, lid; I, Dewar flask (90 mm × 200 mm); J, CO_2 cooling jet. Cell detail: 1, sample space; 2, glass cell, 4.5 mm × 45 mm; 3, thermocouple junction; 4, inner ceramic probe, 3 mm; 5, surface of blocks; 6, outer ceramic cover; 7, sauereisen cement; 8, thermocouple leads.

erally, DTA involves the use of a thermocouple or thermistor that is embedded in, or placed around, the sample. A corresponding sensor is embedded in or placed around some inert reference material. The two are then heated or cooled according to some linear heating or cooling program; the differential signal that arises when the sample and the reference thermal properties do not coincide is recorded with respect to time or temperature. Fig. 7-1 shows a cell that is suitable for measuring temperatures of transition. The sample is located around the thermocouple somewhere in the geometrical center of the cell. The differential signal is affected not only by the specific heat of melting or the specific heat of some solid-solid state transformation but also by the thermal permeability and the thermal conductivity of the sample and the reference material.[†]

The cell shown in Fig. 7-2 overcomes some of these difficulties. Here the only property that will affect the differential signal is the heat capacity and the specific heat of any particular transformation that occurs in the sample. Since the thermocouple is placed around the sample rather than in the

[†] Since the sample and the reference may not coincide particularly well in any temperature range, it is sometimes necessary to mix sample and reference materials together. This is the diluted sample technique. By mixing from 50–90% reference material, which may be aluminum oxide or carborundum or some other inert material, with the sample, it is possible to obtain a differential signal which is essentially zero until some major physical transformation in the sample occurs.

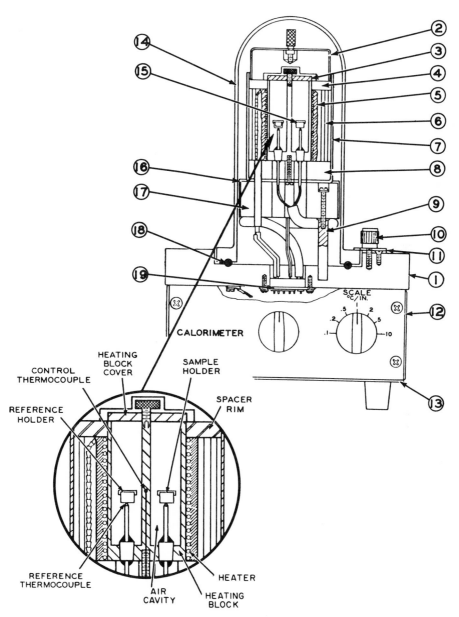

Fig. 7-2. Perimeter thermocouple cell design (6): 1, base plate; 2, insulating lid; 3, heating-block cover; 4, spacer rim; 5, heater; 6, Fiberfrax ceramic fiber; 7, housing; 8, housing insulator; 9, leg; 10, thumbscrew; 11, bell-jar clamp; 12, cabinet; 13, cabinet bottom; 14, bell jar; 15, sample holder; 16, upper sleeve; 17, insulator block; 18, neoprene O-ring; 19, connector.

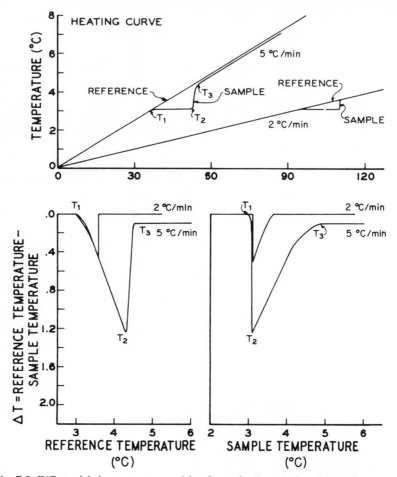

Fig. 7-3. Differential thermograms resulting from simple endothermal melting process.

center of the sample, the thermal permeability and thermal conductivity of the sample material will not affect the differential thermal signal. The importance of removing these phenomena from the differential thermal signal for most thermometric measurements has been outlined recently (2, 6, 7). A cell capable of calorimetric and temperature measurements has been reported but is not commercially available as is the cell in Fig. 7-2 (8).

The differential thermal phenomena are most easily understood in terms of the heating curve shown in Fig. 7-3. As the sample is heated, the reference material heats linearly with respect to time. When the sample undergoes a physical transformation requiring heat (an endothermal transformation) at temperature T_1, the sample will become isothermal and will no longer follow the heating program. From T_1 to T_2 the isothermal range exists. At temperature T_2, the last portion of the sample is transformed and the sample then heats rapidly to the reference-material temperature. The slope of the line from T_2 to T_3 is proportional to the heat capacity of the cell and the rest of the apparatus. The vertex of the differential thermal curve corresponds to temperature T_2 in well designed apparatus. This curve applies to both cells in Figs. 7-1 and 7-2.

A differential thermogram usually shows the differential-temperature signal as well as the actual-temperature signal of the sample.† The differential thermal curves will move as the heating rate of the sample is changed because of the change in the lag of the block or the reference material (9, 10, 11). Since well-behaved endothermal processes for pure inorganic and organic compounds generally do not move when the heating rate is changed within a few orders of magnitude (from 1–20°C/min), recording the sample temperature in the sample itself is a more desirable method. For operations where an extra thermocouple cannot be placed in the cell or where the necessary electrical equipment does not exist for using the sample thermocouple simultaneously for the differential- and sample-temperature measurement, it is possible to obtain a corrected and replotted differential thermogram in which the sample temperature is expressed directly (11). This is achieved by adding algebraically the differential temperature to the recorded block or reference temperature and replotting the differential thermogram.

When the sample temperature is measured within the sample compartment, the differential thermogram is conveniently plotted on an x–y recorder with the differential temperature on the y-axis and the sample temperature on the x-axis (1, 2). It is customary to show endothermal phenomena as downward-sloping peaks and exothermal phenomena as upward-sloping peaks. When the temperature of the system somewhere not within the sample itself is recorded, two strip-chart recorders may be used, one for the differential temperature and the other for the block or reference temperature (12). It is important in this second technique that some device be arranged to transfer a signal simultaneously to the two recorders so that position marks may be made on the two records for future correlation. Greater resolution of endothermal or exothermal peaks can be obtained by speeding up the recorders, an impossibility with x–y recording.

Several satisfactory commercial instruments are available for organic and inorganic differential thermal analysis; representative models are described in Table 7-1. Operating variables encountered in differential thermal analysis are outlined briefly in Table 7-2.

† If the temperature of the reference material or the temperature of the block is measured, the temperature axis of the differential thermogram will then be linear as compared to the reference line in Fig. 7-3. This is not the actual temperature of the sample.

TABLE 7-1

Some Commercial Instruments for Differential Thermal Analysis
and Differential Scanning Calorimetry

Instrument	Description
Aminco Thermoanalyzer No. 4-4442	Part of a larger thermometric setup. Although originally designed for inorganic work, organic thermometry and calorimetry are possible. Temperature range: 0 to 1500°C.
Stone DTA Apparatus	Much the same application as the Aminco machine. Temperature range: 0 to 1500°C.
Perkin-Elmer Differential Scanning Calorimeter DSCl and DSClB	The only scanning calorimeter available. With calibration, the temperature measurements compare well to DTA. The instrument was specifically designed as an organic calorimeter and as such is excellent. Temperature range: − 100 to 600°C.
Du Pont 900 Differential Thermal Analyzer	Can be equipped with a large number of DTA cells and other thermoanalytical equipment. Very flexible, good temperature accuracy, uses cell shown in Fig. 7-2 for calorimetry. Temperature range: − 100 to 1600°C.

TABLE 7-2

Effect of Various Operating Parameters on the Thermogram

Parameter	Effect	
	Differential thermal analysis	Differential scanning calorimetry
Increase heating rate	*Base temperature recorded in sample:* Increases height and area of peak, increases vertex temperature for chemical reactions, does not effect vertex temperature of 1° phase transformations.	Increases peak height but not area. Kinetic or chemical-reaction peaks move to higher temperatures, phase transformations do not move appreciably. Isothermal to program-signal increases. Decreases peak resolution.
	Baser temperature not recorded in sample, also time-base systems: Increases peak height but not area, moves vertex of both chemical reactions and 1° phase transformation to higher temperatures.	
	General: Decreases peak resolution and increases all imbalance signals.	

TABLE 7-2 (*continued*)

	Effect	
Parameter	Differential thermal analysis	Differential scanning calorimetry
Discontinuous or varying heating rate	*Base temperature recorded in sample:* Variable base line, spurous "peaks" appear. Temperature values of real peaks are not seriously affected. Large errors in peak area. Noise increases. *Base temperature not recorded in sample and time-base recording:* Causes serious errors in peak area and temperature location. Also, all of the above.	An indication of instrument malfunction. Spurous "peaks" appear. Base-line noise increases.
Sample size	*Base temperature recorded in sample:* Small samples yield sharpest and most reproducible peaks. Very large samples distort peaks into cusps, which are not satisfactory. Increase area of peak and decrease resolution. *Base temperature not recorded in sample:* Large samples decrease peak resolution and increase peak area and width. Increased sample size moves 1° phase changes to higher temperatures.	Larger samples increase peak area and decrease resolution. Very large samples introduce erorrs in peak area and temperatrue measurement. Very small samples permit closer approach to equilibrium conditions.
Thermal conductivity of of sample	*General:* Increased thermal conductivity decreases system response time; results in narrower, steeper peaks.	Very little relative effect.
Atmosphere	*General:* Aside from chemical reaction with the sample, very little effect. Helium is an exception. The very high thermal conductivity of this gas carries heat away from the sample and decreases the differential effect. This decreases the total sensitivity and increases signal noise in some cases.	
Particle size of sample	Very small particles can lower the general sensitivity by decreasing the thermal conductivity. Chemical reactions can be greatly effected.	For 1° phase changes, very little effect on peak area and location in most cases. Peak broadening can occur on micronscale particles. Chemical reactions can be greatly effected.

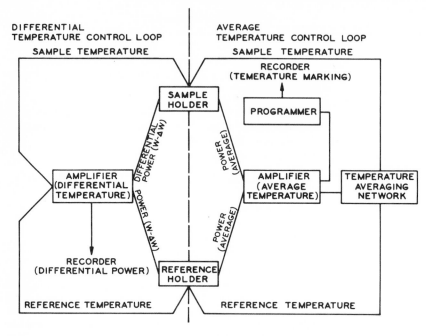

Fig. 7-4. Block diagram of DSC-1B (*13*).

7-2. DIFFERENTIAL SCANNING CALORIMETRY

Differential scanning calorimetry, unlike differential thermal analysis, maintains both the sample and the reference material at a linear heating rate. The sample is not permitted to lag behind the heating program during an endothermal transformation, nor to run in front of the heating program during an exothermal transformation. This condition is obtained by having individual furnaces for the sample and reference material. The instrument is illustrated in Figs. 7-4 and 7-5. The differential scanning calorimeter cell contains a sample and a reference pan. Under the sample and under the reference pan are located individual platinum resistance thermometers and individual heaters. The control module of the apparatus generates a linear resistance program that corresponds to the platinum resistance thermometers undergoing either a linear heating or a linear cooling rate.

Power is supplied to the heaters so that the platinum resistance thermometers not only equal the resistance program of that machine but also stay in balance with respect to one another. During an endothermal transformation, when the sample attempts to become isothermal, additional power is supplied to the heater under the sample plate. During exothermal transformation, less power is supplied to the heater under the sample plate. The differential power between the sample and reference material is recorded on the strip-chart recorder. A base-line deflection signifies some inequality between the sample and the reference material either with respect to heat capacity or rate of heat consumption. Since the program is generated within the apparatus, direct measurement of the sample temperature is not necessary. A sequence of marking pips is provided every degree down the side of the chart by the programmer mechanism. Temperatures can be read from this strip to approximately 0.5°C if the system has been calibrated with melting-point standards. Heats of transformation can be read to a few hundredths of a calorie per gram. Sample size for the differential scanning calorimeter and differential thermal analysis is approximately the same, 25 mg or less. With the differential scanning calorimeter an inert reference material is not necessary. The samples are encapsulated in flat aluminum pills. Reactive materials can be handled on platinum or mica. The dilute sample technique is usually not employed in differential scanning calorimetry since the problems encountered in the apparatus shown in Fig. 7-1 do not exist in DSC. The operation of the differential scanning calorimeter has been outlined in detail by Watson *et al.* (*13*). Two commercial instruments, the Perkin–Elmer differential scanning calorimeter Models DSC 1 and DSC 1B, are available for this technique (see Table 7-1).

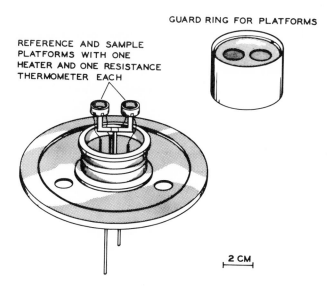

Fig. 7-5. Differential scanning calorimeter cell (*14*).

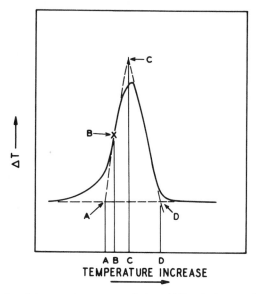

Fig. 7-6. Methods of temperature extrapolation (*15*): A, intersection of the extrapolated straight-line portion of the low-temperature side of the peak with the base line; B, deflection point of the low-temperature side; C, extrapolated peak; D, extrapolated base-line return.

7-3. APPLICATIONS

A. Determination of Purity by Melting-Point Depression

Both differential thermal analysis and differential scanning calorimetry can be easily applied to the determination of purity by melting-point depression or boiling-point elevation. Differential thermal analysis probably affords a more precise method, since results have been reported to the nearest 0.05°C with a well-designed piece of equipment (*6, 8*). The differential thermogram can be interpreted as follows: (a) The onset of melting is signified by the first departure of the base line from the normal. (b) The conclusion of melting is the vertex of the differential thermogram. (c) The reattainment of equilibrium between the reference and sample material is indicated by the conclusion of the differential curve. Various methods of base-line extrapolation are detailed in Fig. 7-6 (*15*). The vertex of the endotherm is usually a sensitive indication of the melting point. Vassalo and Harden (*15*) found that C most accurately reflected the melting point as conventionally reported. Other workers have found that A represents the boiling point most accurately as reported from conventional ebullioscopic measurements (*11, 16*).

In addition to the simple and direct measurement of some point on the

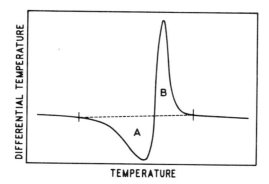

Fig. 7-7. Differential thermogram obtained when a sample containing 1.01% of 4-methylbenzophenone was run against triply recrystallized benzophenone (*17*). Both areas A and B are integrated; the ratio is compared with a "mismatch" blank made with both cells filled with triply recrystallized benzophenone.

differential curve, it is also possible to employ a purified active reference material. In this technique, a double differential curve is obtained. If the sample and the reference material are of identical purity, no signal will be shown on the differential curve since both the sample and the reference undergo exactly the same transformations. The endothermal signal from the sample is exactly equal to the endothermal signal of the reference, and no differential signal will appear. These curves are shown in Fig. 7-7 from the work of Bowman and Rogers (*17*). The technique has also been applied to the study of solid–solid transformations in an inorganic material by Barrall and Rogers (*18*).

B. Determination of Purity by Melting Range

With the exception of a few notable materials, such as camphor, the melting-point–depression constant is very small for most organic compounds. For example, in a 99.5 mole % material such as a normal paraffin, the observed melting-point depression is $\approx 0.3\,°C$ below the 100 mole % material; therefore, great accuracy in the measurement of the vertex of the endothermal minimum is required. This operation is extremely difficult. However, the shape of the differential thermal or the differential scanning calorimeter curve is quite sensitive to the impurity content of the material. The melting range is a more precise measure of impurity content than the temperature at the endothermal vertex. DTA can be applied here as well; however, the scanning calorimeter is somewhat more convenient to use because of its operating principles. Figure 7-8 shows a family of curves generated with National Bureau of Standards benzoic acid and two samples of impure material. Large changes in the shapes of these curves occur with the addition of $<0.2\%$

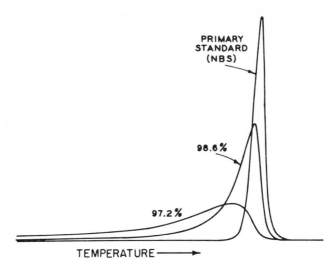

Fig. 7-8. Effect of purity on DSC melting-peak shapes for benzoic acid (*19*).

impurity. These recordings can be utilized on an empirical basis to compare an unknown with a highly pure material; the shapes of these curves have been quantitated, and the actual mole percent of impurity can be derived from the differential scanning calorimeter curve (*19*). This method is extremely convenient, since it is unnecessary to know precisely the melting point of 100 mole % material to obtain a reasonably good estimate of the purity of highly pure materials. The method can be questioned on the grounds that the operating van't Hoff equation is valid only under equilibrium conditions. However, very pure materials of molecular weight below 1000 generally attain equilibrium rapidly. Thus, the technique is ideally suited for the evaluation of zone-refined materials that are 99–99.99 mole % pure.

The melting of a compound is a first-order transition that involves a characteristic latent heat of fusion, ΔH_F, which occurs at a characteristic temperature, T_0. In principle, the melting transition for an absolutely pure, perfectly crystalline compound should be infinitely sharp. However, the presence of even minute amounts of impurities or crystalline defects broadens the melting range and lowers the final melting point from T_0 to some lesser value, T_m. The properties associated with the melting of the material that may be determined by thermal measurement are the melting point (a simple temperature measurement) and the heat of fusion (a calorimetric determination). With the differential scanning calorimeter, these determinations correspond to an abscissa measurement and an area measurement. These are combined to form an analysis of the peak shape, which is related to the purity. The differential scanning calorimeter measures the thermal energy per unit time, dq/dt, transferred to or from the sample as the temperature of the sample holder is changed at a linear rate, dT/dt (19). If there were no thermal lags in the system, the readout of the instrument would be directly proportional to dq/dT_s, i.e., the energy change in the sample per degree, the proportionality constant being the scanning rate:

$$\frac{dq}{dt} = \left(\frac{dT_s}{dt}\right)\left(\frac{dq}{dT_s}\right) \tag{7-1}$$

In the range where no transition occurs, dq/dT_s is the ordinary heat capacity of the sample. In the transition region, we may consider the quantity to represent the effective heat capacity of the sample due to the energy required to accomplish the transition. Thus, for an absolutely pure compound having an essentially zero melting range, dq/dT_s would become infinite at T_0. For an impure material, however, dq/dT_s is finite and a function of the sample temperature such that

$$\frac{dq}{dT_s} = \frac{\Delta q(T_0 - T_m)}{(T_0 - T_s)^2} \tag{7-2}$$

where the melting point depression due to impurity is

$$T_0 - T_m = \frac{RT_0^2 X_2}{\Delta H_F} \tag{7-3}$$

and

Δq = total heat of fusion of the sample (cal)
ΔH_F = molar heat of fusion of the sample, (cal/mole)
R = molar gas constant = 1.987 cal/mole/°C
X_2 = mole fraction of the impurity

These relationships, which describe the rate of melting of the compound as a function of sample temperature, are derived from the van't Hoff equation. The theoretical background and derivation of the equation is well understood. These simple considerations cannot be applied directly because of various instrumental parameters that independently shape the scanning calorimeter curve. These parameters can be evaluated in a single step by examining a highly pure material such as semiconductor-grade indium metal furnished in purities as high as 99.999%. Even this ultrapure material will not yield the theoretically sharp curve because of thermal-lag factors introduced by the instrument and the way the sample is encapsulated in the scanning calorimeter pan.

The slope of the ultrapure-indium peak is superimposed on the curve

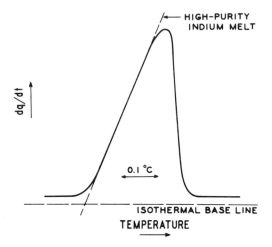

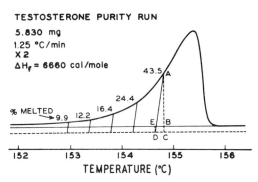

Fig. 7-9. Purity determination by differential scanning calorimetry (*19*).

of the sample (Fig. 7-9); the base-line displacement due to the heat capacity of the sample is also shown. This is obtained in the following heating program:

1. At a temperature 30–50°C below the melting transition, obtain the isothermal base line on the chart.

2. Turn on the program. The recorder will deflect by an amount equivalent to the heat capacity of the system and cell heating constants. This is the scanning base line.

3. 10–20°C after the transition, turn off the program and obtain a new isothermal base line. This should be within 4% of the base line obtained in 1.

In practice, a sample close to 2 mg is heated at 1.2–10°C/min; the attenuation of the apparatus will be 2–8 mcal/sec. Smaller sample sizes are recommended for very high purity compounds. Slower heating rates are advisable in many cases. However, with extremely broad-melting samples, it is desirable to increase the heating rate in order to increase the vertical height of the peak. The extrapolated temperature shown as D in Fig. 7-9 is the sample temperature (T_s) for the fraction melting at that point. The scanning calorimeter curve is integrated from the curve to the solid base line up to that point determined by line A–B. The dashed base line in Fig. 7-9 is the instrument base line which would be recorded if the sample pan and sample were not present; that is, the distance BC is the displacement due to the total heat capacity of the pan and sample. This is usually determined by calculation rather than experiment since the correction is small in any case, and one can tolerate a large error in the estimate of the distance BC. The solid base line is constructed between the point of departure and the point of return of the melting endotherm from the scanning base line. The fraction of the sample melted, F, is calculated by dividing this area by the total area of the endotherm. This is F in Eq. (7-4),

$$T_s = T_0 - (T_0 - T_m)/F \qquad (7\text{-}4)$$

where T_s = sample temperature at which fraction F is melted, T_0 = melting point of 100-mole % material, T_m = true melting point of the impure sample. It is easily seen that T_s is plotted as a function of $1/F$, then the slope of the line will be the melting-point depression, $T_0 - T_m$. Thus, the depression has been obtained without having any knowledge of T_0 or T_m. Figure 7-10(a) shows a plot of T_s versus $1/F$ for the DSC run shown in Fig. 7-9. The sample purity is calculated using Eq. (7-3) and the sample molar heat of fusion, ΔH_F. The molar heat of fusion is calculated from the total endothermal area between departure from and return to the scanning base line and a suitable calibration factor.

Unfortunately for the direct application of this method, most materials, particularly organic samples, have considerable premelting. This causes the T_s versus $1/F$ plot to be a curve rather than a straight line. A solution to the problem of reading the slope, however, is readily available. If the total area under the melting curve is A, the partial areas measured for the $1/F$ plot are a_1, a_2, and so on, and the low-temperature area, which is neglected by drawing the tangent scanning base line, is x. Then, for each a, the true $1/F_n$ is $(A + x)/(a_n + x)$. The value of x may be small with respect to any value of a, but when a is small, the neglect of x will be very significant. Since a is smallest at the lowest temperatures, the most serious errors due to the neglect of x occur in this portion of the plot. The error is such that $1/F$ is larger than it should be at lower values of T_s, which results in a concave upward appearance of the initial $1/F$ plot. Fortunately, the fact that the portion x of the melting area is not experimentally observable is not a serious problem, although the labor

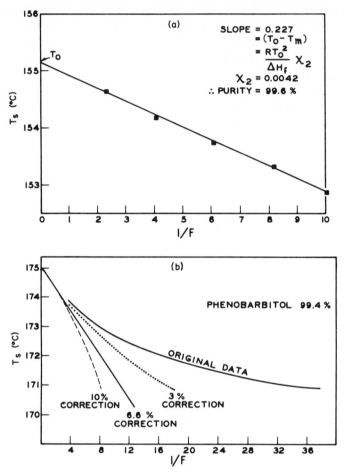

Fig. 7-10. (a) Testosterone purity determination (corrected) (*19*); (b) graphical linearization of $1/F$ plot.

involved in an absolute purity determination is increased somewhat over simple, direct plotting. The value of x is treated as a parameter to be determined from the experimental data. The procedure is to adjust x so that the corrected $1/F$ plot is a straight line. This linearization process is illustrated in Fig. 7-10(b) for the data obtained on a sample of phenobarbital of 99.4% purity. The true value of x was obtained by trial and error. The first estimate of the required correction was such that x/A is equal to 0.03, or 3%. Even though this is a small correction to the total area, the replotted data (dotted line) show the very great sensitivity of points at large values of $1/F$ to small errors in the initial melting region. A value of x equal to 6.6% of A was found to give the required straight line. If the areas are overcorrected, the plot becomes concave downward as shown by the dashed line in Fig. 7-10(b). There is only one value of x that will linearize the plot. Since low values of $1/F$ are affected only slightly by the choice of x, the estimates are made most quickly by extrapolating linearly the initial slope of the curve to the temperature corresponding to the largest value of $1/F$. This point is then adjusted by choosing x so that it falls on the extrapolated line. All of the points are similarly corrected and replotted. The procedure is repeated until a straight line is obtained. Usually two successive approximations will yield the correct value of x to sufficient accuracy. Purity is then calculated from the slope of the new line. The above procedure is not at all arbitrary, as only one value of x will satisfy the linearity requirement.

C. Determination of Boiling Point by Differential Thermal Analysis

Differential thermal analysis has been used by several workers for the determination of boiling points as a function of pressure (*11, 15, 16*). This method is capable of yielding a complete Cox chart of boiling point as a function of pressure over the sample within a matter of hours. The technique has been found to be extremely valuable with relatively pure materials isolated from a gas chromatograph or a very small zone-refining operation. The sample size found effective by most workers is 0.2 mg or less.

Since samples have measurable vapor pressures at temperatures far below the boiling point, DTA and DSC base lines will show some extensive drift prior to the actual onset of the boiling endotherm. The present authors have found that the portion of the DTA curve that most closely compares to the conventional ebullioscopic boiling point is the extrapolated onset temperature, A, of Fig. 7-6. The vertex temperature is dependent to some extent on the amount of sample thermographed.

The boiling-point method for DSC approximates that used for DTA. The sample, distributed on a powder or as a drop of pure liquid, is sealed in an aluminum planchet furnished by the Perkin–Elmer Company especially for liquids. Two small pinholes are then punched in the top and the sample scanned as usual at 10°C/min. The same temperature extrapolation is employed. Open cups cannot be used in most cases because of preboiling vaporization.

D. Determination of Rate of Freezing by Differential Scanning Calorimetry and Differential Thermal Analysis

Isothermal rates of freezing can be determined with a high degree of accuracy by DTA (*20*) or DSC techniques. In practice, the apparatus

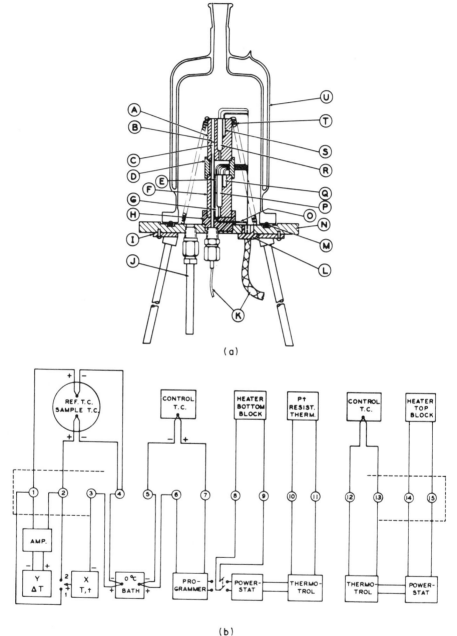

(a)

(b)

Fig. 7-11. Rate-of-freezing apparatus (20): (a) Cell design: A, top conditioning block; B, sample thermocouple; C, sample tube; D, marinite insulator; E, program-

Fig. 7-12. Phase diagram for naphthalene in benzoic acid (21). A. Iso-
tropic melt. B. Pure benzoic acid in
equilibrium with the melt. The melt
composition is shown by the intersection of the temperature ordinate with
the X-Y liquidus line. C. Pure
naphthalene in equilibrium with the
melt; Y-Z is the liquidus line. Y.
Eutectic point composition.

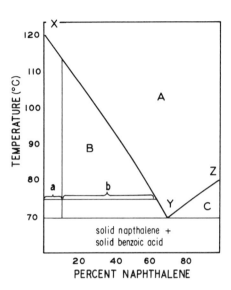

is brought to one predetermined temperature, the sample to another
temperature. The temperature of the apparatus is usually below the freezing point of the material. The molten sample is placed on the pan or in the
cell of the apparatus and differential power expenditure or differential
temperature is recorded as a function of time. The equipment, if properly
poised, quickly reattains equilibrium; freezing can be noted by an exothermal swing of the recorder needle. The rate of freezing is proportional
to the slope of the curve, the half-time to freezing can be computed in the
usual fashion, and the total amount of heat consumed in the freezing
process can be measured by integrating the area of the curve. An apparatus
suitable for this determination is shown in Fig. 7-11 (20). Although
applications of isothermal freezing-rate measurements are well known in
the literature of purity determinations, they are generally tedious and time
consuming. The use of DTA or DSC can greatly improve the accuracy
and the speed of the individual determinations.

ming thermocouple; F, bottom crystallization block; G, reference tube; H, marinite
seat; I, supporting tripod; J, copper tubing as gas inlet; K, electrical leads to recording system; L, multiple-pin feedthrough; M, Neoprene O-ring; N, supporting aluminum plate; O, reference thermocouple; P, R, cartridge heaters; Q, platinum resistance
thermometer; S, temperature-controlling thermocouple; T, tension springs; U,
vacuum-jacketed borosilicate bell jar. (b) Block diagram of circuitry.

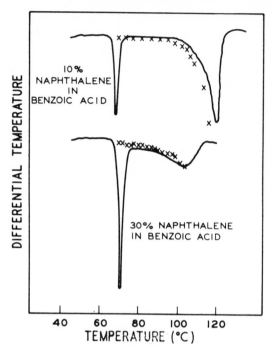

Fig. 7-13. Comparison of the calculated melting rate of benzoic acid with the actual thermogram (*21*): du Pont 900 DTA with 2-mm diam. sample tubes at a heating rate of 20°C/min.

E. Determination of Phase Diagrams

One of the least understood properties of a mixture to be zone-refined is the phase diagram of the mixture as a function of temperature and composition. This is a paradox, since the phase relationships are usually the working basis of most purification processes. A zone-refined eutectic is as much a mixture after 100 passes as before, for example. Classical methods of calorimetry are tedious and cannot be carried out on a routine basis for many mixtures. However, both DTA and DSC are capable of producing reasonably good working phase diagrams for two- and three-component systems containing several eutectics in a matter of hours. Visser and Wallace (*21*), Joncich and Bailey (*22*), and Gray (*23*) have reported phase diagrams of moderate complexity determined by DTA and DSC.

The naphthalene–benzoic acid system is an excellent example of the capabilities of DTA in phase-diagram studies (*21*). Under the conditions of the diagram (Fig. 7-12), only three compositions will show thermograms characteristic of pure compounds: pure benzoic acid (X), pure naphthalene (Z), and the eutectic at Y. All other possible compositions will yield two melting peaks (see Fig. 7-13). The first peak will be at the eutectic temperature, T_e; the second peak will move, depending on the composition, along the liquidus line X–Y or Y–Z. The lever rule applies in the calculation of the melting rate as follows:

$$\text{percent melt} = \frac{a}{a + b} \times 100$$

Terms a and b have composition values as illustrated in Fig. 7-12. The x-points in Fig. 7-13 were calculated by the lever rule for 10% and 30% naphthalene. The points were adjusted by assuming a value for the vertex

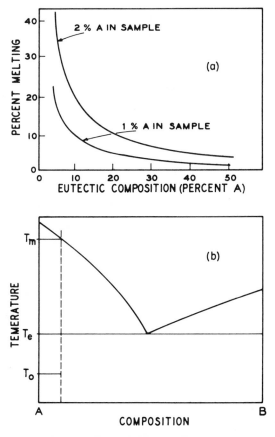

Fig. 7-14. Distribution of thermal effects in the presence of a eutectic-containing mixture (21). (a) percent of total sample melting at the eutectic temperature versus eutectic composition; (b) simple eutectic-containing phase diagram.

of the endotherm. In general, the sharpness of the second endotherm
characterizes the purity of the sample.

The melting of a typical eutectic sample is shown in Fig. 7-14(a) and
(b). From T_0 to T_e, the sample heats with no endotherms. At T_e, a
sharp endotherm occurs as the eutectic component melts (20% of the
sample in this case). From T_e to T_m, the pure A component melts at a
continuously increasing rate. At T_m, the vertex of the A component (last
endotherm on heating) occurs. All of the previous discussion assumes that
the sample mixture has been melted together and slowly cooled. The
eutectic may not form if the materials are cocrystallized from solution by
evaporation. Rapid cooling of the melt can disturb the eutectic formation
as well. The formation of solid solutions will cause significant deviations
of the generated phase diagram from ideality. Changes in the crystal
habitat can also cause unusual phase curves [see Fig. 7-15 (22)]. In this
case, the peritectic temperature is 140°C by DTA [148°C by classical
techniques (24)] and crystal rearrangements occur at 97, 148, 170, and
187°C for the phenanthrene–anthracene system.

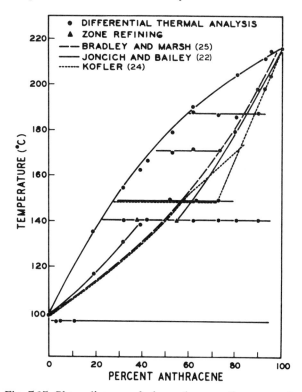

Fig. 7-15. Phase diagram of phenanthrene–anthracene system.

Alternative to using temperatures in the determination of a phase diagram and the eutectic composition, the heat of fusion of the eutectic mixture (usually the first peak as in Fig. 7-13) can be used. The eutectic heat of fusion is plotted as a function of temperature on both sides of the eutectic composition. Two lines will join the points for a simple single-eutectic binary mixture. Gray has demonstrated this technique for the terphenylmethane–stilbene system with DSC (*23*).

7-4. CONCLUSIONS

Differential thermal analysis and differential scanning calorimetry can be applied to almost any thermal method proposed for purity determination. Although many of the original methods are extremely tedious, the differential thermal techniques permit these extremely difficult methods to be applied in a routine fashion for rapid characterization of purity. Scanning calorimeter runs can be extremely useful in characterizing the degree of purification during zone refining. The methods are sufficiently rapid and accurate for following fractional crystallization and fractional freezing on large amounts of material. Since DTA and DSC are usually non-destructive, extremely costly samples can be recovered readily. Theoretically fractional freezing, fractional precipitation from solution, and analytical control of these operations may be accomplished in one piece of equipment.

ACKNOWLEDGMENTS

The authors are pleased to acknowledge the courtesy of E. I. du Pont de Nemours and Company, Instrument Products Division, for Figs. 2, 12, 13, and 14; to Perkin–Elmer Company for Figs. 5, 8, 9, 10a, and 10b; to *Analytical Chemistry* for Figs. 4, 6, 11, and 15; and to *Talanta* for Fig. 7. The authors are also indebted to Dr. A. P. Gray of the Perkin–Elmer Company for reading the manuscript and making several helpful suggestions which materially improved the section on purity determination by DSC.

REFERENCES

1. P. D. Garn, *Thermoanalytical Methods of Investigation*, Academic, New York, 1965.

2. P. E. Slade, Jr. and L. T. Jenkins, eds., *Techniques and Methods of Polymer Evaluation—Thermal Analysis*, Vol. 1, Dekker, New York, 1966.

3. W. W. Wendlandt, *Thermal Methods of Analysis*, Wiley-Interscience, New York, 1964.

4. R. L. Reed, L. Weber, and B. S. Gottfried, *Ind. Eng. Chem. Fundamentals*, **4**, 38 (1965).

5. E. M. Barrall II, unpublished results.

6. I. M. Sarasohn, Conference on Spectroscopy, Instrumentation, and Chemistry, San Francisco, October 1964.

7. E. M. Barrall II, R. S. Porter, and J. F. Johnson, *Anal. Chem.*, **36**, 2172 (1964).

8. E. M. Barrall II, R. S. Porter, and J. F. Johnson, *J. Phys. Chem.*, **70**, 385 (1966).
9. E. M. Barrall II and L. B. Rogers, *Anal. Chem.*, **34**, 1101 (1962).
10. E. M. Barrall II, J. F. Gernert, R. S. Porter, and J. F. Johnson, *Anal. Chem.*, **35**, 1837 (1963).
11. A. A. Krawetz and T. Tovrog, *Rev. Sci. Instr.*, **33**, 1465 (1962).
12. B. Wunderlich and D. M. Bodily, *J. Polymer Sci.*, **C6**, 137 (1964).
13. E. S. Watson, M. J. O'Neil, J. Justin, and N. Brenner, *Anal. Chem.*, **36**, 1233 (1964).
14. Perkin–Elmer Corporation, *Thermal Analysis Newsletter No. 6*, Norwalk, Conn., 1967.
15. D. A. Vassalo and J. C. Harden, *Anal. Chem.*, **34**, 132 (1962).
16. E. M. Barrall II, R. S. Porter, and J. F. Johnson, *Anal. Chem.*, **37**, 1053 (1965).
17. P. B. Bowman and L. B. Rogers, *Talanta,* **14**, 377 (1967).
18. E. M. Barrall and L. B. Rogers, *Anal. Chem.*, **36**, 1405 (1964).
19. Perkin–Elmer Corporation, *Thermal Analysis Newsletter No. 5*, Norwalk, Conn., 1967.
20. J. Chiu, *Anal. Chem.*, **36**, 2058 (1964).
21. M. J. Visser and W. H. Wallace, 17th Pittsburgh Conference (1966); also *Du Pont Thermogram,* **3**, No. 2, April 1966.
22. M. J. Joncich and D. R. Bailey, *Anal. Chem.*, **32**, 1578 (1960).
23. A. P. Gray, private communication, July 1967.
24. A. Kofler, *Monatsh. Chem.*, **86**, 301 (1955).
25. G. Bradley and J. K. Marsh, *J. Chem. Soc.*, **1933**, 650 (1933).

8 ELECTRICAL RESISTANCE-RATIO MEASUREMENT

G. T. Murray

MATERIALS RESEARCH CORPORATION
ORANGEBURG, NEW YORK

8-1. INTRODUCTION

The quest for the true physical, chemical, and mechanical properties of materials has led to the need for ultrapure research materials. As these high purity materials become available, it is essential that analytical tools for characterization of purity advance concomitantly. Analytical techniques for detection and identification of trace impurities in metals and semiconducting materials have made considerable strides in recent years. Mass spectroscopy, microprobe analysis, neutron-activation analysis, and chromatographic techniques have opened new dimensions to the search for foreign elements in the parts-per-million and lower concentration levels. Despite these advances, there is still a need for some simple measure of "over-all" purity.

Researchers have resorted to one of the more basic physical properties, namely electrical resistance, to define the purity of metals. The resistance to the passage of electrons through a metal is extremely sensitive to trace impurities, particularly at low temperatures; in addition, the measurement of resistance is relatively simple. In order to avoid the complications arising from making dimensional measurements, the ratio of the resistance at room temperature to that at some low temperature, e.g., that of liquid helium, is most often employed as the measure of purity. In fact, the term *resistance ratio* as a measure of metal purity is now of such common usage that without specifying, it is assumed to refer to the ratio of the electrical resistance at room temperature to that at liquid-helium temperature (4.2°K).

8-2. THEORY

The resistivity of a metal can be conveniently divided into three parts:

$$\rho_T = \rho_{th} + \rho_d + \rho_i$$

where

ρ_T = total resistivity
ρ_{th} = resistivity due to thermal lattice vibrations
ρ_d = resistivity due to lattice imperfections (consisting primarily of vacancies, dislocations and grain boundaries)
ρ_i = resistivity contribution due to impurity atoms

The sum $(\rho_d + \rho_i)$ is essentially temperature independent, whereas ρ_{th} is strongly temperature dependent $(\rho_{th} \sim T^5)$, and approaches zero at $0°K$. The resistivity near $0°K$ thus affords a measure of $\rho_d + \rho_i$; the contribution due to lattice thermal vibrations is suppressed. The variation of ρ_T with temperature in terms of the components ρ_{th} and $(\rho_d + \rho_i)$ is depicted in Fig. 8-1. Point defects (vacancies) contribute to the resistivity to about the same extent as impurity atoms per unit concentration. However, the number of the former in well-annealed metals is much smaller than the latter. Dislocations of a typical density of $10^7/cm^2$ contribute an insignificant amount to the R/R ratio. In the highest-purity metals obtained to date (10^{-5} to 10^{-6} atom % impurity concentration), the contribution of ρ_d is still small compared to ρ_i. For the present the resistivity near $0°K$ is essentially a good measure of the ρ_i contribution. In practice it is much more convenient to use the resistance ratio, $R_{298°K}/R_{4.2°K}$, than the absolute resistivity in order to eliminate the specimen shape factor.

The resistivity as well as the ratio measurement must be treated with caution for several reasons. The impurity element in question is not de-

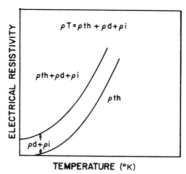

Fig. 8-1. Idealized resistivity of a metal near absolute zero. Lower curve is effect of thermal lattice scattering only.

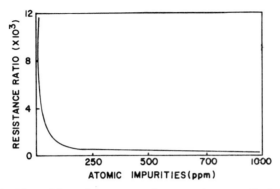

Fig. 8-2. Effect of impurity concentration on resistance ratio for metals.

fined; different impurities have vastly different effects on ρ_i. In addition, as only impurity elements in solid solution are effective electron-scattering centers, nothing is learned about the impurity-atom content in precipitate (compound) form. Finally, even for impurity atoms in solid solution, the resistance-ratio measurement is a sensitive measure of the state of purity only in concentrations in the range of about 100 ppm or less of foreign-atom content. This is illustrated in Fig. 8-2 where the variation of resistance ratio with concentration of interstitial atoms (O_2, N_2, and C) in refractory metals has been estimated (1). For purposes of computation the resistivity data of Ang and Wert (2) have been utilized. This computation shows that one can reduce the impurity level from 500 to 250 ppm without appreciably affecting the ratio, whereas a reduction from 5 to 2.5 ppm has a marked effect.

8-3. EXPERIMENTAL

Two methods are currently used for resistance-ratio measurements. The conventional "four-point probe" method is identical to that employed for many years for resistivity or resistance measurements. A suitable current is passed through the specimen while the potential drop across an arbitrary segment of a rod specimen is measured via two potential-contact leads placed somewhere between the two current-contact leads. The measurement is made at room temperature, and again, without disturbing the current and voltage contacts, while the entire assembly is immersed in liquid helium.

More recently, a contactless method has often been employed that is based upon the characteristic decay of magnetically induced eddy currents (3). If a steady-state magnetic field, H_0, is applied to a sample and then suddenly removed, the voltage, $V(t)$, generated in a pickup coil of N

TABLE 8-1

Resistance Ratios of Some High-Purity Metals

Metal	R/R	Reference
Aluminum	26,000	(5)
Beryllium	3,300	(5)
Bismuth	670	(5)
Cadmium	38,000	(5)
Cobalt	300	(5)
Copper	40,000	(6)
Gadolinium	100	(7)
Gold	2,080	(6)
Iron	400	(5)
Molybdenum	14,000	(7)
Nickel	3,300	(5)
Niobium	1,380	(7)
Palladium	2,700	(5)
Platinum	3,700	(6)
Rhenium	55,000	(5)
Rhodium	500	(5)
Ruthenium	65	(5)
Silver	830	(5)
Tantalum (zone refined)	2,100	(7)
Tantalum (high-vacuum annealed)	7,000	(7)
Tin	100,000	(5)
Tungsten	90,000	(7)
Vanadium	120	(7)
Zinc	42,000	(6)
Zirconium	250	(5)

turns surrounding the sample approaches a simple exponential decay of time constant γ, which is directly related to ρ by

$$V(t) = 10N\rho H_0 \exp(-t/\gamma).$$

For a circular–cross-section specimen of radius R,

$$\rho = 2.17\mu \frac{R^2 \times 10^{-9}}{\gamma} \quad \text{ohm-cm}$$

where $\mu = 1$ for nonmagnetic materials.

The tail end of the decay curve of voltage versus time yields an experimental value for γ from which ρ is computed. Again, the measurements are made at room and liquid-helium temperatures in order to obtain the ratio. The eddy-current method avoids possible contact errors and also permits the measurement of irregularly shaped specimens by merely taking the ratio of τ_R (time for 63% decay) at the two temperatures.

8-4. RESISTANCE-RATIO DATA

Since 1958 the resistance ratio has been considered a qualitative indication of purity. One of the earlier papers on this subject was that by Kunzler and Wernick (4). During the past ten years, however, great strides have been made in metal purification. The highest R/R values measured on metals prior to 1964 have been compiled and published (5). During the past few years a number of metals have been purified by electron-beam zone melting in the writer's laboratory. The resistance ratios of these metals have been measured by researchers in several laboratories. From these measurements and from measurements made by the writer, another list of highest R/R values has emerged. In addition, the Cryogenics Laboratory of the National Bureau of Standards has accumulated a considerable amount of R/R data on high-purity metals. These three sources of data have been used to compile the listing in Table 8-1.

Undoubtedly, some measurements have been overlooked or have never been reported. Nevertheless, it is believed that the compilation in Table 8-1 represents reasonably well the status of metal purity in 1968. The current widespread usage of the R/R measurement is evidence that, despite its limitations, it can be used with proper precautions and interpretations to yield a sensitive, qualitative measure of metal purity.

REFERENCES

1. A. A. Johnson and G. T. Murray, ARPA Symposium on "Analytical Characterization of Materials," January 1964; Materials Research Corp., unpublished work.
2. C. Ang and C. Wert, *Trans. AIME*, **197**, 1032 (1953).
3. C. P. Bean, R. W. De Blois, and L. B. Nesbitt, *J. Appl. Phys.*, **30**, 1976 (1959).
4. E. Kunzler and J. Wernick, *Trans. AIME*, **212**, 856 (1958).
5. W. G. Pfann, *Zone Melting*, 2nd ed., Wiley, New York, 1966, p. 146.
6. Cryogenics Laboratory, National Bureau of Standards, Boulder, Colorado: B. Powell, private communication, 1967.
7. Materials Research Corp., unpublished work.

PART **II**
PREPARATIVE METHODS

9

REDUCTION OF CYCLOHEXANE CONTENT OF BENZENE IN A COLUMN CRYSTALLIZER UNDER STEADY FLOW CONDITIONS

J. D. Henry, Jr., M. D. Danyi, and J. E. Powers

DEPARTMENT OF CHEMICAL AND
METALLURGICAL ENGINEERING
UNIVERSITY OF MICHIGAN
ANN ARBOR, MICHIGAN

9-1. INTRODUCTION

Solvents of ultrahigh purity have unique and unusual applications. One example is the extraction of carbonaceous materials from meteorites with benzene and the analysis of the extract in efforts to determine the possibility of life forms outside those on earth. These efforts are hampered by impurities in the benzene used as solvent (1).

Crystallization provides an excellent basis for the removal of trace quantities of impurities from materials. Column crystallization is a procedure by which countercurrent contacting of crystal and the melt can be readily carried out in the laboratory and is suited to the purification of solvents on a preparative scale. Benzene is especially suited for such treatment because it freezes at moderately low temperatures.

Recent theoretical analyses of column crystallization have proved to be successful in correlating experimental results and have served to identify the primary variables that influence the purity of the product. More important, such developments make it possible to design laboratory-scale (as well as commercial-scale) separations based on results of a limited amount of laboratory work.

Therefore, the purpose of this contribution is to describe a combined theoretical and experimental procedure for operating a column crystallizer under steady-state conditions with continuous feed and product removal to bring about a significant reduction in the cyclohexane content of benzene.

9-2. PROCESS DESCRIPTION

Column crystallization in its various ramifications has been described in Fractional Solidification (2). A column crystallizer is formed of two concentric tubes with a close-fitting spiral in the annular space (3). Freezing, purification, and melting sections are included in a single unit; the spiral serves to transport crystals from the freezing to the melting section (see Fig. 9-1).

In the purification of solvents forming a eutectic* with impurities, the primary separation is brought about by formation of crystals in the freezing section. Two factors tend to limit the purity of the solid phase: (a) As a result of the freezing process, impurities are concentrated in the mother liquor that surrounds the newly formed crystal and therefore contaminate it. (b) In addition, small amounts of impurity become intimately associated with the crystal itself as the result of slight solid solubility, adsorption, occlusion, or other factors.

The solid phase (crystals plus adhering liquid) is augered up out of the freezing section and through the purification region of the column. As the crystals travel through this region, they are washed with a countercurrent stream of purified liquid produced at the top of the column by melting of the crystals. Thus, the purpose of the purification section is to decrease the impurity content of the adhering liquid; the impurity content of the crystals themselves is not changed as they pass through this section.

Several factors tend to limit the separation achieved in the purification section. The solid phase with relatively high impurity content is continually being transported toward the region of high purity. Diffusion or back-mixing tends to eliminate the concentration gradient. Finally, as the wash fluid is produced by melting crystals that are themselves impure, the composition of the adhering liquid (and hence the purity of the product) cannot be reduced below a lower limit by the washing action. Therefore,

---

* Most organic solvents are of this type. In particular, cyclohexane and benzene form a eutectic (4). Column crystallization has also been applied to separate binary mixtures that form solid solutions (5, 6, 7).

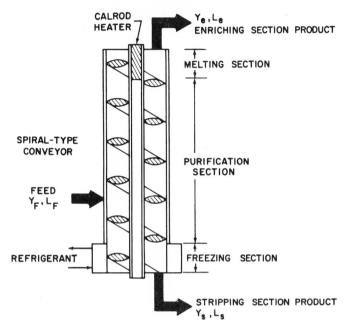

Fig. 9-1. Schildknecht-type column crystallizer operated with continuous feed and product removal.

in attempting to produce ultrapure material in a column crystallizer, the concentration of the impurity within the crystal must be minimized.

Figure 9-1 illustrates operation with continuous feed and product removal. Column crystallization offers significant advantages when operated in this manner because the feed and *both* product streams can be transported as liquids.

9-3. THEORY

Several theoretical analyses of the batch operation of column crystallizers have been presented in the literature (*6, 8, 9*). Recently, the importance of impurity in the crystal has been recognized and incorporated in the analysis (*5, 10*). More recently (*11*), the analysis has been extended to include the factors that influence operation with continuous feed and produce removal as illustrated in Fig. 9-1.

As in the case of batch operation (*10*), analysis is restricted to the processes that take place in the purification section. The washing action is described mathematically in terms of mass transfer between the washing and adhering liquid as determined by the mass-transfer factor, Ka. The diffusive or back-mixing effects are represented in the form of Fick's law with a coefficient of eddy diffusion, D. Internal and external flows that dominate the analysis are the mass-flow rate of crystals from the freezing to the melting section, C, the rate of flow of adhering liquid with the crystals, L', and the mass-flow rates out the enriching section (pure end), L_e, and out the stripping section, L_s. The composition of the wash liquid in the column at the point of feed entry, $Y(Z_F)$, and the constant impurity content of the crystal, ϵ, play important roles, as do miscellaneous column dimensions and physical properties of the system as defined in the List of Symbols. Standard mathematical procedures were used to obtain two equations relating the composition of wash liquid at any point, Z (measured from the freezing section), in the column, $Y(Z)$, above and below the point of feed entry, Z_F. The results are presented in the following paragraphs.

Enriching section ($Z > Z_F$, pure end)

$$\frac{(C - L_e)\, Y(Z) - (\epsilon C - Y_e L_e)}{(C - L_e)\, Y(Z_F) - (\epsilon C - Y_e L_e)} = \exp\left[-\frac{(C - L_e)(Z - Z_F)}{\left(\rho_l D A \phi + \dfrac{L'(L' + C - L_e)}{\rho_l K a A}\right)}\right]$$

$$(9\text{-}1)$$

Stripping section ($Z < Z_F$, impure end)

$$\frac{(C + L_s)\, Y(Z) - (\epsilon C + Y_s L_s)}{(C + L_s)\, Y(0) - (\epsilon C + Y_s L_s)} = \exp\left[-\frac{(C + L_s)Z}{\left(\rho_l D A \phi + \dfrac{L'(L' + C + L_s)}{\rho_l K a A}\right)}\right]$$

$$(9\text{-}2)$$

Equations (9-1) and (9-2) provide a quantitative description of the column operation and is suitable for design purposes, provided some experimental data are available for a particular column and system from which such parameters as L', Ka, and $D\phi$ can be evaluated. These factors will depend primarily on the motion (oscillation as well as rotation of the spiral) and for operation at fixed values of these variables can be considered to be constants. Furthermore, the theory suggests that for continuous production of high-purity product, the crystal rate, C, should be as high as is physically possible. At fixed conditions of spiral motion and constant crystal rates, Eqs. (9-1) and (9-2) can be simplified somewhat:

Enriching section

$$\frac{(C - L_e)\, Y(Z) - (\epsilon C - Y_e L_e)}{(C - L_e)\, Y(Z_F) - (\epsilon C - Y_e L_e)} = \exp\left[-\frac{(C - L_e)(Z - Z_F)}{(K_1 - K_2 L_e)}\right] \qquad (9\text{-}3)$$

Stripping section

$$\frac{(C + L_z)\, Y(Z) - (\epsilon C + Y_s L_s)}{(C + L_s)\, Y(0) - (\epsilon C + Y_s L_s)} = \exp\left[-\frac{(C + L_s)Z}{(K_1 + K_2 L_s)}\right] \quad (9\text{-}4)$$

This might not appear to be much of a simplification; it is indeed expeditious to use a computer in applying it for design purposes. However, it is the simplest form of the two equations that, when solved simultaneously, will predict the influence of feed location (Z_F) and product draw-off rates (L_e and L_s) on the purity of product ($Y_e = Y(h)$, where h is the length of the purification section) with operation at constant crystal rates with fixed column geometry and spiral motion. It is important to note that the values of K_1 and K_2 can be determined by choosing them in such a manner that Eqs. (9-3) and (9-4) match the experimentally determined concentration profiles.

Several conclusions can be drawn by applying these equations with reasonable values of the design paraments, K_1 and K_2:

1. In the production of ultrapure solvent, where primary emphasis is put on obtaining material of very high purity and the yield of product is relatively unimportant (i.e., the value of the product is much greater than that of the feed), the feed should be entered very near the freezing section.

2. The rates of the product withdrawal greatly influence the product purity. Increasing the rate of withdrawal of impure product, L_s, affects the product purity in two ways: (a) An increase in L_s provides for more effective washing in the stripping section because this net flow is counter-current to that of the crystals in the stripping section. [Note that the terms C and L_s are additive in Eqs. (9-2) and (9-4).] (b) More important, the impurity content of the crystals is found to be directly related to the impurity content of the mother liquor in the freezing section, i.e., a $Y(0) = Y_s$. If L_s is increased at fixed L_e, Y_s is decreased as a result of material-balance considerations, approaching the impurity content of the feed material as an absolute lower limit. Therefore, an increase in L_s will result in a decrease in ϵ and yield a product of higher purity. Naturally, as L_s is increased at fixed L_e, the yield of high-purity product per unit feed decreases.

Increasing the rate of withdrawal of purified product, L_e, likewise influences the product purity in two ways: (a) From mass-balance considerations, it follows that an increase in L_e should tend to increase Y_e at constant L_s. (b) More important, as L_e is increased at constant crystal rate, C, less wash liquid is returned as reflux; most is taken as product. [Note that the difference in the rates, $(C - L_e)$, appears in Eqs. (9-1) and (9-3).]

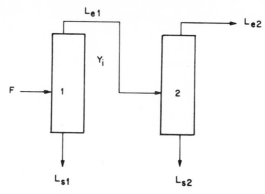

Fig. 9-2. Two-pass sequence for production of ultrapure benzene.

3. For a given set of operating conditions, decreasing L_e and increasing L_s without limit will not produce a product with no impurities. Instead, a lower limit of purity equal to ϵ produced by crystallizing feed material will be obtained. If material of higher purity is desired (or if production of significant quantities of material is anticipated), it will be necessary (or desirable) to make the separation in two or more passes as illustrated in Fig. 9-2.

9-4. EXPERIMENTS

The experimental part of this investigation was carried out to establish that the cyclohexane content of benzene could be reduced significantly by processing in a column crystallizer under steady-flow conditions of operation. Several runs were made to establish the validity of the design equations. Therefore, product was obtained only in small amounts sufficient for the purpose of analysis, and only single-pass operation was employed.

A. Equipment

The basic column has been described in detail elsewhere (10). Basically, the column was in the form of an annulus 60 cm long defined by a glass tube with 2.8 cm I.D. and a stainless steel tube of 1.27 cm O.D. The spiral conveyor was of lenticular shape with a pitch of 1 cm (12). The freezing, purification, and melting sections had lengths of 8, 50 and 5 cm, respectively. The freezing section consisted of a concentric jacket through which a refrigerant was circulated. Sample taps were located at 6-cm intervals in the purification section. The crystals at the top of the column were melted by means of an electrical-resistance heater. The product was removed from the top of the melting section by means of an overflow tube located 56 cm above the freezing section. The column was open to the atmosphere at the top, but the entire column was enclosed in an insulated and refrigerated box to prevent heat leak to the column. Feed and bottoms draw-off rates were controlled by proportioning pumps.

Analyses were made with an F & M Model 5750 chromatograph equipped with a flame-ionization detector. The unit yielded quantitative determinations of cyclohexane content down to 1 ppm after calibration.

B. Reagents

Phillips benzene containing 1500 ppm cyclohexane as the major impurity, was used for three experiments. Phillips cyclohexane was added to the pure benzene in three other experiments. This material contained 28,000 ppm cyclohexane. Both the benzene and cyclohexane were donated by the Phillips Petroleum Company.

C. Procedure

All experiments were made at a spiral rotation rate of 59 rpm and a frequency and amplitude of 290 osc/min and 1 mm, respectively. The feed entered at a point 4 cm above the top of the freezing section; the crystal rate, C, was held as close as possible to 2.9 g/min. The bottom-product rate was essentially constant at 3.2 g/min. The feed composition was either 1500 or 28,000 ppm cyclohexane in benzene. The feed rate, F (and therefore the overhead-product rate, L_e), was varied in such a manner as to provide a test of the design equations. The operating conditions are summarized in Table 9-1.

Considerable care was taken to assure steady-state conditions so that meaningful data could be obtained. The control of the refrigerant temperature had to be adjusted during start-up, and a purging procedure was followed to reduce the time required to reach steady state. These procedures are described in some detail in the following paragraphs.

The column was filled with 300 ml of liquid feed material, the spiral motion was established, and the feed and bottoms product pumps started. The coolant temperature to the freezing section was reduced from 20°C to −2°C for the case of the 1500-ppm cyclohexane feed at a rate of 20°C/hr. A slow approach is necessary to prevent the column from plugging. The temperature difference between the refrigerant and the liquid in the freezing section (which is a function of the freezing-section composition and the crystal rate) was maintained at approximately 4°C. The crystals were allowed to form and be carried up through the column until the annulus was completely filled with the crystal–liquid slurry. The resistance heater was then turned on and the voltage adjusted to provide sufficient power to maintain a crystal–liquid interface at the top of the

TABLE 9-1

Operating Data for the Separation of Benzene–Cyclohexane Mixtures

Parameter	Run					
	1	2	3	5A	5B	9
	Experimental values					
Y_F (ppm C_6H_{12})	28,000	28,000	28,000	1500	1500	1500
Z_F (cm)	4.0	4.0	4.0	4.0	4.0	4.0
F (g/min)	4.2	4.0	5.3	5.3	4.7	3.5
L_e (g/min)	0.68	1.0	2.3	1.8	1.2	0.30
C (g/min)	2.9	2.9	2.9	2.6	2.9	2.9
L_e/C	0.23	0.34	0.79	0.69	0.42	0.10
L_e/F	0.16	0.25	0.43	0.34	0.25	0.86
Y_s (ppm C_6H_{12})	33,900	37,000	37,000	2090	2540	2140
Y_e (ppm C_6H_{12})	40	60	370	16	4.0	1.0
	Calculated values					
Y_e (ppm C_6H_{12})[a]	40	57	440	24	3.0	1.1
ϵ (ppm C_6H_{12})	40	57	57	2.1		1.0

[a] Calculated from Eqs. (9-1) and (9-2).

column, i.e., in the melting section. By measuring the voltage supplied to the heater and relating the energy output to the heat of fusion, the crystal rate was calculated. Adjustments in the refrigerant temperature were then made to obtain the desired crystal rate.

Once the crystal rate had been established and the column had been operating for approximately one hour, a purging procedure was initiated. The heater was turned off and the crystals were allowed to fill the column up to the overflow tube, at which time the heater was again turned on. This process flushes the bulk of the impurities from the top section of the column and is repeated at least one more time during the unsteady-state period. Once this flushing was completed, samples were collected from the overflow tube into glass vials every 30 to 60 minutes. The samples were immediately analyzed using the gas chromatograph until two consecutive samples were of the same composition, indicating that steady-state operation had been attained. Product was collected after steady state was achieved. In addition, in order to obtain added information with which to test the design equations, a composition profile for the column was obtained at the end of the experiment in the following manner: The heater, pumps, spiral, and refrigerant were turned off. Samples of approximately 1 ml were withdrawn through the sample taps using individual syringes, starting with the top sample tap and proceeding downward in order.

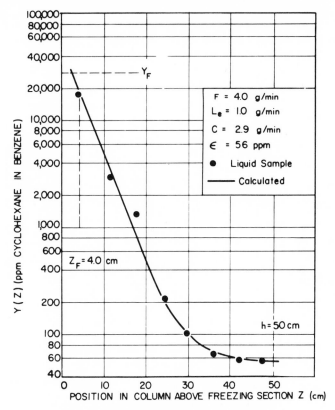

Fig. 9-3. Free-liquid concentration profile.

D. Results

Experimentally determined values of the compositions of both product streams obtained under steady-state conditions are listed in Table 9-1, together with values of the other process variables. Results of a typical concentration-profile determination are plotted as points on Fig. 9-3. Product purity concentrations are plotted versus the ratio of pure product to crystal rate in Fig. 9-4. As can be seen, it was possible to produce benzene containing 1 ppm cyclohexane from a feed containing 1500 ppm by a single pass through a column crystallizer.

9-5. COMPARISON OF EXPERIMENTAL RESULTS WITH CALCULATIONS USING DESIGN EQUATIONS

In order to relate theory and experiments, it was necessary to determine the functional form of the relation

$$\epsilon = f(Y_s) \tag{9-5}$$

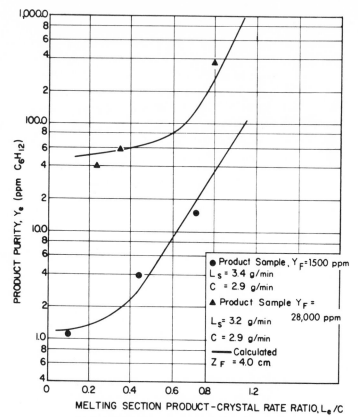

Fig. 9-4. Effect of product–crystal rate ratio on product purity.

Data from the concentration profiles determined for the six runs listed in Table 9-1 plus other runs made under batch conditions were analyzed to yield values of ϵ. Results of such analyses are listed in Table 9-1. These and other results are presented in Fig. 9-5. These data are well represented over the entire composition range by a constant value of distribution ratio, k,

$$k \approx \frac{\epsilon}{Y_s} = 1.42 \times 10^{-3} \tag{9-6}$$

This relation was used together with experimental values of the operating parameters and empirical values of K_1 and K_2 to predict values of Y_e for the conditions listed in Table 9-1. The results of these calculations are included in Table 9-1 and are seen to be in good agreement with the experimentally determined values. Calculated values are also plotted as lines on Fig. 9-4 for further comparison and to illustrate the dominant trend. It is noted that theoretical predictions indicate that little increase in purity is to be expected below an L_e/C ratio of 0.2 for the 1500-ppm feed. The experimental value obtained at an L_e/C ratio of 0.1 for this feed appears to be in agreement with this prediction.

Equations (9-3) and (9-4) serve to relate impurity content to position throughout the column as well as at the draw-off points. Another test of the design equations is to calculate a concentration profile using empirical values of K_1 and K_2. Calculated values are plotted as a line on Fig. 9-3 and are found to be in agreement with experimental values.

9-6. TWO-PASS OPERATION

As indicated by theoretical and experimental results presented in Fig. 9-4, the column and operating conditions described in this presentation cannot be used to reduce the cyclohexane content below 1 ppm from 1500-ppm material as feed, nor below 40 ppm from a synthetic 28,000-ppm feed. If material below 1 ppm is desired, two-pass operation as illustrated in Fig. 9-2 is required. Two-pass operation was not attempted in the course of this investigation because the precision of the available analytical technique (GLC) fell off sharply below 1 ppm cyclohexane

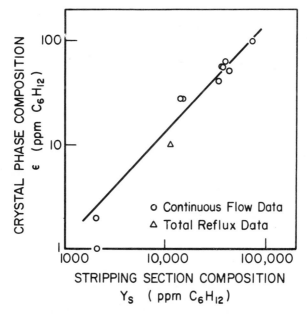

Fig. 9-5. Effect of freezing-section composition on impurity entrainment in the crystal phase. [Calculated from Eq. (9-1) and (9-2) and experimental concentration profiles.]

content. However, the design equations were applied to determine under what conditions it might be desirable to use a two-pass arrangement to produce material of 1-ppm purity. The feed and crystal rates were constrained at 5 g/min for each pass. An optimum value of impurity content for this intermediate product, Y_i, was determined to be 75 ppm. The time required to start up the column for each operation was estimated to be five hours. On the basis of these calculations, it was determined that one pass should be used for a desired total production of 2.0 liters or less. A total of 27 hours would be required. For quantities of purified benzene (3 ppm cyclohexane) greater than 2.0 liters, two passes should be used.

9-7. SUMMARY AND CONCLUSIONS

One pass through a column crystallizer under steady-flow conditions produces benzene containing 1 ppm cyclohexane. Excellent agreement between experimental results and calculations based on design equations developed from a theoretical model indicate that it should be possible to apply the design equations to determine optimum processing conditions.

LIST OF SYMBOLS

A area of column cross section, L^2
C crystal rate, $M\theta^{-1}$
D effective diffusion coefficient, $L^2\theta^{-1}$
Ka over-all mass-transfer coefficient, θ^{-1}
h length of purification section, L
L' adhering liquid, $M\theta^{-1}$
X composition of impurity in crystal phase, ppm wt.
Y composition of impurity in free liquid, ppm wt.
Z position in column, measured from top of freezing section, L
ρ density, ML^{-3}
ϕ volume fraction free liquid
ϵ constant composition of impurity in crystal phase, ppm wt.

Subscripts

e melting section product
F feed to column
l free liquid
s stripping section

REFERENCES

1. W. G. Meinschein, N. Bartholomew, and D. J. Hennessy, *Ann. N. Y. Acad. Sci.*, 108, 553 (1963).
2. R. Albertins, W. C. Gates, and J. E. Powers, in *Fractional Solidification*, Vol. 1 (M. Zief and W. R. Wilcox, eds.), Dekker, New York, 1967.

3. H. Schildknecht, *Z. Anal. Chem.,* 181, 254 (1961).

4. J. Timmermans, *Physico-Chemical Constants of Pure Organic Compounds,* Elsevier, Amsterdam, 1950.

5. W. C. Gates, Jr., Ph.D. Dissertation, Univ. Michigan, Ann Arbor, 1967.

6. J. E. Powers, in *Symposium über Zonenschmelzen und Kolonnenkristallisieren* (H. Schildknecht, ed.), Kernforschungzentrum, Karslruhe, 1963, p. 57.

7. H. Schildknecht and J. Breiter, Symposium on Crystallization, Joint IMIG–AIChE Meeting, Mexico City, 1967.

8. A. G. Anikin, *Dokl. Akad. Nauk SSSR,* 151(5), 1139 (1963).

9. A. G. Anikin, *Russ. J. Phys. Chem. (English Transl.),* 37(3), 377 (1963).

10. R. Albertins, Ph.D. Dissertation, Univ. Michigan, Ann Arbor, 1967.

11. J. D. Henry, Jr., Ph.D. Dissertation, 1968, Univ. Michigan, Ann Arbor.

12. Specialty Design Co., Ann Arbor, Mich.

10 PURIFICATION OF AROMATIC AMINES

Bernard Pouyet

UNIVERSITY OF LYON
LYON, FRANCE

10-1. INTRODUCTION

A study of the photochemical behavior of aromatic amines requires highly purified material. Although commercial sources of excellent purity are reported to be available, these substances are usually altered on storage by the action of air and light. Aniline, for example, may be orange or reddish colored; the melting point may vary between -6.35 and $-6.65°C$. Completely pure product, however, is colorless (*1*) and melts at $-6.0°C$. A gradation in properties is absolutely forbidden in photochemistry, since the behavior under irradiation depends on the impurities present in the initial product.

Fractional distillation does not remove impurities efficiently—some colored impurities remain in the distillate—whereas they can be removed by successive crystallization or fractional crystallization. Purification by zone melting affords excellent results, but the method has been supplemented by column crystallization in our laboratory for the following reasons: (a) Amines are relatively viscous near the solidification point; they tend to supercool, crystallize with difficulty. (b) Minimum quantities of 500 ml were required. (c) The melting-point range of compounds investigated extended from -30 to $+15°C$.

10-2. EXPERIMENTAL

All amines were first fractionally distilled in vacuo to remove most of the ionic contaminants (water particularly). We then purified the distillate in a column crystallizer having one inlet for feed and two outlets for products designed for continuous operation (*2, 3*). Substantial purification was effected in four hours. The important details of our crystallizer are the following:

spiral

outer diameter	35 mm
inner diameter	15 mm
total length of column	60 cm
rotation of the spiral	70 rpm

10-3. RESULTS

The melting point and optical density in the near ultraviolet were selected as the most sensitive measurements for organic impurities. Table 10-1 shows the values obtained with the same starting materials by column crystallization (A) and zone melting (B). The efficiency of zone melting is slightly higher. When the product from A is purified further in the column crystallizer (C and D), the product approximates zone-refined material. Optical density appears to be a more sensitive criterion of purity than the melting point.

In another series of experiments (E), relatively impure commercial amines were introduced into the crystallizer directly. The importance of starting with purified material is readily apparent.

The influence of take-off rate was one parameter investigated. With 2,3-dimethylaniline the optical density of the product remained unchanged until a flow rate of 0.3 ml/min was attained (Fig. 10-1).

10-4. SUMMARY

Purification of aromatic amines by column crystallization affords product comparable to that obtained by zone melting. The speed of the process

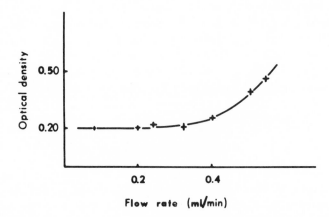

Fig. 10-1. Effect of flow rate on optical density for 2,3-dimethylaniline.

TABLE 10-1

Purification of Amines

Amine		Melting point (°C)		Optical density (1-cm tube)	
		Before purification	After purification	Before purification	After purification
Aniline				λ = 340 mμ	
	A[a]	−6.10	−6.00	0.215	0.210
	B	—	−6.00	—	0.195
	C	—	−6.00	—	0.210
	D	—	−6.00	—	0.200
	E	−6.4	−6.10	>2	0.220
o-Toluidine				λ = 365 mμ	
	A	−23.80	−23.70	0.080	0.050
	B	—	−23.70	—	0.030
	C	—	−23.70	—	0.050
	D	—	−23.70	—	0.035
	E	−24.7	−23.85	1.90	0.090
m-Toluidine				λ = 340 mμ	
	A	−30.10	−30.05	0.150	0.120
	B	—	−30.05	—	0.100
	C	—	−30.05	—	0.120
	D	—	−30.05	—	0.110
	E	−33.1	−30.20	>2.0	0.115
2,3-Dimethylaniline				λ = 340 mμ	
	A	3.40	3.80	0.320	0.310
	B	—	3.80	—	0.300
	C	—	3.80	—	0.310
	D	—	3.80	—	0.300
	E	−1.2	3.30	2.0	0.340
2,4-Dimethylaniline				λ = 390 mμ	
	A	−15.10	−14.90	0.230	0.225
	B	—	−14.90	—	0.215
	C	—	−14.90	—	—
	D	—	−14.90	—	0.225
	E	—	—	—	0.220
2,5-Dimethylaniline				λ = 360 mμ	
	A	15.30	15.70	0.290	0.275
	B	—	15.75	—	0.250
	C	—	15.70	—	0.275
	D	—	15.70	—	0.255
	E	13.2	15.70	2.0	0.300
2,6-Dimethylaniline				λ = 364 mμ	
	A	10.80	11.25	0.210	0.200
	B	—	11.25	—	0.180
	C	—	11.25	—	0.200
	D	—	11.25	—	0.185
	E	8.7	11.10	>2.0	0.210

[a] A = column crystallization of distilled amine (1 pass)
B = zone melting of distilled amine
C = A (2 passes)
D = A (3 passes)
E = column crystallization of commercial amines.

and ease of continuous operation make column crystallization a worth-while laboratory or industrial preparative technique. Columns can be arranged in series as suggested by Maas and Schildknecht (4).

REFERENCES

1. G. Armanet and B. Pouyet, *Bull. Soc. Chim. France,* **1966**, 1931.
2. H. Schildknecht and H. Vetter, *Angew. Chem.,* **73**, 121 (1961).
3. R. Albertins, W. C. Gates, and J. E. Powers, in *Fractional Solidification,* Vol. 1 (M. Zief and W. R. Wilcox, eds.), Dekker, New York, 1967, p. 351.
4. K. Maas and H. Schildknecht, Symposium über Zonenschmelzen, Karlsruhe, 1963.

11
THE FREEZING STAIRCASE METHOD*

Charles Proffer Saylor

NATIONAL BUREAU OF STANDARDS
WASHINGTON, D. C.

11-1. GENERAL DESCRIPTION OF THE METHOD

The freezing staircase technique of purification (*1*) depends on repeated controlled crystallizations with continuing removal of rejected impurities. An annular chamber, which may be either vertical or tilted but must not be horizontal, is slowly rotated in a space that is thermostated at a temperature a few degrees above the melting point of the substance being purified. The space inside the container has rectangular cross section and is half- to three-quarters filled with the substance being purified. Except where it is locally cooled, this material is liquid and flows to the low side of the cavity. Immediately outside the container and in close proximity to its opposed sides are the cooled surfaces of a heat-absorbing metal, maintained a few degrees lower than the melting point of the substance. Extending between these opposed metal surfaces, therefore, a solid phase is preserved from front to back in the washer-shaped cavity.

Figure 11-1 shows the cavity, the meniscus which is the uppermost surface of the liquid phase, two sets of metal coolers (one set extends inward from the rim and the other outward from the center), and two regions of solid phase. The portions shown would represent a sector of a device which would also have about 7 additional sets of coolers.

As the container rotates, the crystalline portions attached to the walls move with the chamber. The leading edges of each solid region move slowly away from the coolers, then melt. At the same time, the trailing

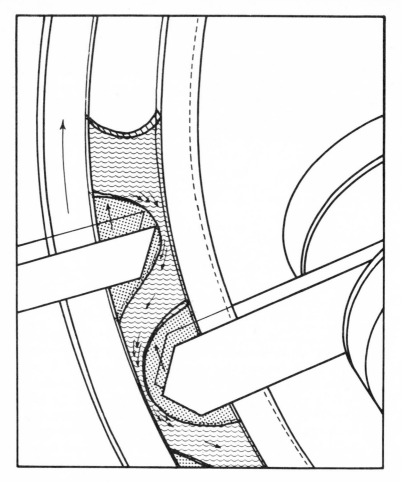

Fig. 11-1. Perspective drawing of the last two stages of a freezing staircase apparatus. The material being purified is confined in part of an annular space of rectangular cross section. Heated above the melting point, it is locally cooled by external metal shields forming crystalline solids, indicated by stippling. The solids move clockwise with the apparatus. They melt on their leading (clockwise) edges and grow on the trailing (counterclockwise) edges.

edges move closer to the metallic cooler and the crystalline solid grows. If a channel of liquid is maintained between each solid portion and the adjacent wall of the vessel, the position of the meniscus will not move. Counterclockwise through each of the channels will flow a volume of liquid that exceeds the clockwise transport of solid matter in the degree that liquids occupy more volume than their own crystalline phases.

Impurities which are rejected by the solid join the flowing stream of liquid and move down to the right under the conditions shown in Fig. 11-1. When the apparatus is operated properly, these impurities cannot return to this part of the system except by entering into the solid phase at one of the growing liquid-crystal interfaces. Backflow of rejected impurities can be prevented by limiting the width of the channel between crystal and wall. Although the required narrowness of this channel depends on rate of translation, degree of contamination, and specific characteristics of substances, a condition where the cross section of the open space is 5% of the annulus will usually be successful. Since clockwise backmixing or diffusion of impurities is avoided, impurities rapidly increase at the counterclockwise end of the charge.

When the apparatus has been operating for a sufficient period without addition or removal of materials, the distribution of impurities reaches a more or less steady condition in the different parts of the apparatus. The composition of the liquid immediately trailing any crystalline region is the composition from which the solid is forming. Since the liquid leading the solid region is replenished entirely by melting of solid, liquid composition in the space just after the solid equals that of the solid portion. The actual impurity retention coefficient, as used here, is simply

$$k = \frac{\text{impurities in liquid formed by melting of a crystalline stage}}{\text{impurities in liquid from which a crystalline stage freezes}}$$

This k should not be confused with k_0, the hypothetical solid solution coefficient, nor with the k defined by Burton et al. (2) as the effective distribution coefficient at any moment. While their factor k differs from k_0 because of inhomogeneities in the liquid phase, they do not take into account unpredictable contaminations that are a result of liquid occlusion by the solid, the phenomenon that is often the controlling effect.

11-2. CONDITIONS THAT ARE ACHIEVED IN PRACTICE

Tests were performed to determine the single stage effectiveness of removal of impurities by the staircase method as a function of starting purity and rate of growth of the solid phase. For this purpose naphthalene contaminated with 1,4-dibromobenzene, 2-chloronaphthalene, and the hydrocarbon-soluble dye Oil Red (duPont) was used. The impurities were added in the weight ratio 2:2:1. Various trial concentrations were used, but for the experiments described here, the total impurity was 1%. The starting naphthalene contained about 0.4% of solid-insoluble impurity. From geometrical and crystallographic considerations, it was inferred that the dibromobenzene and the dye would not form solid solutions with the naphthalene. 2-Chloronaphthalene, because of its geometrical and dimensional similarity to 2-naphthol and 2-naphthylamine, was included on the

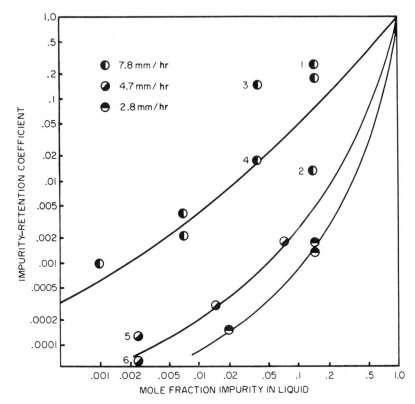

Fig. 11-2. Effectiveness of purification as a function of starting contamination and linear rate of growth. The observations of retention coefficient are for one crystallization stage. In each curve the relative retentions are illustrated as a function of the mole fraction of impurities in the immediate liquid from which the solid is forming. Each curve represents a particular rate of crystal growth. The reproducibility of retention at each stage is poor since the inclusion of impurities is accidental and depends on crystal orientation, supersaturation conditions, shape of the cooling region, and coincidences of nucleation.

assumption that it would form solid solutions. For the measurements the outside diameter of the annulus was 104 mm, the small diameter 89 mm, and the thickness of the chamber 0.5 mm. The inner space was held at a temperature near 100°C, whereas the coolers were connected to copper radiating sheets in the room. Their temperatures, therefore, were not exactly known.

The data of Fig. 11-2 were obtained by a very simple yet adequate colorimetric procedure. The obvious and more generally satisfactory analytical methods are inadequate for this purpose because they would not give instantaneous results for changing compositions in a closed apparatus.

A series of solutions of Oil Red in 1-methylnaphthalene was prepared. The series ranged between 0.0316 and 1×10^{-7} weight fraction of dye, its concentration in adjacent members differing by $\sqrt{10}$. These reference fluids were introduced into multiple cells made by cutting 2-mm wide slots part way across a standard $75 \times 25 \times 1$ mm microscope slide. The slotted slide was held between two other slides and sealed by allowing warm corn syrup to flow by capillarity between adjacent glass surfaces. A slight displacement allowed for insertion of a closing cover cut from another slide. There was thus a series of chambers, 2 mm by 20 mm and 1 mm thick which contained the 12 prepared liquids. When this device was inserted into the thermostated space of the staircase apparatus, the essential instant comparisons could be made between portions of the substance being purified and the reference standards. This helped a great deal with strongly contaminated liquid phases. Accidents of crystal growth in such cases cause abrupt changes in composition of yield. The accuracy of results was much improved by using a low power magnifier to increase the subtended angle of field.

Solutions of Oil Red in naphthalene or in the optically similar methylnaphthalene have two principal absorption bands. One in the blue green, extending from about 450 to 580 nm, has its strongest absorbance at about 520 nm. Another in the ultraviolet is strongest at about 320 nm. Simple inspection with a white background was fully adequate for the purposes of this study except at the extreme ends of the purity range being studied. At concentrations of impurity above 5%, the nearly equal deep redness of all materials lowered the accuracy, and measurements based upon freezing point as determined inside the apparatus were used as supplementary information. Below a mass fraction of 1×10^{-6} the pink color could not be seen directly with white light. The line along the edges of the chamber, however, still showed an interpretable color. This is tantamount to increasing the optical path length. The edge technique had to be used with great caution to assure that there was no liquid of different composition along the distorted optical path and that the conditions for refraction at the interfaces were equivalent. The results must be treated as having high likelihood of error in such cases. Another help in dealing with very low concentrations is the use of an extreme metamer of white light. Two colors are metameric (3) when they are visually identical but spectroscopically dissimilar. Thus, if we take white light, absorb out the green region with, for example, a magenta filter (Kodak 34 or 34A), and add a spectroscopically pure green until the effect is acceptable as white, the resultant will be one of the many possible metamers of the comparison white. Since the absorption of this dye is about 3 times as great at 520 nm as for the integrated green part of the spectrum, the sensitivity is increased accordingly. By using the 546-nm line of mercury in combination with the blue and red as produced by a minus green (magenta) filter, a different metameric white was produced. While this mixture was theoretically less sensitive than the one using 520 nm plus magenta, it was immensely more convenient.

From the foregoing it is clear that points 5 and 6 (Fig. 11-2) are actually less accurate than might be inferred from their nearness. It is hard to interpret the real accuracy at the low concentration for these points, but at other points in the figure, it is believed the basic results are not in error by more than 30%.

In Fig. 11-2, the actual impurity retention coefficient k is plotted against the mole fraction of impurity in the immediate liquid from which the solid is forming, both on a logarithmic scale. Three different linear rates of crystal growth (actually the linear rate of the midpoint of the annulus) were used to obtain these measurements. These are identifiable by the indicated symbols. Although smooth lines have been drawn, these lines do not indicate a theoretical relation between a starting level of impurity and the proportion of an impurity that is retained by the solid; they serve merely to coordinate and tie together the three series of values.

Reproducibility of some points is very low. Consider points 1 and 2. These results correspond to about 16 mole percent of combined known solid-insoluble impurities in the feed liquid as judged by the absorption of the sample and by the depression of the freezing point and to 7.8 mm/hr of travel. In the case of point 1, approximately 27% of the impurity originally in the liquid is retained in the solid, whereas for point 2 the retention is 1.3%. The corresponding amounts of impurity in the solid portion are 4.3% and 0.2%. When the amount of impurity in the feed liquid was about 0.5% (points 3 and 4), the ratio between retention coefficients for the two determinations dropped from 21 to 9.

The disparity between points 1 and 2 originates not with an inadequacy of analytical methods, but in the general characteristics of crystal-growth methods of purification. When crystals grow, particularly those for which at least one impurity is insoluble or slightly soluble in the solid phase, the major retention of impurity in the solid is often by entrapment, not solid solution. In the present case the Oil Red and the 1,4-dibromobenzene are insoluble in the solid. Under these conditions, even the 2-chloronaphthalene is primarily retained by accident, by an occlusion of mother liquor that is stimulated by augmentation of the other impurities, those which are solid insoluble. There is a distinct increase in concentration even of the solid-soluble ones as compared with what would be inferred from the composition of the adjacent bulk liquid and an experimental evaluation of the solubility coefficient.

Fig. 11-3. Conditions for which initial concentration of impurity or rate of growth is too high. The impurities build up in the immediate vicinity of the growing inter- face, depressing the freezing point of the contact liquid below that more distance away. This fosters growth of extensions from the growing surface, polycrystallinity, and encapsulation of already rejected impurities. Notice here the dissymmetry of the solid portion with respect to the cooling blades and the flattening opposite the point of the cooler. These effects are caused by the depression of freezing point on the right where the concentration of impurities is higher.

Figure 11-3 illustrates this accidental nature of the impurity entering the "solid" phase. Here the cooled portion, the solid, is polycrystalline. The entrapped impurities, seen as irregular blackening, occur in nonsolid- solution form as cysts between the individual, relatively pure crystals. It is significant that all parts of the solid are not equally contaminated. En- trapment of mother liquor is greater in the portion below the midpoint of the growing surface. Thermal stirring in the liquid causes a counterclock- wise movement. The impurities rejected by the upper portion of the solid flow in laminar fashion past the lower portion, increasing the probability of occlusion and increasing the concentration of impurity in the occluded spaces.

The differences between points 5 and 6 (Fig. 11-2), however, are basically analytical. Point 6, for example, corresponded to a concentration of 6 parts in 10^8 after crystallization and remelting—barely at the level of detectability. At point 5 the concentration after purification was ap- proximately twice as great. At such impurity levels, points 5 and 6 can be considered as fortuitously close.

11-3. MECHANISM BY WHICH IMPURITIES ENTER A PRODUCT; MEANS OF CONTROLLING THE CONTAMINATION

Although the major sources of contamination vary greatly from system to system, in any method of purification depending on growth of crystals the following are potentially important:

1. Solid solution
2. Occlusion of mother liquor in the spaces between individual crystals
3. Adsorption
4. The accidents associated with nucleation
5. Mixing of concentrated contaminants with the growth fluid
6. Molecular occlusion (clathrate formation, point defects, etc.).

Sources 1 and 2 have been treated here. Adsorption occurs with very finely divided crystalline substances but is not ordinarily an important effect when continuously growing large crystals are utilized. This leaves us with sources associated with seed formation, the back mixing of rejected impurities, and intracrystalline sealing off.

Figure 11-4 shows an area where nucleation has occurred. Initial spontaneous seeds were followed by formation of a fine network during crystal growth. No significant separation of the impurity occurred. The impurity is visible as a dark stain. As crystallization proceeded and the areas of the solid phase enlarged, the size of the crystallites increased. The rejected impurities are caught in the midst of the moss-like solid; no effective purification results. Since the crystals occupy less volume than the liquid from which they form, the liquid concentrated with rejected impurities is pulled into the interstices between the crystallites. Clearly, in any operation of purification by crystal growth, spontaneous nucleation should be avoided by every possible means. The attainment of this result is one of the principal merits of the method being described here.

Source 5, the mixing at every stage of impurities which have hypothetically already been removed, is an insidious degenerating influence upon many techniques of purification by partial solidification. Stirring of the liquid is an essential condition if the increase in impurity near the surface where growth occurs is to be held within manageable limits. Yet, when we melt and mix in a system in which there is neither liquid flow nor systematic removal of rejected impurities, the materials from the impure end of a space tend to be carried backward, step by step, to the pure substance portion (4). This common form of degradation of an achieved purity is avoided with a peculiar degree of success by the method described here; there is a continuous open path of liquid from the pure to the impure end along which a continuing stream carries the rejected im-

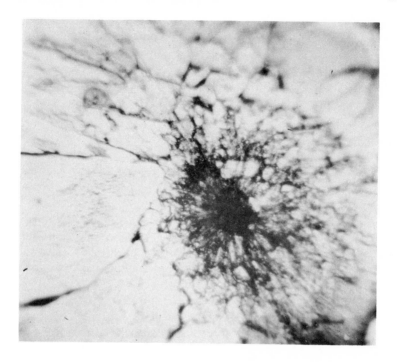

Fig. 11-4. Contamination of solid associated with supercooling and spontaneous nucleation. A nearly pure sample of 1,4-dichlorobenzene was deliberately contaminated with 0.5% of Bunker C oil (a petroleum tail very high in bitumens). This mixture was melted in a sheet 0.2 mm thick and cooled until nucleation occurred. From a point slightly below and to the right of the middle of the picture, where the first growth took place, mossy crystals spread out faster than could be interpreted by eye, encapsulating much impurity near the center. Farther out the impurity is entrapped between the crystals. Away from the center, stripes of inclusion are caught within the crystal or between the crystal and the glass windows.

purities to a point from which they can be removed without interrupting the process.

Molecular occlusion, particularly of the kind discovered by Bengen (5), which has subsequently come to be known as clathrate (6) formation, shares with adsorption the unusual characteristic that the proportion of impurity which enters the solid phase increases at progressively higher purities. The abnormally open crystal structure that is necessary for this condition is distinctly rare. It would be interesting to learn whether, with urea, the typical clathrate former, a large proportion of impurities travel to what would normally be the pure substance end.

Except for true or equilibrium solid solution and possibly molecular occlusion, the freezing staircase method avoids each of the enumerated sources of contamination. Thus, there is no spontaneous nucleation except perhaps during the first few minutes of a long continuing operation; the single crystals grow on one side and melt on the other while maintaining their identity, with the result that they steadily become more perfect; the rejected impurities flow away from the pure portions; and the purity level of the entire batch can be raised by withdrawal of small volumes which contain the concentrated impurities.

The method shares certain difficulties with other crystallization techniques. For example there are matters related to the anisotropy of crystal growth. For best results, a substance being purified must have at least two directions along which crystal growth can take place at a significant rate. By survival, crystals can then become oriented so that directions of relatively rapid growth lie nearly in the plane of rotation. Without satisfactory orientation, a "sport"* may appear, particularly if it can grow faster in the needed direction than the established seed. This effect is particularly important when we are confronted by an unusual crystal with extreme needle-like characteristics. The probability of the "sport" formation is then high even at very low rates of growth. Extreme needles are rare for materials which grow from their own melt as compared with those which grow from solutions. Another compound, carbon tetrabromide, which was originally chosen for study in the belief that much more rapid growth would be possible than with other molecular crystals, turned out to be interesting. The forecast had been based on the symmetry of the molecule and the low viscosity of its melt, but it neglected the low energy of the surfaces. The concentration of impurity in the region of growing carbon tetrabromide can build up only very slightly before the substance forms new units of different orientation. A similar effect with this material has been observed by Jackson and Hunt (7). The solid phase then grows around the impurity. The tolerable speed of advance in the system is therefore much lower than had been anticipated. As a consequence, the widths of the channels between the crystals and the walls of the container must be very accurately controlled. This necessitates accurate and changing control of temperature or position of the coolers.

11-4. PATTERNS OF IMPURITY DISTRIBUTION

One stage of purification and part of another are shown in Fig. 11-5. The picture was taken during the early part of a purification operation. The solid portions have stabilized themselves into the single-crystal con-

---

* Probably by analogy with the same word as used in genetics, a "sport," in crystal growth, is a crystalline portion of slightly different orientation that is in contact with the crystal upon which it appears, whereas a "volunteer" initiates at some distance.

Fig. 11-5. Two illustrative stages during purification. Each solid portion is mono-crystalline and nearly perfect. The concentration of impurities builds up at the trailing (growing) edge but these rejected impurities flow away, counterclockwise with the liquid phase. Where the liquid from the space between the crystals meets the liquid at the lower right corner there is a discontinuity. On both sides the surface follows the isotherm for equilibrium between the solid and the liquid of contact. Here, as in Fig. 11-3, the dissymmetry is caused by depression of freezing point on the side where concentration of impurities is higher.

dition but the impurities have not yet flowed to the counterclockwise end of the apparatus. The picture shows the front and back metallic blades which, from the outside, cool the material in the chamber. Behind every-thing can be seen the dim outline of the radiator that serves to cool the back metallic blade. The space between the crystals has not yet been cleared of the colored impurities, and the increase of impurity content in immediate contact with the upper crystal can clearly be seen. Likewise the liquid formed by melting of the lower crystal is more pure than the space into which it discharges. This, of course, would change in a short time. As the liquid flows downward between the lower crystal and the walls of the vessel, it tends to follow the surface of the crystal be-cause, in this case, the impurities are more dense than the compound. The skin of augmented impurity content near the surface of the lower crystal increases in concentration and thickness along the direction of flow.

A particularly notable feature is an indentation in the bottom surface of the lower crystal. The liquid from the upper space surges out and holds its identity until it mingles with the lower fluid. Around the cool metal blades the lines of equal temperature follow smooth curves, the forms of which can be established either with thermocouple probes or by progressively changing the temperature and observing the pattern of a pure crystal in a pure liquid. The indentation, therefore, represents the place at which the composition of the liquid changes. The crystal interface follows different isothermal lines on opposite sides of the compositional transition.

11-5. DISTRIBUTION OF IMPURITIES IN A RUNNING APPARATUS

A mass-balance equation coordinating the compositions in an apparatus of this kind can be written. For the data illustrated in Fig. 11-2, however, the ratio between solid-insoluble impurity in the solid and liquid phases varies by a factor greater than 2000. Moreover, there is no intimation of what happens to k at starting impurity levels below 0.1%. The coefficient k, therefore, cannot be considered even as a parameter. Nevertheless, when compositions stabilize, (1) any liquid portion contains all ingredients in the same concentrations as they are present in the solid portion from which the liquid forms, (2) the sum of the masses of the constituents in the parts equals those of the whole.

The following terms differ from those customarily employed for other processes because of conditions (1) and the recognition here of the great variability of k:

S_1 = mass of solid 1, the solid that forms from liquid 0 at the beginning of the sequence
L_1 = mass of liquid 1, that which forms by the melting of solid 1
C_1 = fraction of impurity in both solid 1 and liquid 1
$k_1 = C_1/C_0$
$\vdots \qquad \vdots$
$k_n = C_n/C_{n-1}.$

Then, for an existing charge in which the mass fraction of a particular impurity is C and the masses of the successive solid and liquid portions are L_0, S_1, L_1 through L_n,

$$C[L_0 + S_1 + L_1 + S_2 + L_2 \cdots + S_n + L_n] = C_0[L_0 + k_1(S_1 + L_1) \\ + k_1 k_2(S_2 + L_2) \cdots + (k_1 k_2 \cdots k_n)(S_n + L_n)]$$

From this, the concentration of an impurity at the end from which the wheel turns can be computed. Similarly,

$$C[L_0 + S_1 \cdots L_n] = C_n \left[\left(\frac{1}{k_1} \cdot \frac{1}{k_2} \cdots \frac{1}{k_n} \right) L_0 \right.$$
$$\left. + \left(\frac{1}{k_2} \cdot \frac{1}{k_3} \cdots \frac{1}{k_n} \right) (S_1 + L_1) \cdots + \frac{1}{k_n} (S_{n-1} + L_{n-1}) + S_n + L_n \right]$$

which gives the remaining concentration of the impurity after n successive crystallizations. Obviously, if we remove liquid L_0, containing $C_0 L_0$ of impurity, and replace it with an equal volume of a material of the same composition as the original charge, containing CL_0 of impurity, the entire succession of compositions will be changed.

So long as k remains so uncertain (an analytical expression to approximate the data of Fig. 11-2 has doubtful merit), it seems futile to use equations of this type except for the purpose of fostering an understanding of the process or facilitating judgments about impurity contents which are far below the level of determinability.

11-6. FEATURES OF THE FREEZING STAIRCASE METHOD

The freezing staircase method of purification has the following characteristics:

1. Except during the first moments of a new operation, crystal nucleation of every kind is avoided. At each solid stage, the crystalline portions melt on one edge and grow on the other.

2. If the rate of growth is held to an adequately low level and the concentration of impurities is controlled, those crystallites which are most perfectly oriented for continuing growth in the demanded direction will increase in size at the expense of their neighbors. Ultimately only one crystal remains at each stage. During sustained operation of the system, this crystal, by growing farther and farther away from the initial site of nucleation, will achieve an ever increasing state of perfection.

3. There is a positive flow of liquid in a direction opposite to the rotation of the vessel. This carries the impurities toward the reverse end of the vessel in an uninterrupted stream.

4. By removing the concentrated impurities plus a little extra liquid at least once for each revolution of the vessel, the purity of the material in advance of the first stage can be kept at a value that is only momentarily less pure than that of the starting substance. The great increase in concentration of impurities during the slow growth of nearly perfect crystals results in the loss of only a small fraction of the feed substance.

5. The entire operation requires rigid controls. The rate of freezing

that will cause multiple crystals to form at any but the first stage must never be allowed.

6. The channels between the crystals and the containing vessel walls must never be entirely closed off (except when withdrawal or addition operations are being carried out). The channels must remain sufficiently narrow that linear flow through the channels will be rapid enough to prevent back diffusion of impurities.

7. In the form described, the system has limited value for substances that are unstable at their melting points.

8. A container material inert to the substance being purified is necessary.

9. With purification carried out by random nucleation and disordered crystal growth, the retention of impurity by entrapment is usually many times as great as that which takes place by solid solution. For compounds and large molecules it is often many thousands of times as great. The salient advantage of the method described here is that, except for the first or in extreme cases the first two crystallization stages, the effectiveness of each stage is limited only by solid solution. The principal disadvantage is that any apparatus is limited to the finite number of crystallization stages that are represented by the cooler pairs which are introduced. On the other hand, a limiting purification factor of 0.5 for many methods must be raised to a very high power before it becomes as small as the 0.0001^{10} which can reasonably be predicted for ten stages by this technique. The prediction is limited by the requirement that the trend of Fig. 11-2 continues at lower concentration—at least, that k does not rise sharply at points to the left of the diagram.

REFERENCES

1. *Natl. Bur. Std. (U. S.) Tech. News Bull.*, **49**, 210 (1965).
2. J. A. Burton, R. C. Prim, and W. P. Schlichter, *J. Chem. Phys.*, **21**, 1987 (1953).
3. I. Nimeroff and J. A. Yurow, *J. Opt. Soc. Am.*, **55**, 185 (1965).
4. W. G. Pfann, "Zone Melting," 2nd ed., Wiley, New York, 1966, pp. 33 and 43.
5. F. Bengen, D. B. Patent application OZ12438 (March 18, 1940) or 869070 (1940).
6. H. M. Powell, *J. Chem. Soc.*, 1948, p. 61.
7. K. A. Jackson and J. D. Hunt, *Acta Met.*, **13**, 1212 (1965).

12

PURIFICATION OF ALUMINUM

John L. Dewey

REYNOLDS METALS COMPANY
REDUCTION RESEARCH DIVISION
SHEFFIELD, ALABAMA

12-1. INTRODUCTION

Continuous progressive freezing can produce up to 99.99% aluminum from normal Hall-process metal more economically than the electrolytic refining cell process. It can produce 99.999% aluminum from refining-cell product in a single step; other metals such as zinc or lead may be similarly treated. Although the process has been described previously (*1, 2, 3*), additional aspects of plant design and operation are discussed in this chapter.

A schematic view of the purification unit is shown in Fig. 12-1. Feed metal from a holding furnace flows into a mold heated by a controlled-temperature furnace. A stirrer mixes the feed with the molten metal in the mold and continuously sweeps it across the freezing interface of an ingot whereon a defined portion, less than the amount of feed, continuously freezes out as purified product. The excess of feed over product overflows to a second purification unit, a holding furnace, or other recovery means. The stirrer produces highly efficient and uniform purification conditions over the ingot face, and continuous overflow keeps the impurity level of the molten metal constant.

The degree of purification depends upon the impurity concentration of the melt, and the mass-transfer conditions at the interface as set by the physical properties of the melt, the ingot diameter, d, the distance, z, between the bottom of the stirrer and the freezing interface, and the rotation rate, ω, of the stirrer.

139

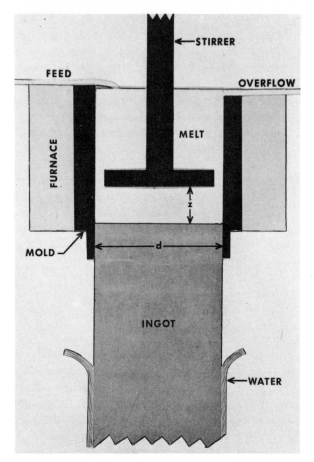

Fig. 12-1. Essential components of continuous progressive freezing.

Table 12-1 shows production data during the preparation of a 20-in. diam aluminum ingot (99.96% pure) produced at 93 lb/hr from a 99.82% aluminum feed stock.

12-2. THERMAL DESIGN

Thermal design is directed toward (a) providing sufficient heat input from the furnace to maintain a constant melt temperature in the mold, (b) removing from the ingot the heat of freezing and cooling and the heat transferred from the melt by convection, and (c) positioning the cooling section with respect to the freezing interface to help keep the interface flat.

Heat flow down the ingot consists of the convectively transferred heat and the heat released on freezing and cooling the product to its final temperature. The length of cooled ingot above the saw cut needed to remove this heat, and the length of the uncooled ingot between the interface and the cooling zone can be estimated from a two-dimensional electrical analog model. For pure aluminum a water-cooled length of 1½ ingot diameters and an uncooled length of 1 diameter have been satisfactory. The ingot is cooled to about 93.3°C and isotherms within about ¼ diameter of the interface are substantially flat and perpendicular to the axis.

TABLE 12-1

Production Data: 20-in. Diameter Ingot[a]

	Impurities (%)			Rate (lb/hr)	k_{eff}	
	Fe	Si	Total		Fe	Si
Ingot						
4.3 ft	0.0092	0.0155	0.041	93	0.131	0.167
8.5 ft	0.0076	0.0145	0.038	93	0.108	0.156
Feed	0.0639	0.045	0.181	940		
Overflow	0.0702	0.0931	0.200	847		

[a] Stirrer rotation rate = 140 rpm; ingot growth rate = 3.5 in./h; stirrer–interface separation = 5 in.

A. Stirrer Design

Stirring is an essential part of the process. The preferred stirrer design (1) causes the molten metal to rotate around the axis of the ingot while being drawn downward along the mold wall to the interface, thence inward toward the common axis of the stirrer and ingot, and upward away from the common axis. It provides good diffusion conditions over the entire interface.

This design provides an additional benefit that has only recently been understood. The effects of this design, and of another comprising a small-diameter impeller offset from the axis, were observed for aluminum crystallization in the plant and for dissolving wax in kerosene in a model. The offset impeller gave a uniform solution rate of wax over the entire surface while the surface remained smooth. The axial stirrer left the wax surface in a highly irregular, pitted and gouged condition, originally considered unsuitable. In the plant, however, the axial stirrer gave the desired results while the impeller gave poor purification over most of the interface area.

Thomas and Westwater (4) provide an explanation; Fig. 12-2 is a

Fig. 12-2. Dendrite growth at freezing interface of n-octadecane growing at 0.366 in./hr. The size of the view is 0.0300×0.0157 in. (Reprinted by permission of L. J. Thomas and J. W. Westwater.)

reproduction of one of their photographs of the freezing interface of n-octadecane growing at a rate of 0.366 in./hr. The dark areas are fully frozen n-octadecane, and the light streaks are crystalline dendrites that have grown upward into the melt, at times as far as 0.005 in. No doubt the aluminum interface has a similar tendency to dendrite growth and the harsh scouring action of the axial stirrer is necessary to flatten the dendrites and reduce entrapment of impurities. Stirring by electrical induction or an off-center impeller may stir the bulk liquid equally satisfactorily but give poor purification because they do not inhibit dendrite growth. The 20-in. diam. unit has operated with k_{eff} values only 25% higher than k_0 at commercial production rates, giving purification in a single pass that would require a number of zone-refining passes.

As noted by Wolten and Wilcox (5), many solutions that exhibit monotectic points should be separable by zone refining or progressive freezing. Thus, freeze separation of zinc from lead might permit zinc blast-furnace plants to produce die-casting metal directly and eliminate the step of distilling prime western-grade zinc. In the past, however, droplets of the heavy, lead-rich liquid have been trapped by the freezing zinc and the separation has been unsatisfactory. The effective surface-scouring action of the aluminum purification apparatus should reduce the trapping. Since many of the other impurity elements are soluble in the lead, a zinc ingot of good purity may be prepared.

The most favorable conditions for purification are also the most favorable for crystal growth. Purified aluminum ingots comprise variously oriented crystals up to 3 or 4 in. in diameter that may extend for several feet along the ingot. The variation of crystal size over a diameter shows qualitatively the variation of purification. No attempt has been made to produce a single-crystal ingot.

B. Materials of Construction

Aluminum near its melting point reacts slowly with Al_2O_3 and more rapidly with Si and Fe compounds. For 99.99% Al or lower, CS grade graphite, calcium aluminate-bonded tabular alumina casting mix, and Vesuvius Crucible Company's Alumelt have been used. Alumelt should be stripped of glaze and washed with molten aluminum before use. For higher purities calcium aluminate-bonded tabular alumina and fired pure alumina shapes will avoid contamination with carbon.

The feed-melting furnace can be a major source of contamination. Its interior lining should be formed from the above materials and high-purity mortar. For 99.99% Al or less, a mixture of high-purity cryolite and Bayer process alumina (6) may be used for the bottom lining.

12-3. CONTROLS

Control requirements in decreasing order of criticality are ingot-lowering rate, melt temperature in the mold, stirrer rotation rate, feed composition, interface-to-stirrer separation, feed rate, feed temperature, and cooling-water rate. Suitable control units, either manual or automatic, are readily available. Instruments are selected for their ability to maintain a constant condition over a long period of time rather than for accuracy of measurement.

The molten metal in the mold is kept around 5.5°C above the solidus temperature. It is controlled with a gas-fired furnace in turn controlled by a motorized valve assembly responsive to a control thermocouple located near the heated edge of the mold, operating through a Leeds and Northrup Model H temperature recorder with retransmitting slide wire and a Leeds and Northrup position-adjust temperature controller. The temperature-control range was less than 5.5°C at the thermocouple junction and less than 0.55°C in the molten metal. The range can be reduced by using an adjustable zero-adjustable range recorder.

The ingot-lowering mechanism should be adjustable for pulling rates between about 1 and 10 in./hr and free of jerkiness. Hydraulic units are favored. The hydraulic lowering mechanism for a direct-chill casting unit has been used. For continuous operation a device patented by Treadway and Davis is preferred (7).

The stirrer is mounted on a hydraulic lifter for easy positioning and for rapid removal from the unit. Its position is adjusted frequently during the first hour or two of a run and infrequently after the interface position has stabilized. The interface position is measured by a dip-stick while the stirrer is momentarily stopped.

Because of the large holdup of molten metal in the mold, the feed rate and feed temperature require only nominal control. Manual control of feed rate based on depth of the metal flowing over a weir has given satisfactory results; automatic control may also be used. Feed metal is held at about 700°C; the feed launder is heated to prevent freezeup. The exit-water temperature is kept below about 60°C. No detrimental effects of excess cooling water have been observed.

12-4. OPERATION

A starting ingot of impure metal a little smaller in diameter than the mold is prepared separately and positioned in the unit. The portion of ingot in the mold is melted with the cooling water flowing, the stirrer is inserted to a relatively high position, feed is started, and the temperature of the melt is adjusted to about 665°C. Production then is started at a slow rate and the mold-furnace temperature is lowered simultaneously. The interface level drops initially and then steadies. Production rate is then increased in steps with concurrent adjustment of stirrer position and mold-furnace temperature. The interface position is measured every five to ten minutes during the first hour, less frequently thereafter; the mold-furnace temperature is adjusted to stabilize the interface near the bottom of the mold furnace. The unit is shut down by performing the following steps in order: (a) stop ingot pulling, (b) stop feed, (c) remove stirrer, (d) shut off furnace and allow ingot to freeze in the mold, and (e) shut off cooling water. The unit may be held in standby condition at any step by adjusting the mold-furnace temperature.

In practice the stirrer–interface separation and the stirrer rotation rate are fixed; product purity is adjusted by varying the feed stock, the ratio of product to feed, and the production rate. The separation is usually 4 to 8 in. The rotation rate is near the maximum value consistent with thermal design that will not produce a vortex on the molten metal surface sufficient to pull air into the melt.

12-5. SAFETY

Hazards of the process are similar to those of direct-chill casting of aluminum except that a larger amount of molten aluminum is in the mold. The area beneath the mold should be designed to prevent entrapment of water if any conceivable type of spill should occur (a pound of molten aluminum will generate 10 cubic feet of steam).

Spillage can result from breakage or from driving the interface out of the mold. The latter problem is avoided by extending the mold below the mold-furnace bottom. An extension of 10 inches has worked satisfactorily, but greater lengths can be employed for large-diameter ingots. Since heat loss through the ingot increases as the interface drops, the system tends to be self-stabilizing; but a combination of excessive melt temperature and excessive ingot pull rate or a sudden fall of the ingot can be troublesome. All control instruments should be designed to fail safely; the interface position should be controlled carefully during startup.

REFERENCES

1. J. L. Dewey, U. S. Patent 3,163,895 (1965).
2. J. L. Dewey, *J. Metals,* 17, 940 (1965).
3. M. Zief and W. R. Wilcox, eds., *Fractional Solidification,* Vol. I, Dekker, New York, 1967.
4. L. J. Thomas and J. W. Westwater, *Chem. Eng. Progr. Symp. Ser.,* 59(41), 155 (1963).
5. G. M. Wolten and W. R. Wilcox, in *Fractional Solidification,* Vol. I (M. Zief and W. R. Wilcox, eds.), Dekker, New York, 1967, Chapter 2.
6. J. L. Dewey, U. S. Patent 3,093,570 (1963).
7. R. F. Treadway and B. K. Davis, U. S. Patent 3,238,577 (1966).

13

CONCENTRATION OF HUMIC ACIDS IN NATURAL WATERS

Joseph Shapiro

UNIVERSITY OF MINNESOTA
MINNEAPOLIS, MINNESOTA

Studies of the biological and chemical phenomena of natural waters have long suggested that the dissolved organic substances found in such waters are of importance. With the advent of infrared spectrophotometry and gas chromatography, investigations of such substances have only recently been successful. Even with these new instruments, however, the organics are present in too dilute solution for measurement. Yellow humic acids, for example, are present in natural waters in the order of 1–20 mg/liter; extraction from lake waters by polar solvents is possible, but the extraction is much more efficient from more concentrated solutions. Most workers have used vacuum distillation for such a concentration step, but the possibility of altering unknown chemical structures during distillation clearly exists. A safer method is progressive freezing, the concentration of lake waters by removing most of the water in the form of ice.

13-1. PROCEDURE

The basic procedure is essentially that used in commercial ice making (agitation of the solution at a controlled rate of freezing). Air agitation and brine freezing are the usual techniques. In the laboratory air stirring causes the formation of aerosols and losses by splashing. Therefore, an apparatus based on mechanical stirring was constructed. This apparatus (Fig. 13-1) consists of a 55-gal stainless steel drum wrapped on the outside with 120 ft of $\frac{1}{2}$-in. copper tubing soldered to the drum for conduction and filled with Freon 12. The tubing is connected to a $\frac{1}{2}$-hp compressor; the system is insulated with Fiberglas.

After the drum is filled with about 45 gal of lake water, the compressor is started. A single stirrer with a four-bladed propeller 2 in. in diameter is powered by a $\frac{1}{30}$-hp motor. The stirrer is positioned vertically in the

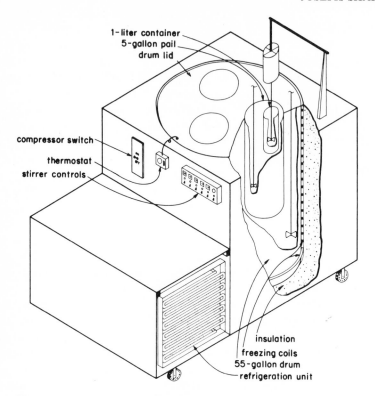

Fig. 13-1. Apparatus for concentration of humic acids in natural waters.

center of the drum with the blades bent so that the thrust is downward. The propeller should be at least 8 in. below the surface. A convenient support for the stirrer is a wooden board with a central hole through which the shaft may pass (Note 1). The volume of unfrozen solution will be reduced to about 5–10 gal in 48 hr continuous operation. At this point the compressor is turned off and the concentrate is removed by pumping. In one model a central hole in the bottom of the drum was connected to a pipe and valve for this purpose. This is feasible because with the refrigeration limited to the sides of the drum no ice forms on the bottom. Upon removal of the concentrate the ice generally cracks with a resounding noise because of new stresses. Removal of the ice may be accomplished either by melting or by breaking with an ice pick.

Frequently it is desired to concentrate lake water to an even greater extent. The drum is used as a brine bath by placing in it about 35 gallons of water containing 2 lb/gal of sodium chloride or 2 lb/gal of sodium nitrate. The drum lid, from which three large and two small holes are cut out, is positioned; then a thermostat and stirrer are inserted into the brine through the small holes. The thermostat is usually set at -5 to $-7°C$. Through the lid are suspended three 5-gal stainless steel cream pails (Note 2). In this manner three 15–17-liter lots may be concentrated; stirring is similar to that for the drum except that variable-speed stirrers are advisable. The propeller is positioned about two thirds of the way into the solution and the stirring rate is adjusted to create a vortex. As freezing proceeds, the stirrer is raised periodically to allow the ice to advance upward (Note 3). Simultaneously the stirrer is slowed to prevent splashing. Reduced stirring rate also allows the liquid level to subside so that it lies below the ice level and thus prevents loss of concentrate onto the ice shoulder. In this manner three 15-liter volumes may be concentrated to about ½ liter in 8–9 hr (Note 4), whereupon the concentrate may be recovered by siphoning from the cavity in the ice.

If further concentration is desired, one of the 5-gal pails is filled with brine; a stirrer for circulation of the brine is added. Then a 1-liter stainless steel container is suspended into this brine through a hole in a Plexiglas lid. A stirrer is placed into the liter container and the sample is treated as described for the 15-liter volumes. As any losses at this stage represent loss of a large portion of the original sample, it is advisable to begin by stirring quickly enough to form a deep vortex, and then to slow the stirring rate while periodically raising the stirrer. Concentration is carried out to the stage desired or to the point at which cloudy ice indicates entrapment of solute (Notes 5 and 6).

At this point the original 200 liters will have been concentrated to perhaps 200 ml, a factor of 1000; now acidification and solvent extraction will yield the bulk of the humic acids (Note 7).

As quantitative analysis of trace amounts of humic acids is impossible, the recovery achieved is unknown. Reconcentration of melted ice, however, indicates that the recovery must be very close to 100%. By similar techniques Baker (1, 2) consistently recorded 100% recovery of organic materials; these results approximate those of Kobayashi and Lee (3), Shapiro (4, 5) and Wilson et al. (6). In fact, Baker's work shows that recovery is sufficiently nonspecific so that an internal standard may be used to estimate recovery of other organics by means of gas–liquid chromatography.

NOTES

1. On occasion stirring creates waves which threaten to spill the water. The waves are easily damped by suspending a 1 liter Erlenmeyer flask so that its flat bottom projects about 2 inches below the water surface at the periphery of the drum.

2. The liquid level in the pails should be at or just above the level in

the drum to prevent floating. As floating may still occur due to the density of the brine or removal of the concentrate, Plexiglas covers for the pails support lead weights.

3. Even with stirring, supercooling may produce a slushy mass. This condition will gradually correct itself.

4. The rate of freezing of the 3 containers may be speeded by increasing the rate of stirring of the brine.

5. If entrapment occurs near the end of a run, a heat gun may be used to melt the last-formed ice. If serious entrapment has occurred, retain the concentrate, melt the ice, and begin again with the more dilute solution.

6. The method is best suited to dilute solutions. As a general rule, the more concentrated the solution the slower must be the freezing rate and the faster the rate of stirring to avoid entrapment.

7. For small volumes the procedure described by Baker (2) can be employed. Here solutions (<1 liter) are placed in a round-bottomed flask which is rotated in a salt–ice bath. In any event the freezing rate must be controllable; rapid freezing with acetone–dry-ice mixtures is to be avoided. If volatile solutions are present, recovery is greatly aided by a tight-fitting cover with a small hole for the stirring rod.

REFERENCES

1. R. A. Baker, *J. Water Pollution Control Federation,* 37, 1164 (1965).
2. R. A. Baker, *Water Res.,* 1, 61 (1967).
3. S. Kobayashi and G. F. Lee, *Anal. Chem.,* 36, 2197 (1964).
4. J. Shapiro, *Science,* 133, 2063 (1961).
5. J. Shapiro, *Anal. Chem.,* 39, 280 (1967).
6. T. E. Wilson, D. J. Evans, and M. L. Theriot, *Appl. Microbiol.,* 12, 96 (1964).

14 FRACTIONATION OF POLYSTYRENE

Joseph D. Loconti

U. S. ARMY NATICK LABORATORIES
NATICK, MASSACHUSETTS

14-1. INTRODUCTION

All polymers consist of a mixture of molecules; the distribution of molecular weight is broad or narrow depending on the type of polymer and method of synthesis. Some properties of a polymer are strongly influenced by the shape of the molecular-weight distribution curve; it is therefore important to be able to determine this curve. Several methods for determining distribution are fractional precipitation, ultracentrifugation, chromatographic fractionation, and gel-permeation chromatography. Each has certain assets and limitations. The development of a freezing-fractionation process adds still another method with its own unique contribution to the fractionation process.

Polymer fractionation by a fractional-solidification process can be obtained by progressive freezing or by zone melting. The unidirectional freezing of a dilute solution of polystyrene in benzene yields a frozen ingot in which the polymer has been redistributed on a molecular-weight basis; the highest molecular species appear in the first-frozen end, with successively lower molecular weights in the direction of the opposite end (*1, 2*). In the zone-melting method the highest molecular species will appear in the first-melted end of the ingot.

14-2. METHOD A: PROGRESSIVE FREEZING

A zone refiner patterned after one designed at the National Bureau of Standards (*3*) was built in our shop and used for this work. A clamp is attached to the carriage in place of one of the heaters. A test tube 1⅜ in. I.D. $\times$ 28 in. long is attached in an upright position to the clamp near its upper end. With the zone refiner in the raised position, a 4-in. diam $\times$ 28 in. deep Dewar flask is positioned beneath the tube with the bottom of the tube even with the top of the Dewar. The carriage is adjusted so that a downward pass will carry the tube into the Dewar up to the point at which the tube is clamped.

With the tube in the raised position, a 30-in. motor-driven glass stirrer is inserted to about 1 in. above the bottom. The stirrer is mounted independently of the tube so that it remains at a fixed height when the tube is lowered into the Dewar flask. A G. K. Heller dc variable-speed-gear motor (slow-speed shaft operating at 0–277 rpm and high-speed shaft at 0–5000 rpm) is used to drive the stirrer. A speed is chosen so that air is not sucked into the vortex, about 200–300 rpm depending upon the blades of the stirrer.

A solution of 250 mg of 305,000 viscosity average molecular weight polystyrene in 250 ml freshly redistilled benzene is poured into the tube, filling it to a height of 10 in. A 500-ml separatory funnel with an elongated exit end is positioned above the tube with the exit end just below the surface of the polystyrene solution. The funnel, containing 500 ml of freshly distilled benzene, is closed air tight with a silicone-greased stopper (Note 1). The Dewar, resting inside a shallow pan to catch overflow, is filled right to the brim with a slurry of finely powdered dry ice in alcohol. The zone refiner is set for a downward travel of 1.25 in./hr and turned on (Note 2). The stirrer is started and the stopcock of the separatory funnel opened wide. Freezing of the benzene solution begins shortly after the end of the tube becomes immersed in the dry-ice–alcohol bath. When steady state is reached, the freezing front will remain about 0.5 in. below the paddle of the stirrer. As the tube is lowered, the level of the liquid phase drops below the end of the separatory funnel, which is mounted independently of the zone refiner; benzene in the funnel is replaced by air and flows into the tube to maintain the level constant (Note 3). Refrigerant displaced by the lowering tube overflows the top of the Dewar and is thus maintained at a constant level (Note 4).

When all of the benzene has been added and about 3 in. of liquid remains unfrozen, the speed of the stirrer is reduced to avoid splashing; the stirrer is stopped just before it emerges from the solution. The last inch of solution is allowed to freeze without stirring. The total length of frozen ingot is 26.4 in.

After freezing is complete, the Dewar is quickly emptied of refrigerant, and the tube, supported by wadding, is placed in the empty Dewar. It will remain frozen for several hours. The Dewar and tube are now tilted so that the open end is angled slightly downward. An electrically heated copper disc (Note 5), attached to the end of copper tubing, is inserted in the tube and held against the ingot. The melt flows from the tube directly into test tubes; 25-ml fractions are collected until the whole ingot is melted (Note 6). This method of collecting fractions does not result in any detectable remixing or contamination of one fraction with another. The last bit of one fraction to be melted is very similar in composition to the first bit of the succeeding fraction. This results in rinsing the tube with solutions quite similar to the first-melted portion of each fraction.

Polystyrene is recovered by evaporating the solvent in tared aluminum dishes. The polymer is then weighed and dissolved in toluene. Viscosity of the fractions is measured in toluene at 0.3% concentration. Intrinsic viscosities are calculated according to Hart (4) and molecular weights from the data of Alfrey et al. (5).

The results of this separation are shown in Table 14-1. Most of the

TABLE 14-1

Distribution of Polystyrene in Frozen Ingot

Fraction solidified	Weight of solute (mg)	W/v % solute	M.W. $\times 10^{-5}$
0.1	6.0	0.008	5.3
0.2	7.5	0.010	5.3
0.3	4.5	0.006	—
0.4	3.0	0.004	5.2
0.5	2.5	0.003	—
0.6	1.5	0.002	—
0.7	3.0	0.004	5.2
0.8	8.0	0.011	5.0
0.85	9.0	0.024	4.9
0.88	9.0	0.040	4.8
0.905	13.1	0.069	4.3
0.926	21.3	0.134	3.6
0.945	23.2	0.161	3.2
0.962	31.3	0.243	2.9
0.977	33.1	0.291	2.5
0.990	31.7	0.321	2.1
1.00	36.6	0.483	1.7

polymer has been redistributed to the last-solidified end, with 85% being found in the last tenth of the ingot. Molecular weights along the frozen ingot are shown in the last column, while Table 14-2 gives the cumulative weight percent versus molecular weight of the fractionated polymer.

14-3. METHOD B: ZONE MELTING

Fractionation can also be obtained by a regular zone melting procedure (1, 2) in a cold room at 0°C or less. A glass tube 1 $\times$ 20 in. is nearly

TABLE 14-2

Molecular-Weight Distribution of Polystyrene

Cumulative wt %	M.W. $\times 10^{-5}$
15	1.6
20	1.8
30	2.15
40	2.5
50	2.8
60	3.15
70	3.5
80	4.6
90	5.2
100	5.3

filled with liquid benzene, which is then allowed to freeze so that the solid ingot occupies 19 in. of the tube. A Teflon catheter, previously inserted and centered in the tube, now occupies the axis of the ingot (Note 7). The flexible catheter relieves pressure buildup that occurs at the start of each pass and thus prevents cracking of the glass tube.

The remaining inch of the tube is filled with a 5% solution of polystyrene in benzene and allowed to freeze. Zone melting with a single heater is started at the end of the ingot containing polymer at the rate of 2 in./hr. Zone width (1 in.) is kept uniform by slow rotation of the tube at 2 rpm. The rotation is achieved by use of a pulley attached to the slow forward-drive motor of the zone melter. After 10 passes the polymer is uniformly distributed along the length of the ingot.

After the tube is warmed slightly with the hand to free the ingot from the walls, the end of the tube is cut off; the ingot is then pulled out by the projecting catheter. The ingot is now cut by a hot wire into sections and the polymer is analyzed as in Method A. The highest molecular species will be found at the first-melted end of the ingot.

14-4. OTHER METHODS

Polymer fractionation can also be performed by fractional precipitation from a solvent–nonsolvent system (6), by elution chromatography (7, 8), and by gel-permeation chromatography (9). Fractional precipitation is a laborious, time-consuming method used only when there is no other recourse. Elution chromatography has been widely used in both the Desreux method, which uses a solvent gradient in a chromatographic column, and in the Baker and Williams method which combines solvent gradient with a temperature gradient. Gel-permeation chromatography is the newest and quickest method available for fractionation, but requires expensive equipment.

The procedures described are for the molecular-weight fractionation of polymers. It should also be useful for the actual purification of polymers. Removing such impurities as catalyst fragments, ultraviolet absorbers, and plasticizers should be readily achieved because of the large difference in molecular size between these substances and the polymer. More complex, but also possible, is the separation of copolymers from any constituent homopolymer content, as well as separation of copolymer on a composition basis. In these proposed purifications, the use of the bulk polymer rather than a solution appears practical.

NOTES

1. Care must be taken to prevent contamination of the benzene by the grease.

2. The rate of freezing is critical for good separation; an erratic rate will result in poor separation. Thus, it is important that downward travel of the tube remain constant.

3. At a freezing rate of 1.25 in./hr most of the polymer is rejected by the freezing front, resulting in increasing concentration in the liquid phase. Because fractionation efficiency decreases with increasing concentration, the continuous addition of benzene prevents concentration buildup.

4. Since change in level of refrigerant results in a change in freezing rate, continuous refrigerant overflow assures a constant level. When displacement of refrigerant by the descending tube is greater than decrease in volume due to loss of dry ice, the level remains constant. If the level drops below the brim, it should not be adjusted by the addition of more dry ice.

5. The melter has an output of about 10 W; it consists of a $1\frac{5}{16}$-in. diameter copper disc $\frac{1}{16}$ in. thick, silver-soldered to the end of a 30-in. length of $\frac{1}{4}$-in. copper tubing. A short length of glass-insulated nichrome resistance wire is inserted in the end of the copper tube, touching the center of the disc. The ends of the nichrome are connected to electrical leads inserted into the other end of the tube. The disc temperature is varied through the use of a variable transformer.

6. As the bulk of polymer is found in the last-solidified end of the ingot, it is necessary to collect smaller factions, e.g., 5 ml, at this end.

7. Because of volume increase at the melting end of the ingot, fracture of the tube is a common occurrence unless some compensation for pressure buildup is introduced. This is achieved by inserting along the axis of the tube a thin-walled $\frac{1}{8}$-in. teflon catheter, heat-sealed at one end. The catheter is kept straight by insertion of a rigid welding rod inside the

catheter. A $\frac{1}{32}$-in. annular space between catheter wall and rod offers sufficient volume to relieve pressure buildup. The catheter tubing is available from Pennsylvania Fluorocarbon Co., Inc., Holley St. and Madison Ave., Clifton Heights, Pennsylvania.

REFERENCES

1. J. D. Loconti and J. W. Cahill, *J. Polymer Sci.,* 1, 3163M (1963).
2. J. D. Loconti and J. W. Cahill, *J. Polymer Sci.,* 49, 52 (1961).
3. *Natl. Bur. Std. (U. S.) Tech. News Bull.,* 39, 81 (1955).
4. V. E. Hart, *J. Polymer Sci.,* 17, 215 (1955).
5. T. Alfrey, A. Bartovics, and H. Mark, *J. Am. Chem. Soc.,* 65, 2319 (1943).
6. G. V. Schulz and A. Dinglinger, *Z. Physik. Chem.,* B-43, 47 (1939).
7. V. Desreux, *Rec. Trav. Chim.,* 68, 789 (1949).
8. C. A. Baker and R. J. P. Williams, *J. Chem. Soc.,* 2352 (1956).
9. J. C. Moore, *J. Polymer Sci.,* A2, 835 (1964).

15

PURIFICATION AND GROWTH OF LARGE ANTHRACENE CRYSTALS

John N. Sherwood

DEPARTMENT OF PURE AND APPLIED CHEMISTRY
UNIVERSITY OF STRATHCLYDE
GLASGOW, SCOTLAND

15-1. INTRODUCTION

Anthracene may be extracted from coal-tar distillates or synthesized. Material from both sources is commercially available. There is little difference in total impurity content between the synthetic anthracene and good samples of coal-tar anthracene (usually designated blue fluorescent); the major difference is the type of impurity present. The total impurity content of both materials is approximately 1%, and further purification is necessary before single-crystal growth can be attempted. The major impurities in the two types of material have been isolated and identified by gas–liquid chromatography and optical and mass spectroscopy.

Anthraquinone, anthrone, carbazole, fluorene, 9,10-dihydroanthracene, tetracene and traces of other aromatic hydrocarbons are found in blue fluorescent anthracene (1–3); bianthryl (0.4 wt %) and traces of anthraquinone, anthrone and 9,10-dihydroanthracene contaminate synthetic anthracene (4). Segregation coefficients have been determined for some of these impurities (1). At high concentrations the impurities segregate efficiently from the solid during normal freezing. The impurity content can therefore be reduced by zone refining. In some cases, however, the segregation process becomes less efficient at low impurity concentrations, and long periods of zone refining would be needed to yield a small increase in over-all purity. This is particularly true for the removal of carbazole. Carbazole forms solid solutions with anthracene (4) and, at low concentrations, has a segregation coefficient close to unity (*1*). Since the carbazole content of the starting material may be as high as 0.1%, it is advisable to carry out some preliminary purification to remove this compound.

The most efficient method for the removal of carbazole (*5–7*) is continuous-absorption chromatography (*7*). This process has the added advantage that it also serves to remove other polar impurities and to reduce the concentrations of all impurities to levels where the efficiency of the subsequent zone-refining process is increased. When this process is followed by distillation or sublimation under reduced pressure and, finally, zone refining, material of the high purity required for single-crystal growth is obtained.

15-2. PROCEDURE

A. Purification

1. Chromatography

The chromatographic separation is carried out as depicted in Fig. 15-1. The design is basically that of Sangster and Irvine (*7*) (Note 1).

The column, A, is packed with grade-1 neutral alumina slurried in *n*-hexane (Note 2). The lower end of the column is closed by a coarse sinter to prevent the passage of the alumina into flask B. Sufficient *n*-hexane to fill the flask is added to the top of the column and allowed to flow through into the flask. Strongly absorbed impurities are thereby removed from the solvent. Care should be taken to ensure that the absorbent in the column is covered with *n*-hexane at all times and that a small head of liquid stands above the absorbent.

Before all the hexane has passed through the column, impure anthracene is placed upon the sinter in the head flask, C, and the system is flushed with dry, oxygen-free nitrogen to expel air; a continuous slow stream of nitrogen is then maintained through the apparatus during the remainder of the process to minimize oxidation. When all the air has been expelled, the flask is heated and *n*-hexane distilled to the top of the column, where it condenses and drips onto the anthracene. The warm hexane dissolves the anthracene, which rapidly passes in solution through the column into the flask. By adjusting the boiling rate, a steady head of *n*-hexane can be maintained in C. Overfilling, and hence the running back of the impure anthracene solution into B, can be prevented by the incorporation of an automatic leveling device. A float interrupts a light beam incident upon a photocell, causing the flask heater to be switched off. When float falls below the beam, the heater is switched on again, and so on.

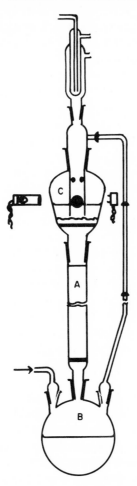

Fig. 15-1. Apparatus for continuous absorption chromatography.

As the process proceeds, more anthracene can be added from time to time. The total amount will vary with column size and packing. A 2 × 36-in. column will pass about 10–15 g anthracene per day and will last 3–5 days before repacking (Note 3). The more polar and less soluble impurities are absorbed at the top of the column. As the elution proceeds, distinct impurity bands "tail" down the column. Since the anthracene is added continuously, separate bands do not form. Particularly noticeable are red and green bands at the head of the column, due to anthraquinone and tetracene respectively, and a light brown coloration, due to tarry materials, which gradually spreads down the column. This brown impurity proceeds more rapidly than other visible impurities, and the process should be stopped before this band reaches the foot of the column (Note 4). To obtain the maximum amount of purified material from the process, the addition of impure anthracene should be stopped when the light brown color has covered three quarters of the column length; boiling can then be continued until all the anthracene has been eluted from the column. Complete removal can be determined by examining the eluate for the characteristic blue fluorescence of anthracene. Alternatively, the distillation of *n*-hexane can be stopped when the light brown color approaches the bottom of the column; the residual anthracene is discarded with the alumina.

As the *n*-hexane in the flask cools, the anthracene crystallizes from the solution as blue fluorescent flakes and can be filtered off. The remaining anthracene is obtained by distilling off the solvent. The latter stages of solvent removal should be carried out by pumping on the cold concentrated solution to prevent excessive oxidation of the anthracene.

Since it is often difficult to assess the true position of the lower end of the light brown impurity band, it is possible that some of this impurity will pass through the column. It is therefore advisable to carry out the chromatographic purification twice. As purer material is used the second time, the column has a longer life. This repetition will afford the removal of all strongly absorbed impurities. The major purpose, the removal of carbazole, is definitely achieved (Note 5).

2. Sublimation

The carbazole-free anthracene from the chromatographic purification still contains those nonpolar impurities soluble in hexane, along with a high proportion of solvent. The apparatus usually used for removal of these contaminants is a combined sublimation apparatus and zone-refining tube (Fig. 15-2). The chromatographed anthracene is loaded into the left-hand bulb, this tube is then sealed and the apparatus is evacuated. A heating tape is wrapped around the bulb and the anthracene sublimed under continuous evacuation into the second bulb. The most volatile impurities are pumped off and trapped. When approximately 90–95% of the anthracene has passed over, the remaining impure anthracene is sealed in the first bulb by melting the constriction. At this stage the cold sublimed anthracene has a yellow color due to anthraquinone carried over during the sublimation. This is particularly noticeable at the tail end of the sublimed material (the yellow color of pure, hot anthracene should not be confused with impurity).

The anthracene is then resublimed into the third bulb and again sealed at the constriction. Pure nitrogen is added to 1 atm pressure and the anthracene is melted into the zone-refining tube. While the material is still liquid the pressure is reduced to 0.5 atm, the anthracene is allowed

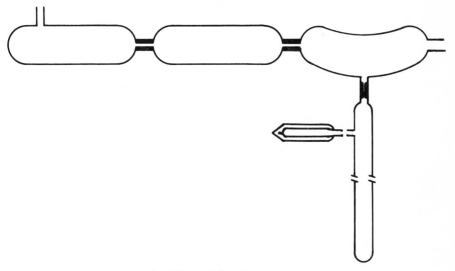

Fig. 15-2. Sublimation apparatus.

to solidify from the lower end of the zone-refining tube and the tube is sealed off at the constriction.

3. Zone Refining

The zone-refining process can be carried out with any of the usual forms of zone-refining apparatus. These and other basic details of the zone-refining process have been adequately described elsewhere (8).

The refining is best carried out in thick-walled pyrex tubing (2–3 mm wall) to reduce the possibility of breakage, which often occurs as a result of the considerable increase in volume on melting. Tube fracture can also be avoided by including air or water coolers above the heaters to stabilize the width of the molten zone and by commencing zone melting at the free surface; attempts to initiate zones in the solid inevitably results in fracture of the tube. The presence of inert gas in the tube prevents serious sublimation of anthracene up the tube.

In the author's laboratory the usual practice is to pass 30 to 50 zones of length 0.5 to 1 in. down a 2- to 3-ft column of anthracene. The initial 10 zones are passed at a rate of 2 in./hr and the remainder at 1 in./hr. The heaters should be maintained at as low a temperature as possible to minimize thermal decomposition. All processes in which anthracene is melted should be carried out in darkness or nonactinic light, since daylight induces photoreaction in the hot liquid, thus generating impurities during refining (Note 6).

The most obvious change in the appearance of the material during zone refining is the concentration of yellow anthraquinone at the lower end of the tube, together with some dark brown material.

When zone refining is completed the tube is cracked open; the upper and lower extremes of the ingot are rejected. Most impurities segregate downward. A number of impurities in organic systems, however, have segregation coefficients greater than unity; thus, even though no obvious impurity has this property in the present case, it is a wise precaution to reject the upper extreme. Since some sublimation always occurs at the upper end of the ingot, this portion contains a higher proportion of impurities than are found in the center portion.

The center portion of the ingot is combined with other similar material, sublimed in a two-stage sublimation apparatus, melted into a second zone-refining tube to which a crystal-growth vessel is attached, and sealed. This material is then zone refined again as described above. On this occasion no yellow anthraquinone should be observed in the sublimed material. During the zone refining the anthracene forms large clear crystals, a good indication of the high purity of the material. On completion of zone refining the top portion of the ingot is melted into the empty upper part of the zone-refining tube; the center portion is melted into the crystal-growth tube and sealed. In this way the transfer is effected without exposing the anthracene to atmospheric oxidation, and the crystal is grown in the same atmosphere used for the final refining. This operation should be carried out in the dark (Note 6).

4. Purity of the Material

The initial step of the purification procedure yields material that can be shown by spectrophotometric and gas–liquid chromatographic techniques to contain 100–1000 ppm total impurity. The greater part of these impurities are refined out during the first zone refining to yield material containing 10–50 ppm total impurity. Beyond this stage analytical techniques are too insensitive to permit accurate measurement, but from a knowledge of the segregation coefficients for the major impurities Sloan (1) has shown that the probable final impurity content will be less than 0.1 ppm. Material of this purity can be obtained only by exercising extreme care during the process. It is essential to check the improvement in purity obtained at each stage during purification.

B. Crystal Growth

In addition to the requirement of highly pure material, the basic necessities for the growth of organic crystals from the melt are the selection and propagation of the seed crystals. The former is usually effected by the design of the containing tube and the latter by controlled cooling in a thermally stable oven.

1. Design of Growth Oven

Most ovens designed for the growth of crystals of organic compounds from the melt are based upon the Bridgman method (9) in which controlled cooling is carried out by slowly lowering the crystal-growth tube through a vertical temperature gradient from the hot to the cold end. A number of ways of achieving a suitably sharp gradient have been described (10) (Note 7). The most convenient way is to arrange two isothermal furnaces separated by a nonconducting baffle such that the upper portion is approximately 10° above the melting temperature and the lower portion 10° below the melting temperature. Figure 15-3 depicts such an arrangement constructed basically of concentric glass tubes (Note 8). This type of arrangement has the considerable advantage that the progress of the crystal can be observed throughout the growth process. Gradients of 20°/cm stable to ±0.01°C can be attained in such an apparatus. The melting-point isothermal is level with the baffle center (11).

2. Seeding the Crystal

The generation of the single crystal is more dependent on growth-vessel design than on the incorporation of a seed crystal in the vessel. Various types of growth vessel have been used (11). The simpler of these rarely yield one single crystal but usually form several aligned crystals. Greater success is achieved by using a growth vessel in which specific seed selection occurs; suitable vessels are shown in Fig. 15-4. The charge added from the zone-refining tube is melted and crystallization initiated by cooling the tip of the vessel (Notes 9, 10). The vessel is then suspended in the growth oven so that the tip is just below the melting-point isothermal; the system is then allowed to come to equilibrium. When equilibrium has been achieved the vessel is slowly lowered through the temperature gradient. The rates of growth of organic crystals of the anthracene type are considerably lower than those for other solid systems (11). Under the temperature conditions quoted above, lowering rates in excess of 2 mm/hr inevitably result in the formation of multicrystals of poor quality (12); lower rates yield crystals of excellent quality from ultrapure material.

As the vessel descends, the crystallites grow until several large crystallites occupy the tube just below the capillary. Some of these grow up the capillary. If the capillary is straight, most of these crystallites will continue to grow into the wider upper tube. The bent capillary, however, inevitably selects one particular seed, which grows into the upper tube as a large single crystal (Notes 11, 12).

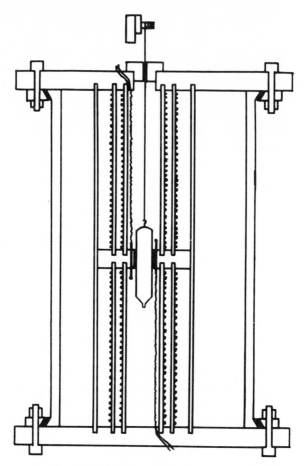

Fig. 15-3. Crystal-growing oven (Note 8).

When growth is complete, the crystal in the tube is removed from the oven and allowed to cool rapidly for a short period to let the crystal break away from the tube wall. There is usually a "sharp crack" as this occurs. The crystal and tube are then transferred to an annealing oven at 200°C and cooled to room temperature over 2 to 3 days. After this period the tube can be cut open (at A–A in Fig. 15-4) for removal of the crystal boule from the tube (Note 13).

3. Crystal Appearance and Perfection

Anthracene crystals grown from pure material are clear and free from striations. They have a very pale yellow color in thick specimens and a blue fluorescence in sunlight and ultraviolet light.

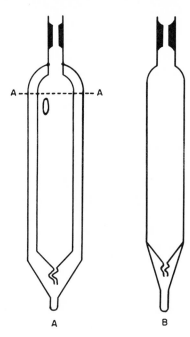

Fig. 15-4. Crystal-growing vessels (Note 10).

In the "as grown" condition the crystals contain a high degree of extrinsic disorder, and they should be well annealed before further study *(13)*.

There is no obvious visual difference between good crystals grown from synthetic or coal tar material. For some purposes, however, crystals grown from synthetic anthracene appear to be more intrinsic in character (Note 14). Both types of crystal contain 10^6–10^8 dislocations/cm^2 as grown but this dislocation content can be reduced by prolonged annealing *(14)*.

The over-all impurity of the final crystal should be considerably less than 0.1 ppm (Section 2.A.3). This will be distributed along the crystal in a manner determined by the segregation coefficients of the separate impurities. The lower end of the boule will always be the most pure portion.

4. Crystal Orientation

The cutting of the crystal for future studies can be carried out with a sharp blade or a solvent-soaked string saw. An optical finish can be obtained by solvent polishing.

The location of the crystallographic planes is easily determined. Examination of the crystal boule will usually reveal the positions of cleavage cracks. By placing a sharp blade against one of these and applying a steady pressure in the direction of the crack the crystal can be cleaved apart readily. The cleavage face is the (001), *ab* plane. The location of the ⟨100⟩, *a* direction in this plane can be obtained by using the polarizing microscope (*15*) or the double refraction of the crystal (*16*). With this information, along with the relative positions of the other crystallographic axes (*17*), the crystal can be cut in any desired orientation.

C. Purification and Growth of Other Organic Solids

Although the above account has been concerned with the preparation of anthracene crystals, the method is basic to the preparation of most organic crystals that can be grown from the melt. By use of this basic technique the following single crystals have been grown (*2*): acetic acid, benzanthracene, benzene, benzoic acid, biphenyl, camphene, chrysene, cyclohexane, hexamethylethane, naphthalene, phenanthrene, pyrene, and succinonitrile.

NOTES

1. Sangster and Irvine (*7*) describe the basic methods, solvents, and so on for the chromatographic purification of a large number of aromatic hydrocarbons. Although the final purity of their products is not quoted, the description of the crystals grown from these materials often conveys an idea of what further purification may be necessary.

2. Dry, aromatic-free *n*-hexane should be used. Reagent-grade *n*-hexane can be purified by shaking with a 1:1, *v*/*v*, mixture of concentrated nitric and sulphuric acids, washing the separated *n*-hexane several times with dilute sodium hydroxide solution and then with water, and finally drying the wet solvent over a solid desiccant and distilling prior to use.

3. Considerable photooxidation can occur on the column; consequently, rapid discoloration of the absorbent will result. This can be prevented by carrying out the process in the dark or nonactinic light, or alternatively, by covering the column.

4. The flow of the solution can be increased by heating the column. This technique also obviates the possibility of the column being blocked by anthracene that has crystallized from the warm solution. Since absorption efficiency decreases with increased temperature, care must be taken to avoid overheating and, hence, boiling the solvent. Heating can be controlled effectively by wrapping electrical heating tape around the column.

5. Experiments using ^{14}C labelled carbazole have proved that this impurity is quantitatively removed by the chromatographic process (*2*).

6. The physical examination of anthracene crystals grown in daylight and in nonactinic light shows that the former contain otherwise undetect-

able amounts of impurities, which have a marked effect upon some physical properties. For example, the fluorescence decay time for crystals grown from anthracene refined under fluorescent light is much shorter than for those refined in nonactinic light. The impurity that causes this effect can be removed by re-zone refining the material in nonactinic light (*4*).

7. Steep temperature gradients of 10–20°/cm are essential to the formation of good single crystals.

8. This design is an adaptation of that described by Sherwood and Thomson (*11*). The present apparatus incorporates four separate oven windings (two upper and two lower) and the separate control of the upper and lower portions of the oven by two thermistor controllers, the sensing elements of which are located 1 in. above and below the baffle respectively.

9. It is essential to initiate crystal seeds before inserting the growth vessel into the oven. Attempts to grow crystals from completely molten samples always results in supercooling and the consequent formation of multicrystals.

10. The type-A vessel has been found to be most suitable. The material fills both the outer and inner portions of the tube and thus provides some thermal insulation for the growing crystal. Where only small quantities of material are available, the type-B vessel can be used; crystals of poorer quality are usually obtained.

11. In addition to aiding in the selection of the crystal seed, the capillary can select the orientation of the growing crystals. If the angle of the capillary to the vessel axis is less than 45° then the *ab*, cleavage, plane will grow parallel to the vessel axis. If the angle is greater than 45° it will grow perpendicular to the vessel axis (*11*).

12. The tube dimensions can be varied; but the tube should always fill the hole in the oven baffle. The capillary should be 1–2 mm diameter and should be bent so that there is no direct path from bottom to top.

13. On occasions the anthracene will adhere strongly to the vessel wall, and release of the crystal without fracture is difficult. This can be prevented by treating the inside surface of the crystal vessel with a silicone release agent and baking before filling. The release agent reacts chemically with the glass surface and subsequent contamination of the crystal is unlikely.

14. Photoconductivity studies show that the synthetic anthracene crystals contain fewer charge-carrier trapping sites than coal-tar anthracene crystals (*18*). This may be a consequence of residual, analytically undetectable amounts of other aromatic hydrocarbons remaining in the crystal lattice. It is obvious that the source material should be chosen in relation to the intended physical examination.

REFERENCES

1. G. J. Sloan, *Mol. Crystals,* 1, 161 (1966).
2. J. N. Sherwood with N. T. Corke, R. Fox, H. M. Hawthorne, G. M. Hood, B. J. McArdle, A. R. McGhie, and D. J. White, unpublished work.
3. J. H. Beynon and R. A. Saunders, *Brit. J. Appl. Phys.,* 11, 128 (1960).
4. G. J. Sloan, private communication.
5. J. M. Clark, *Ind. Eng. Chem.,* 11, 204 (1919).
6. J. Feldman, P. Pantages, and M. Orchin, *J. Am. Chem. Soc.,* 73, 4341 (1951).
7. R. C. Sangster and J. W. Irvine, Jr., *J. Chem. Phys.,* 24, 670 (1956).
8. M. Zief and W. R. Wilcox, *Fractional Solidification,* Vol. 1, Dekker, New York, 1967.
9. P. W. Bridgman, *Proc. Am. Acad. Arts Sci.,* 60, 305 (1925).
10. G. F. Reynolds, in *Physics and Chemistry of the Organic Solid State,* Vol. 1 (D. Fox, M. M. Labes, and A. Weissberger, eds.), Wiley-Interscience, New York, 1963, pp. 223–286.
11. J. N. Sherwood and S. J. Thomson, *J. Sci. Instr.,* 37, 242 (1960).
12. J. N. Sherwood, *Crystal Growth,* Proceedings of the International Conference on Crystal Growth, Boston, 1966, Supplement to *J. Phys. Chem. Solids,* p. 839.
13. J. N. Sherwood and D. J. White, *Phil. Mag.,* 15, 745 (1967).
14. N. T. Corke, A. A. Kawada, and J. N. Sherwood, *Nature,* 213, 62 (1967).
15. R. C. Jarnagin, J. Gilliland, J. S. Kim, and M. Silver, *J. Chem. Phys.,* 39, 573 (1963).
16. M. Gordon, *Acta Met.,* 13, 199 (1965).
17. J. M. Robertson, *Rev. Mod. Phys.,* 30, 155 (1958).
18. D. C. Hoestery and G. M. Letson, *J. Phys. Chem. Solids,* 24, 1611 (1963).

16 PURIFICATION OF INDIUM ANTIMONIDE

A. R. Murray

TEXAS INSTRUMENTS LIMITED
BEDFORD, ENGLAND

16-1. INTRODUCTION

In comparison with other III–V semiconducting compounds, indium antimonide has a low melting point and low vapor pressure in the liquid phase. As simple, reliable techniques can be employed in compounding, zone refining, and growth of single crystals, the purification of InSb has received extensive study (*1–6*). Residual impurity contents approaching those obtained by zone refining of the elemental semiconductors are reported; 77°K mobility values of 1×10^6 cm^2/V-sec are quoted by some workers (*2, 5*).

A variety of experimental techniques involving numerous zone passes have been used in preparing pure single-crystal InSb by zone refining. In other cases, the process is completed by producing a single crystal by the Czochralski method from InSb previously purified by zone refining. A difficulty found with the latter procedure is that contamination is likely to occur when effecting the transfer from refining to crystal-growing apparatus.

The zone purification of InSb will be considered here with particular reference to the physical properties of the material; a method of zone refining in which the ingot is maintained as a single crystal will be described.

16-2. SEGREGATION

The efficiency of the zone-refining process is limited in the case of InSb by the segregation behavior of certain impurity species that are invariably found in the compounded material, particularly zinc and tellurium.

Zinc and cadmium are acceptors in InSb with segregation coefficients (K_{eff}) of 3.0 and 0.26 respectively. Zinc therefore segregates in the direction opposite to that of the zone traverse and degrades the material that is being depleted of solutes with $K_{eff} < 1$. Both elements are volatile over a melt of InSb, and in normal zone refining, redistribution via the vapor phase can occur. The effect can be turned to advantage, however, by evaporating and trapping the contaminants from the molten ingot under high vacuum, as a preliminary stage before zone refining.

The behavior of tellurium in InSb is particularly interesting in that the type of segregation is strongly dependent on the crystallography of the ingot (3, 6). When zone refining is carried out on a polycrystalline InSb ingot, tellurium exhibits a K_{eff} near unity; if the zones are passed through a single crystal (oriented away from $\langle 111 \rangle$ to avoid principal facet formation), the observed K_{eff} is 0.47. Only in the latter case will tellurium be transported by the liquid zone; it is then the limiting donor impurity found after polycrystal zone refining.

16-3. ZONE REFINING

A. Apparatus

InSb is extremely prone to surface contamination even when ultraclean handling techniques are used. This means that the advantage of pre-evaporation is lost if the material must be subsequently transferred to a zone refiner. The difficulty may be overcome by carrying out both operations in a single apparatus without intermediate dismantling; an apparatus suitable for this purpose is shown in Fig. 16-1.

The traveling furnace element (A) is made of nichrome wound on a grooved transparent quartz sleeve, coaxial with the furnace tube (B) which contains the ingot. An advantage of this design is that the entire ingot is completely visible at all stages of the process. The element is tapped off at intervals and power fed individually to each section to give the required temperature distributions. A traveling thermocouple (C) is located in the furnace tube with the hot junction adjacent to the part of the element used for zone refining; this can be used as the sensor in a suitable temperature-control servo system. Provision must be made for operating consecutively in high vacuum and gas.

Fig. 16-1. Apparatus for zone refining of indium antimonide. (Courtesy of Royal Radar Establishment, Malvern, U. K.)

B. Selection of Raw Materials

Considerable effort has been devoted to the production of hyperpure indium and antimony for the preparation of compound semiconductors (7, 8). Both are available in a variety of physical forms and grades of purity; the price is closely geared to quality. Most impurity elements have segregation coefficients that favor removal by zone refining, but high concentrations demand more processing. It is unfortunate that the impurities most likely to impose a final limitation on the properties of the InSb (Zn, Cd, and Te) are often not quoted in impurity specifications for the elements. This is also true of carbon, which, although not electrically active, is usually present in indium and antimony and gives rise to an insoluble coating that interferes with the crystal-growing operation. In general, economics dictate the use of the best available grades of starting materials for the preparation of ultrapure InSb.

C. Pretreatment of the Elements

It is inadvisable to use indium and antimony direct from the supplier's packages; comparative experiments in the author's laboratory have shown that ingots processed from the material as received are ultimately more difficult to purify and prepare in single-crystal form.

Antimony is often provided in the form of zone-refined ingots, which may be reduced in size by melting to allow accommodation in the apparatus used for compounding. A useful surface etch for antimony is concentrated hydrochloric acid to which hydrogen peroxide is added to produce nascent chlorine. The reaction is stopped by addition of excess hydrochloric acid followed by copious rinsing with deionized water.

Indium is usually available in the form of ingots of small cross section. If large masses have to be reduced in size, melting under a pure cover gas is the best procedure. Although indium adheres strongly to smooth quartz, it can be detached with some persuasion from a clean abraded quartz surface. Indium also tends to pick up carbon particles from sooted boats. An ideal container material is vitreous carbon. Concentrated nitric acid etching followed by a deionized water rinse will remove most surface impurities.

D. Compounding

The compound is easily synthesized by mixing the elements in their correct proportions. The method depends on the quantities required. For large-scale commercial preparations, the bottom-pouring method (4, 5) is useful and has the advantage of removing insoluble surface matter. It has also been demonstrated that this technique affords a batch of ingots with uniform impurity content from nonuniform starting elements (5).

For laboratory-scale preparations, it is convenient to combine the elements in a container of the same size as that which will ultimately be used for zone refining. Apparatus of the type shown in Fig. 16-1 is suitable. The first step is to place the etched indium in a clean, smooth quartz boat and melt down under high vacuum or pure hydrogen. After freezing and extraction, the etched antimony is placed on top of the solidified indium mass; the complete charge is reloaded into the apparatus and a clean gas ambient is established. The temperature is then brought up to 540°C over the entire length of the boat until the charge is entirely molten; a normal freeze pass is applied by moving the heater out of coincidence with the boat. This can be followed by zone passes until it is evident that a single phase is present.

It is good practice to add the antimony in slight excess over the stoichiometric ratio to avoid formation of a terminal indium-rich phase, which will cause the ingot to stick to the smooth quartz boat. If the compound is to be vacuum baked (the procedure recommended if highest purity is required), then antimony must be added in sufficient excess to allow for evaporation losses at this stage. This excess should be about 2% for a 4-hr evaporation period. The main object of forming a stoichiometric ingot before the preevaporation and refining is to obtain a visual assessment of the inert matter associated with the material and facilitate its removal. This is important inasmuch as a film of scum on the melt surface will prevent the discharge of zinc and other contaminants. An effective method of removal is to sandblast the top surface of the compounded ingot where foreign matter will have aggregated by flotation and follow with ultrasonic rinsing and etching prior to evaporation. A method of etch-cleaning the ingot surface is given in a note at the end of the text.

E. Boat and Seed Preparation

Under some circumstances an InSb ingot will grow as a single crystal during zone refining without deliberate seeding. The orientation produced in this way is usually ⟨111⟩, which is disadvantageous because of principal facet formation. To ensure that the zones are passed through an ingot of the required crystallography, it is necessary to arrange for them to be generated from a seed crystal with orientation other than ⟨111⟩. The most reliable orientations for maintenance of singularity are of the type ⟨331⟩ and ⟨221⟩. A somewhat tedious but effective way of preparing a seed crystal for horizontal growth is to expose a face of the required orientation on a pulled ingot and grind into the boat with an abrasive slurry, while the oriented face is normal to the boat axis.

It is most important that zone refining be carried out in a boat that is not wetted by molten InSb. Unless such a container is used, single-crystal growth will not be maintained because of the strain imposed by differential contraction of the boat material and InSb (upon cooling after passage of the zone). This applies even when the ingot is detachable from the container after passage of the zone and subsequent cooling; strain can be experimentally verified by passing a zone through a clean, single-crystal InSb charge in a smooth quartz boat. The wetting condition that results gives rise to the type of cross section shown in Fig. 16-2(a); the strain is generated mainly in the shaded regions. The nonwetting condition results in a more rounded cross section shown in Fig. 16-2(b).

A suitable preparation is as follows:

1. The interior of a quartz boat is sandblasted as uniformly as possible with abrasive particles ($30\ \mu$ diam).

2. The boat is then immersed in 48% hydrofluoric acid for 1 min, water-rinsed and dried.

3. Fine-particle silica is applied by spraying from a suspension in acetone or alcohol or by stroking onto the surface a paste of the same composition. Excess particles are blown away after drying.

The source of the silica particles is commercial colloidal silica or the product of reactive decomposition of a silicon halide. The boat is ready for use after firing *in vacuo* to remove water vapor and other impurities. Since the coating readily absorbs water from the atmosphere, it should be stored under vacuum until used.

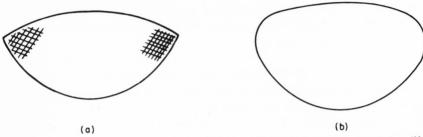

(a)   (b)

Fig. 16-2. Cross-section geometries of indium antimonide ingots produced by different growth conditions: (a) wetted; (b) nonwetted.

F. Preevaporation

The seed and compounded ingot should be etched clean immediately before being placed in the boat. After loading, the system is evacuated to $\sim 1 \times 10^{-5}$ mm Hg; power is applied to the furnace to melt the whole ingot. The power distribution should be adjusted to avoid melting the seed and to give a bulk temperature a few degrees in excess of the melting point of InSb. Too high a melt temperature results in excessive discharge of antimony.

Antimony from the melt should not condense on the seed surface, since this entrapment may interfere with crystal growing. By maintaining the seed at a high enough temperature, entrapment of the condensate is eliminated. A favorable position of heaters with respect to the boat and its contents is shown in Fig. 16-3. It should be noted that with this temperature distribution, condensate is not allowed to collect at the end of the boat where the zone pass terminates. This is to avoid reheating and reverse transportation of the volatilized impurities when the refining zone overruns the end of the ingot in the normal manner. Rather precise adjustment of the relative power inputs to regions C and D is required in order to avoid degrading the seed by surface melting or (if too cool) by arrival of condensate.

A preevaporation of 3–4 hr will remove any zinc contained in InSb almost quantitatively to the condensate.

G. Zone Passes

When the preevaporation is complete, pumping is discontinued and the gas selected as the zone-refining ambient is admitted. Hydrogen, argon, or helium should be carefully treated to remove contaminants, particularly oxygen, since InSb very readily forms oxides that are insoluble in the melt. The gas should be admitted before switching off the heaters; otherwise the ingot will be obscured by antimony depositing on the inner wall of the work tube upon cooling. A slight overpressure can be applied before closing the admission tap.

When the ingot has recrystallized, the refining section of the heating element may be positioned to form and traverse zones of restricted dimensions from the seed. It is necessary to apply a tilt to prevent matter transport; the precise angle is dependent on the zone dimensions. The extent of zone refining necessary to give an appreciable yield of ultrapure material will depend largely on the tellurium content. Low zone-traverse speeds (3 cm/hr) should be employed to suppress the K_{eff} values of the solutes. Higher traverse rates do not give any difficulties with crystal structure when the material has stoichiometric composition; if one component is in excess, constitutional supercooling may occur. Large numbers of passes are not necessary when the ratio of zone length to ingot length is kept small in accordance with normal practice.

H. Control of Structure

The ingot should ideally be maintained in single-crystal form at all times during zone refining. Growth twins may occur, and a situation is sometimes encountered in which large numbers of parallel twins appear. Twinning in InSb is usually initiated on the Sb-terminating external facets and may often be eliminated by slightly altering the position of the seed in the boat or by removing an impurity (particularly oxygen) from the cover gas. In addition, the polar nature of most of the orientations has considerable bearing on the ease of growth of III–V semiconductors. Persistent growth twinning can often be cured by reversing the seed polarity, i.e., rotating through 180°.

It can be argued that the appearance of an occasional growth twin will not greatly affect the efficiency of zone refining. This is not true for gross polycrystallinity, which may be due to wrong polarity or to strain caused by localized wetting arising from defective boat preparation.

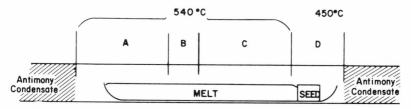

Fig. 16-3. Arrangement of heating zones during preevaporation of indium antimonide melt.

16-4. NOTES ON SURFACE ETCHING OF InSb

A useful method of ensuring a clean surface on an InSb ingot before zone refining or crystal growing is as follows:

1. The ingot is placed in a suitably sized polyethylene trough and supported on small quartz rods to prevent direct contact with the polyethylene.

2. Concentrated nitric acid with a small admixture of concentrated hydrochloric acid is added until the ingot is completely immersed.

3. Reaction is promoted by addition of further small quantities of hydrochloric acid.

4. Reaction is stopped by the addition of excess hydrochloric acid, which should be added at one end of the trough so that the bulk of the reaction mixture is flushed out at the other end. (Obviously, this operation should be carried out in a suitable place, such as a hood.) The hydrochloric acid is in turn flushed away with deionized water and the ingot transferred to a glass or quartz vessel for more prolonged rinsing.

Etchants containing hydrofluoric acid are not recommended, since there is some evidence that F⁻ ions undergo surface adsorption and enter the lattice as interstitial acceptors on subsequent heat treatment. Quartz components of the zone-refining apparatus may be cleaned before use by successive immersions in aqua regia, hydrochloric acid, and deionized water. This treatment is also effective in removing an antimony condensate from the interior of the furnace tube.

REFERENCES

1. T. C. Harman, *J. Electrochem. Soc.*, 103, 128 (1956).
2. K. I. Vinogradova, V. V. Galavanov, D. N. Nasledov, and L. I. Solov'eva, *Sov. Phys. Solid State (English Transl.)*, 1, 364 (1959).
3. K. F. Hulme and J. B. Mullin, *Solid State Electron.*, 5, 211 (1962).
4. S. C. Liang, in *Compound Semiconductors*, Vol. 1, Reinhold (R. K. Willardson and H. L. Goering, eds.), New York, 1962, p. 227.
5. S. G. Parker, O. W. Wilson, and B. H. Barbee, *J. Electrochem. Soc.*, 112, 80 (1965).
6. A. R. Murray, J. A. Baldrey, J. B. Mullin, and O. Jones, *J. Mater. Sci.*, 1, 14 (1966).
7. H. L. Goering, in *Compound Semiconductors*, Vol. 1, Reinhold (R. K. Willardson and H. L. Goering, eds.), New York, 1962, pp. 74–78.
8. R. R. Haberecht, *ibid.*, pp. 92–95.

17

PURIFICATION OF ALKALINE IODIDES (KI, RbI, CsI)

Daniel Ecklin

NEUCHÂTEL UNIVERSITY
NEUCHÂTEL, SWITZERLAND

17-1. INTRODUCTION

When alkaline iodides are molten in a silica container under an air atmosphere, the melt interacts with the silica. During solidification the salt adheres firmly to the walls of the vessel; the adhesion has been ascribed to the exchange of small quantities of oxygen between oxides in the melt and the wall (*1*). Minute quantities of moisture in air can, in addition, hydrolyze iodides to hydroxides. Alkaline oxides and hydroxides quickly devitrify silica. Cristobalite formed in this way breaks when it is cooled below 275°C; thus such devitrified ware can be used only at temperatures above 275°C.

Despite these difficulties, evaluation of container materials proved that silica is still the best choice for the zone melting of alkaline iodides. The purification must be carried out in the total absence of air, moisture, or dust (lime dust is particularly undesirable) with the addition of small quantities of iodine to eliminate oxygen and water ($Cs_2O + I_2 \rightarrow 2CsI + \frac{1}{2}O_2$; $H_2O + I_2 \rightarrow 2HI + \frac{1}{2}O_2$).

17-2. EXPERIMENTAL

A. Apparatus

A quartz tube is sealed to the side of a high-purity silica boat (Note 1) as shown in Fig. 17-1. The front end of the boat is tapered to provide graduated heating for formation of the initial molten zone. Without this

177

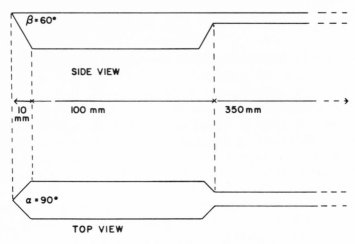

Fig. 17-1. Shape of the silica boat.

precaution, the appreciable volume difference between liquid and solid invariably cracks the boat. A dihedral angle of 90° at the front end insures correct orientation of the first-formed crystal upon solidification of the zone (approximately 10 mm wide). The sealed tube is placed in the zone-melting apparatus (Fig. 17-2) for purification.

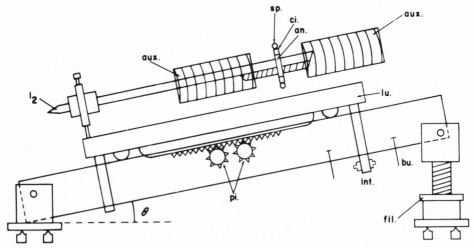

Fig. 17-2. Zone melting apparatus: I₂, Sublimed iodine; aux, auxiliary furnaces; sp, induction coil; ci, cement for ring fixation; an, boron silicide heating ring; lu, carriage moving on ball bearings; θ, tilting angle of the vessel—12° for CsI and RbI, 10° for KI; pi, two pinions alternatively driven with one motor by two magnetic couplings; int, rocking switch; bu, limit shelf; fil, threaded ring for adjusting the angle of tilt. Forward speed, 16.8 mm/hr; backward speed (downward), 10 mm/sec.

B. Procedure

The spectroscopically pure salt is introduced into the boat along with sublimed iodine of the same purity (Note 2). After the system has been evacuated by an oil-diffusion pump (Note 3), the system is gradually heated with a flame until the iodide is completely melted in order to remove the last traces of air and moisture from the melt. The charge is allowed to solidify and the operation is repeated two more times. Finally, small particles of iodine are once more added by sublimation and the tube is then sealed off. The end of the tube is maintained at room temperature so that excess iodine can condense (Note 4). After 20 passes in the zone-melting apparatus the tube is immediately placed in a programmed furnace at 500°C (Note 5). The temperature is slowly reduced to 20°C during approximately 15 hr.

The boat is then broken and the ingot sawed by means of a cotton thread wetted with demineralized water. The cut crystal surfaces are then polished by a disc polishing machine, first with a mixture of water and ethyl alcohol, then diamond paste (1μ) in suspension in isopropyl alcohol. The crystals should be handled only with nylon or Teflon tweezers to prevent possible contamination with metallic ions. Teflon vices permit polishing of crystals in the form of regular parallelepipeds of $10 \times 5 \times 2$ mm.

C. Methods of Analysis

Our efforts have been specially directed toward removal of the alkaline-earth elements. Experience has shown that these close neighbors in the periodic table are indeed the most difficult to separate (2, 3).

Emission spectrophotometry affords only qualitative tests at best. The influence of the matrix (iodine, alkali metal) on the intensity of the line is unknown; the best graphite electrodes available do not attain the purity of our crystals. This technique, however, has helped to establish that Fe, Cu, Zn, Ag, and Si move with the molten zone. Neutron-activation analysis presents many difficulties. Thus Cs^{133} with its large neutron cross section produces the radionuclide Cs^{134} with a long period of decay.

The most sensible and precise method is isotopic dilution followed by mass spectrographic analysis. In practice a weighed portion of sample is dissolved in an appropriate solvent. An aliquot of a stock solution of an isotope different from the isotopes of the element present in the sample is added to the first solution as an internal standard. The mixture of natural isotopes and that of the standard is chemically separated from the other elements in the crystal. The ratio of isotopic concentrations of the desired element is now determined by mass spectrography. From this ratio the original concentration of the element can be calculated. Analyses for calcium and strontium have been made on samples of KI and CsI ingots after the passage of 20 zones. In KI calcium was reduced from 10 to 2.3 ppm, strontium from 5 to 0.03 ppm. The analytical process, however, was long and fastidious.

Flame spectrophotometry (4) was found to be rapid, selective, and precise, and required small quantities of solutions (1.5–2.0 ml). Determinations were carried out with a Jarrell–Ash instrument equipped with an optical grating and an Ebert monochromator with 0.5-meter focal length. Under these conditions the sensitivity of the analysis is limited by the interaction of alkali and alkaline-earth metals (5). The method is most convenient when the impurity concentration remains above 1 ppm. After the passage of 20 zones the detection of impurities is beyond the limits of this apparatus.

D. Summary

The purified crystals were used as standards for ionic conductivity, luminescence, and electronic paramagnetic resonance (6). Results showed that potassium, rubidium, and cesium iodides can be purified by zone melting. Metals such as Cu, Fe, Zn, Ag, Na, Mg, Ca, Sr, and Mn can be lowered by a factor of 10 to 100.

Cesium iodide was obtained particularly pure. The total concentration of impurities did not exceed 1 ppm; the alkaline-earth metals were less than 0.1 ppm.

NOTES

1. Composition of silica boat:

Element	ppm
Calcium	0.4–1.0
Magnesium	0.2
Iron	<0.02
Copper	0.004
Boron	0.01
Antimony	0.01

2. Purity of reagents:

KI*	>99.967
RbI*	>99.943
CsI*	>99.98
I_2†	>99.998

* E. Merck, Darmstadt, Germany.
† Koch-Light Labs, Colnbrook, England.

3. If the vacuum is too high ($<10^{-3}$ Torr) the salts sublime; a molten zone is not formed at all.

4. The vapor pressure of this system is that of the iodine at the coldest point. The iodine vapor pressure is approximately equal to the vapor pressure of the molten alkaline halide. The vapor pressure of the three iodides and iodine amount to 1 Torr at the following temperatures:

747°C for KI
749°C for RbI
737°C for CsI
39.5°C for I_2

During the melting stage, iodine vapor serves as a sink. Alkaline-earth ions (Mg, Ca, Sr, Ba) form volatile iodides that are readily removed.

5. Once the tube is sealed, it is maintained above 300°C. The molten zone remains at 650–750°C, depending on the salt.

REFERENCES

1. H. Wartenberg, *Z. Anorg. Allgem. Chem.,* 273, 257 (1953); *Z. Angew. Chem.,* 69, 258 (1957).
2. R. W. Dreyfus, in *The Art and Science of Growing Crystals* (J. J. Gilman, ed.), Wiley, New York, 1963, p. 21.
3. H. Grundig, *Z. Physik,* 158, 577 (1960); 176, 293, 415 (1963).
4. R. Mavrodineanu and H. Boiteux, *Flame Spectroscopy,* Wiley, New York, 1964.
5. D. Ecklin, *Helv. Chim. Acta,* 50, 1107 (1967).
6. M. Aegerter, Ph.D. Thesis, Univ. of Neuchâtel, Switzerland, 1967.

18 ZONE MELTING OF METAL CHELATE SYSTEMS

Keihei Ueno, Hiroshi Kobayashi, and Hisamitsu Kaneko

DEPARTMENT OF ORGANIC SYNTHESIS
FACULTY OF ENGINEERING
KYUSHU UNIVERSITY
FUKUOKA, JAPAN

18-1. INTRODUCTION

Zone melting has been found to be very effective for obtaining ultrapure materials and for concentrating trace amounts of impurities, when applied to certain types of inner-complex metal chelates. Systems that contain metal chelates may be classified as follows.

A. Class I Systems: Main Component a Metal Chelate

The component to be purified is a metal chelate thermally stable enough on prolonged heating at temperatures slightly higher than its melting point. As metal chelates melt at much lower temperatures than the free metal, this process affords advantages when metal-ion impurities are to be separated. Many metal chelate compounds, however, are not thermally stable under the conditions of operation (Note 1) (*2–4*).

B. Class II Systems: Main Component a Free Ligand, Solid at Room Temperature

Zone melting can also be applied to a free ligand containing trace amounts of its metal chelates. Metal chelates tend to dissolve in excess ligand; therefore, if a ligand is chosen that is easily solidified (under forced cooling, if necessary), zone melting can be employed for the concentration of trace-metal ions after their extraction in the form of metal chelates. In most cases, a large excess of chelating agent is not required for the extraction of metal ions in an aqueous solution. When the extraction is carried out under very mild conditions without destroying the matrix material, however, the samples must be extracted repeatedly with a large excess of chelating agent. Such cases may be encountered in biochemical investigations. For the determination of trace amounts of metal ions in a large excess of ligand, the application of zone melting may be preferable to a conventional metal-ion determination.

In this system the metal chelates need not be stable at their melting points nor show clear melting points. The melting point of the free ligand, however, should be low enough for the metal chelates to dissolve without thermal decomposition (Note 2) (1, 5).

C. Class III Systems: Main Component an Organic Solvent, Solid at Room Temperature

An inert organic solvent that can dissolve the metal chelates to some extent can be employed in place of the free ligand. The sample might be a chelate compound from a crude metal salt, a mixture of a ligand and its metal chelate, or that of a metal chelate and an organic solvent. When these samples are placed on top of a column containing solid solvent, and zone melting is applied to this system, zone chromatographic separation of metal chelates can be expected; the efficiency depends on the segregation coefficients.

18-2. PROCEDURE AND APPARATUS

A. Preparation of Model Sample of Class I

A model sample of Class I was prepared, consisting of chromium acetylacetonate contaminated with trace amounts of iron (III), aluminum (III), and copper (II) chelates (3, 4). Accurately weighed *tris*(acetylacetonato) chromium (III), aluminum (III), and iron (III) were dissolved in benzene. The addition of a chloroform solution of a known weight of *bis* (acetylacetonato)copper (II) into the benzene solution gave a homogeneous solution. The solution was evaporated to dryness under reduced

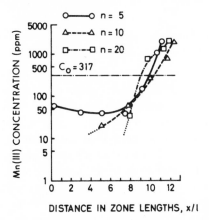

Fig. 18-1. Distribution of Mn(AA)₃ in Cr(AA)₃ after zone melting. Initial concentration of Mn(III) = 317 ppm.

pressure; the residual solid was ground in an agate mortar to give a uniform powder. Initial concentration of aluminum, copper, and iron were 85.2, 25.6 and 29.1 ppm as metal ions respectively.

B. Preparation of Model Sample of Class II

A Class II model sample was prepared, consisting of a trace copper (II) oxinate extracted with a large excess of oxine (5). A solution of 8-hydroxyquinoline (2.70 g) in glacial acetic acid (7 ml) was diluted with 100 ml of deionized water. A copper acetate solution (5 ml) containing 11.985 μg of copper (II) was adjusted to pH 3–4 with aqueous ammonium acetate. Addition of the oxine solution (about 5 ml) gave a yellow pre-

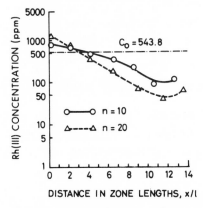

Fig. 18-2. Distribution of Rh(AA)₃ in Cr(AA)₃ after zone melting. Initial concentration of Rh(III) = 543.8 ppm.

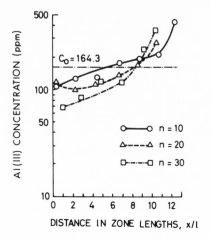

Fig. 18-3. Distribution of Al(AA)$_3$ in Cr(AA)$_3$ after zone melting. Initial concentration of Al(III) $= 164.3$ ppm.

cipitate, which was extracted with chloroform (20 ml). The aqueous layer was mixed with the rest of the oxine solution, the pH of the resulting solution was adjusted to 7 with aqueous ammonia. A yellow precipitate along with the free oxine was extracted with chloroform (100 ml). The chloroform extracts were combined and dried over sodium sulfate. The dried solution was evaported to dryness and the residual solid (2.62 g, 97% recovery) was ground in an agate mortar to give a uniform powder.

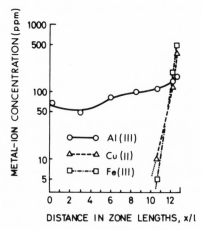

Fig. 18-4. Distribution of metal acetylacetonate chelates in Cr(AA)$_3$ after zone melting: $n = 10$. Initial concentration of metal ion (ppm): Al(III), 85.2; Cu(II), 25.6; Fe(III), 29.1.

C. Preparation of the Column for Zone Melting

About 2.5 g of a powdered sample (Class I) in a glass tube (4 mm I.D., 300 mm in length) was melted under nitrogen. After solidification upon cooling, the tube was sealed under nitrogen. The length of the ingot in the tube was about 150 mm (180 mm for the model sample of Class II).

D. Zone Melting

The apparatus consisted of a hoist, driven by a clock motor, pulling a vertical glass tube upward at a speed of 28 mm/hr. A two-stage nichrome ring heater was controlled at 5–10°C above the melting point of the ingot; the length of the molten zone was 13–15 mm. The required number of passes of the molten zone depends upon the segregation coefficient of the system concerned. Ten passes of the molten zone were sufficient for the model sample of Class I, while 40 passes were required for the Class II sample.

E. Determination of Metal Concentration after Zone Melting (Note 3)

After 10 passes the Class I sample was cut into pieces 20–25 mm long. About 40 mg of a sample from each piece was ground together with three times the amount of spectrographic graphite powder; standard emission spectrophotographic techniques were used with chromium as an internal standard. The analytical line pairs for the impurity elements were Al 3082.155 Å/Cr 3084.56 Å, Fe 2599.396 Å/Cr 2603.570 Å, and Cu 3273.962 Å/Cr 3264.264 Å, respectively. Some typical results are shown in Figs. 18-1–4, where metal concentrations are plotted against the distance in zone lengths, x/l; n = number of zone passes; AA = a univalent acetylacetonate anion. The results show that the chromium ion was separated from iron and copper, which were reduced to levels below the analytical sensitivities of the instruments, while the aluminum ion remained at about 50 ppm in the upper half of the column (Fig. 18-4). Increased number of zone passes did not significantly improve the purification (Fig. 18-3) (4).

On the other hand, the Class II sample was analyzed by standard atomic-absorption spectrophotometry. After 40 passes the bottom 30 mm of the ingot was removed and dissolved in methylisobutylketone to give 25.00 ml of solution. At 3247 Å analysis showed that the fraction contained 11.53 μg of copper (96.2% of the initial quantity of copper ion). Similar experiments on systems containing other metal oxinates such as nickel, cobalt, zinc, and iron showed that the effectiveness of concentration depended upon the particular metal ions involved. Concentration is increasingly effective in the order of Ni, Co, Fe, Zn, and Cu in this system.

NOTES

1. *Tris*(acetylacetonato)chromium (III) and *bis*(acetylacetonato)beryllium (II) are stable; *tris*(acetylacetonato)aluminum (III) decomposes slightly during zone melting. Although the dipivaloylmethane chelates are stable, chelates of ethyl acetoacetate, benzoylacetone, and thenoyltrifluoroacetone decompose easily near the melting points. Chelates of 8-hydroxyquinoline are stable up to 250°C, but give no clear melting points.

2. Thenoyltrifluoroacetone (m.p. 42.5–43.5°), benzoylacetone (m.p. 57–58°) and 8-hydroxyquinoline (m.p. 74–75°) satisfy these conditions. In the systems of 8-hydroxyquinoline and its chelates of various metal ions, very effective concentrations are observed.

3. Analytical methods varied with the nature of the chelate compounds. Visible and atomic-absorption spectrophotometry as well as emission spectrophotography were employed in the authors' work.

REFERENCES

1. K. Ueno, H. Kaneko, and Y. Watanabe, *Microchem. J.*, **10**, 244 (1966).
2. K. Ueno, H. Kaneko, and N. Fujimoto, *Talanta*, **11**, 1371 (1964).
3. H. Kaneko and K. Ueno, *Talanta*, **13**, 1525 (1966).
4. H. Kaneko, H. Kobayashi, and K. Ueno, *Talanta*, **14**, 1403 (1967).
5. H. Kaneko, H. Kanagawa, H. Kobayashi, and K. Ueno, *Talanta*, **14**, 1411 (1967).

19

PURIFICATION OF DIENES

Roger Kieffer

UNIVERSITY OF STRASBOURG
STRASBOURG, FRANCE

The purification of conjugated dienes is complicated by the facility with which these materials polymerize. Although 2,3-dimethyl-1,3-butadiene has been prepared in 99.4 and 99.8% purity by fractional distillation and the intermediate sulfone (*1*), we required higher purity for some applications. We attained our goal by developing apparatus for zone melting organic compounds down to $-140°C$ (*2, 3*). 2,3-Dimethyl-1,3-butadiene and *trans*-1,3-pentadiene have been obtained in purities of 99.98% (*4*) and 99.91% (*5*) respectively.

19-1. APPARATUS

The complete unit consists of three basic parts (see Fig. 19-1): (1) the cooling unit, (2) purification section, and (3) control unit.

The cooling unit consists of a metallic Dewar (22 liter capacity) (a) containing liquid air. Into the Dewar is placed a 5-mm steel-walled vessel (b) equipped with a circulation pump and propane (Note 1). The vessel is sealed by a bolted cap; a copper joint insures a tight seal. The pump (Note 2) maintains the flow of liquid propane at $-180°C$ through the cooler and cold zones of the purification section.

The purification unit consists of a driving mechanism that raises and lowers the sample through seven hot and six cold zones. The product to be purified is contained in a Pyrex tube (10 mm diam) equipped with hooks fashioned at each end. The tube is sealed if the sample is sensitive

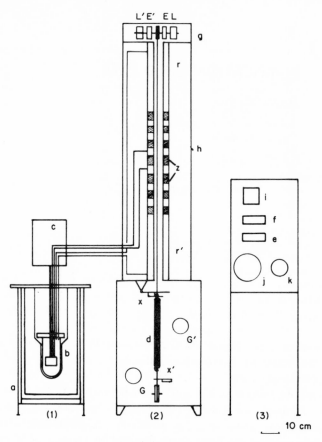

Fig. 19-1. Apparatus for zone melting at low temperatures. (1) Cooling unit: a, Dewar; b, pump; c, motor. (2) Purification section: d, sample tube; h, case; z, hot zones; r, r', coolers; x, x', microswitches; E, E', clutches; L, L', motors; G, G', gloves. (3) Control unit: i, impulse counter; f, temperature regulator; e, temperature indicator; j, transformer; k, rheostat for heating the stuffing box.

to air or oxygen; otherwise the tube is fabricated with a 1–2-mm opening for inserting the sample by means of a syringe. The filled tube, suspended by two wires attached to pulleys, is then placed in the refrigerator at the bottom part of the apparatus until frozen. It is then moved to the top at a speed of 2.5 cm/hr by motor L and electromagnetic clutch E. When the tube reaches the top of its ascent, the microswitch X' actuates a relay that disengages motor L and allows motor L' to return the tube to its original position at a speed of 70 cm/min. The limit switch X then automatically reverses the motors again for the slow ascent.

The detail of the zones is shown in Fig. 19-2. The sample container

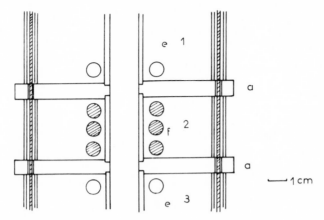

Fig. 19-2. Detail of zones: 1, cold zone; 2, hot zone; 3, cold zone; a, insulating disk; e, cooling tube; f, electrical resistance.

passes through a brass tube (12 mm I.D., 14 mm O.D.). A copper tube (6 mm I.D.) is soldered on to the outside at intervals (e in Fig. 19-2). Cold propane flows through the copper tube and thus provides the six cold zones of the system. The hot zones are formed by wrapping the brass tube with a resistance heater (100-W power). The temperature of the hot zones is measured by a copper–constantan thermocouple and controlled by an electronic regulator.

The hot zones are insulated from the cold zones by 10-mm thicknesses of asbestos. Propane-cooled areas (r, r′ in Fig. 19-1) maintain the sample in the solid form when emerging from central purification section. The entire unit is encased in a box filled with "Perlite," a mineral insulator (3).

Moisture presents delicate problems because the deposition of ice on cold parts prevents movement of the glass tube. We have provided a system of drying by circulating the air through a layer of silica gel. A glove box (G, G′) permits manipulation in the absence of moisture. After each experiment it is necessary to dry the apparatus completely with hot air.

The control unit includes an impulse counter that records the number of passes, a temperature regulator for the hot zones, and a temperature indicator for different parts of the units.

19-2. INFLUENCE OF VARIOUS PARAMETERS

A. Number of Zones

The purity of the sample increases with the number of zones. After a number of passes, however, purity reaches a limiting value. Table 19-1

TABLE 19-1

Purification of Dienes by Zone Melting

Product	Number of zones	Purity of starting material (%)	Purity[a] of different fractions				
			1	2	3	4	5
2,3-Dimethyl-	7	94.85	93.2		93.2	95.0	96.0
1,3-butadiene	21	94.85	94.2		94.2	97.0	98.5
	49	94.85	96.3		96.3	97.4	98.9
	84	94.85	96.3		96.3	97.4	99.6
	7	99.43	97.0	98.8	99.7	99.7	*99.82*
	21	99.43	96.8	98.6	99.7	*99.88*	*99.80*
	35	99.43	96.6	98.6	99.8	*99.90*	*99.95*
	49	99.43	96.6	98.6	*99.84*	*99.92*	*99.98*
	98	99.43	96.5	98.4	*99.92*	*99.95*	*99.98*
1,3-Pentadiene	9	68	62.2	65.3	67.2	68	70
	35	92.8	85.5	89.5	93.3	93.5	94.2
	7	98.7	96.7	98.7	99.7	99.8	99.8
	7	98.7	94.5	98.5	*99.85*	*99.91*	*99.90*
	7	98.7	95.4	98.6	*99.87*	*99.21*	*99.89*
	7	98.7	95.6	98.5	*99.89*	*99.93*	*99.91*
2,4-Dimethyl-	7	97.9	99.1		97.9	97.7	
1,3-pentadiene	14	97.9	99.4	99.3	97.8	97.8	
	35	97.9	99.6	99.2	97.8	97.8	
2,4-Hexadiene	7	98.7	98.4		98.8	98.9	
	14	98.7	98.2		98.5	99.1	
	35	98.7	98.0		99.1	99.5	
2,4-Heptadiene	7	98.3	97		97.6	98.6	
	35	98.3	96.6		98.4	99.4	99.3
3-Methyl 1,3-hexadiene	35	98.2	No purification				
4-Ethyl- 1,3-hexadiene	14	98.0	No purification				
4-Methyl- 1,3-heptadiene	14	98.6	No purification				

[a] Purity values shown in italics were obtained by thermal analysis (6); purity values <99.8% were determined by gas-liquid chromatography.

shows that 2,3-dimethyl-1,3-butadiene is not purified from 49 up to 98 zones.

B. Zone Speed

A speed of 25 mm/hr affords acceptable material more readily than the 50-mm/hr rate. For all of our work with dienes 25 mm/hr was the preferred rate.

C. Polymer Content

Polymerization of diene monomers often occurs spontaneously on storage. The presence of small quantities of polymers ($<1\%$) retards purification excessively; polymers increase the viscosity of the sample and slow down diffusion at the solid–liquid interface.

D. Crystallinity of the Product

If the solid product is a glass, the viscosity is changing continuously; no purification occurs. If the product melts with softening, diffusion can not take place in the viscous media at the liquid–solid interface. This is the explanation for lack of purification in the case of the last three compounds listed in Table 19-1.

E. Purity of the Starting Material

Starting material $<98\%$ pure does not lead to the highest attainable purity. Examination of Table 19-1 shows that 2,3-dimethyl-1,3-butadiene (94.85%) afforded 99.6% material after 12 passes (84 zones). With 99.43% material at the start 5 passes (35 zones) yield a fraction of 99.95% purity. An impure sample must be prepurified to 99% purity. Further purification of the purest fraction affords the best material.

19-3. METHODS OF ANALYSIS

In our experience gas–liquid chromatography was found to be accurate

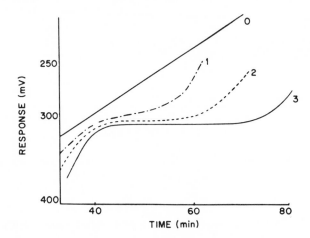

Fig. 19-3. Time–temperature curves of 2,3-dimethyl-1,3-butadiene samples: 0, heating curve (reference); 1, initial product; 2, after 21 zone passes; 3, after 98 zone passes.

to 99.6% purity. We found melting curves at low temperatures accurate to 99.98% purity. The variation of melting point with purity is shown in Fig. 19-3.

NOTES

1. Liquid air cannot be used as the cooling liquid because of its volatility and poor lubricating action in the pump. Liquid propane is entirely satisfactory; it melts at $-195°C$ and possesses a manageable viscosity at $-180°C$.

2. A centrifugal pump does not maintain a sufficiently rapid flow. We used a gear pump, the oil pump of a car engine adapted to work at $-180°C$. An electric motor (0.25 hp) drives the pump via a shaft that passes through a double Teflon gasket lubricated by molybdenum disulfide grease.

3. Originally the unit was enclosed in wood. Recently we replaced the wood with a cylinder of sheet iron soldered at all edges. The new unit is water-tight; it no longer absorbs moisture from the air.

REFERENCES

1. F. Schue, *J. Polymer Sci.*, 4, 259 (1963).
2. A. Deluzarche, R. Kieffer, J. C. Maire, and J. Moritz, French Pat. 994,486 (1964).
3. R. Kieffer, J. C. Maire, A. Deluzarche, and A. Maillard, *Bull. Soc. Chim. (France)*, 633 (1965).
4. R. Kieffer, *Bull. Soc. Chim. (France)*, 3224 (1965).
5. R. Kieffer, International Symposium on Macromolecular Chemistry, Prague, 1965; *J. Polymer Sci. C*, 16, 2829 (1967).
6. R. Kieffer, J. C. Maire, A. Deluzarche, and A. Maillard, *Bull. Soc. Chim. (France)*, 1499 (1964).

20

PURIFICATION OF KILOGRAM QUANTITIES OF AN ORGANIC COMPOUND

J. C. Maire and M. Delmas

DEPARTMENT OF ORGANIC CHEMISTRY
MARSEILLE–SAINT JEROME
MARSEILLE, FRANCE

20-1. INTRODUCTION

Ultrapure organic compounds are usually obtained by employing laboratory-scale zone refiners. Since large-scale production is an attractive possibility, we have been engaged in the development of a zone-refining unit capable of handling approximately two pounds per day. This modest goal permitted us to study most of the problems involved in scale-up operations (1). Although this refiner has not yet been used commercially, we believe that it is applicable to industrial processes. The efficiency of the apparatus has been tested with (a) benzoic acid containing 1% methyl red and (b) octadecanol containing 1% dodecylbenzene. In both cases spectrophotometric analyses of purified fractions paralleled the results obtained with microscale zone refining.

20-2. THE KILOGRAM-SCALE MULTIZONE REFINER

The apparatus shown in Figs. 20-1 and -2 is a four-zone vertical refiner. The heating system is composed of six resistance heaters, a small heater (D) for each zone and two heaters (G) along the length of the aluminum block (total power $= 4 \times D + 2 \times G = 3,500 \, W$). The heaters are regulated by a temperature-control device (T) monitored by a thermocouple (E) to maintain the aluminum block at the preselected temperature. An axial hole in which the ingot is moved up and down is drilled in the block, which is also cut out on the front side in such a way as to produce four molten zones (A) and three cold zones (R). Into each

Fig. 20-1. Kilogram-scale zone refiner used for purifying organic compounds (*1*).
(Courtesy of Centre National de la Recherche Scientifique.)

zone is inserted a thermocouple; the temperature is controlled by means of a galvanometer (B) and a selector switch (S). Three copper-wire coolers are mounted in the spaces between the molten zones. The block is heat-insulated by an asbestos lining covered in turn with aluminum sheets. The sample container is a Pyrex glass tube 1 meter long and 5 cm in diameter. To avoid breakage by expansion on melting, a collapsible Teflon tube (M) is placed inside the container and is held in an axial position by a glass rod. Teflon is inert to ordinary chemicals; no contamination of the product occurs. In most cases the Teflon may be severely deformed after an experiment, but the pyrex container does not break. At the lower end of the container is a needle valve (L), which is used for sampling the refined product.

A. Slow-Motion Mechanism

Some difficulties were encountered in moving the heavy sample tube. It was not possible to use clock-type electrical motors, but hydraulic devices proved to be convenient. The container is balanced by a floating counterweight (F). When water flows into the vessel (K), the counterweight (F) rises and the sample tube is lowered. A 2-cm/hr speed is easily achieved. The necessary cable and pulley systems are shown in Fig. 20-2. When the water level reaches to top of the siphon tube (N) most of the water is quickly siphoned out, the sample tube rises, and the process starts again. A constant flow of water is achieved by means of a capillary tube and a constant-level water tank (H). It is necessary to filter the water through a Pasteur filter (J) and a fritted-glass filter (J') in order to keep the system operating efficiently over a long period of time.

B. Operation and Results

The container is filled outside the unit, attached to the driving cable above the heating block, and moved down to its starting position. A suitable temperature is selected on (T) and the process is started through the main switch (I). When a sufficient number of passes has been achieved, the sample tube is brought to its uppermost position. The lower end of the solid ingot (one zone length) is then introduced within the top heater until this fraction is molten. The tube is then lowered rapidly until the melt emerges below the bottom heater; the liquid is extracted through the needle valve (L). The tube is then raised so that a zone length of the new bottom end of the ingot is molten by the top heater. The tube is again

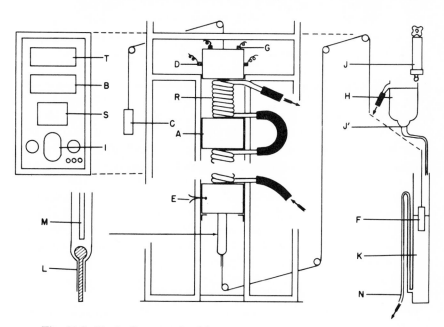

Fig. 20-2. Block diagram of a kilogram-scale multizone zone refiner (6).

lowered, the molten zone is removed and the sampling procedure is continued until the tube is empty.

NOTES

1. Sampling.   In microscale zone refining, sampling of the refined product is usually achieved by slicing the tube. On a large scale this would be inconvenient and expensive.

Our sampling system is not yet satisfactory. As each fraction does not drain completely, some mixing of fractions of differing purity results. A possible solution is a container made of several parts linked by ground-glass joints. Well-defined, uncontaminated fractions would then be available upon disconnecting the joints. An alternative refinement would be a stainless-steel tube fabricated from a sufficient number of segments screwed together.

2. Stirring.   The parameters that influence free convection have already been discussed *(2)*. In order to obtain strong convection currents we consider the cooling system most important for maintaining a temperature difference between the crystallizing and melting interfaces. In addition to the gradient effect, superheating of the molten zone increases free convection by reducing the viscosity of the medium.

An attractive way to improve purification is the reduction of the boundary layer at the freezing interface by forced stirring *(3)*. This has the added advantages of improving the shape of the zone and decreasing the length of the zone relative to the diameter of the ingot *(4)*. Our current investigation of a refiner containing one zone and a stirring mechanism shows that the efficiency of separation is improved by a factor of 10 *(5, 6)*.

3. Continuous Processing.   Most of the literature on zone refining is concerned with multistage batch processes. Although the advantages of continuous zone refining for large-scale operation are obvious, few attempts have been made to develop the zone-void system described in 1955 *(7)*. In our hands the results with the zone-void method applied to a circular charge were not encouraging enough to deserve further investigation *(8)*.

4. Analytical Methods.   In large-scale operation the availability of large samples permits the use of less sophisticated methods [see reference *(9)*, p. 202 for a review of appropriate methods]. Thermal and differential analyses give the most reliable results and are the only independent criteria of purity. The method devised by Rossini *et al.* *(10)* is most reliable, but requires complicated equipment and considerable sample (40–50 g). Skau's method *(11)* revised by Mathieu *(12)* requires only 0.3–0.5 g of sample. We have found that the procedure recommended by

Skau can furnish results comparable to Rossini's method if temperature can be measured accurately to 0.001 °C. We have determined, for example, that zone-refined 2-methyl naphthalene contained <0.03 mole % impurity by Skau's method (*13*).

REFERENCES

1. J. C. Maire and M. A. Delmas, *Rec. Trav. Chim.*, **85**, 268 (1965).

2. W. R. Wilcox and C. R. Wilke, in *Ultrapurification of Semiconductors* (M. S. Brooks and J. K. Kennedy, eds.) Macmillan, New York, 1962, p. 481.

3. N. V. Abramenko, G. M. Dugacheva, and A. G. Anikin, *Vestn. Mosk. Univ.*, **21**, 56 (1966).

4. W. G. Pfann, C. E. Miller, and J. D. Hunt, *Rev. Sci. Instr.*, **37**, 649 (1966).

5. J. Trombetta, Dissertation, Marseille–Saint Jerome, Marseille, 1966.

6. M. Delmas and J. C. Maire, unpublished results.

7. W. G. Pfann, *J. Metals,* **7**, 297 (1955).

8. J. C. Maire, J. Moritz, and R. Kieffer, Symposium für Zonenschmelzen und Kolonnenkristallisieren, Kernforschungzentrum, Karlsruhe, Germany, 1963.

9. W. R. Wilcox, R. Friedenberg, and N. Back, *Chem. Rev.*, **64**, 187 (1964).

10. F. D. Rossini, A. R. Glasgow, and A. J. Streiff, *J. Res. Natl. Bur. Std.*, **35**, 355 (1945).

11. E. L. Skau, *Proc. Am. Acad. Arts Sci.*, **67**, 551 (1932).

12. M. P. Mathieu, *Bull. Soc. Chim. Belges,* **63**, 333 (1954).

13. J. C. Maire and J. Moritz, *Bull. Soc. Chim. (France)*, **89** (1963).

21 RAPID PURIFICATION OF ORGANIC SUBSTANCES

M. J. van Essen, P. F. J. van der Most, and W. M. Smit

INSTITUTE FOR PHYSICAL CHEMISTRY, TNO
ZEIST
THE NETHERLANDS

21-1. INTRODUCTION

Recently a rapid zone refiner has been developed (*1*). This automatic apparatus reduces the time for purification from several days or weeks to a few hours. In this chapter special features of this apparatus along with some purifications are described. Special attention has been given to the analysis of the resulting products, since the literature records such unclearly defined criteria for purity as odor, color or crystal size (*2*).

Most analytical methods permit the determination of specific contaminants. In "highly pure" organic substances however, a multitude of contaminants may be present. Thus a purity determination based on conventional analytical methods will be inadequate as well as time consuming. Recent developments in the measurement and interpretation of temperature–heat-content curves have eliminated this analytical difficulty to a large extent (*3*).

21-2. DISCUSSION AND DESCRIPTION
OF THE APPARATUS

A. Drawbacks of Conventional Apparatus

1. When organic substances are purified in conventional apparatus, separation of impurities does not occur at travel rates exceeding 5 cm/hr. Effective stirring to remove contaminants from the boundary layer at the freezing interface is not provided.

2. To allow for expansion upon melting in a vertical tube, the molten zone is initiated at the open upper end of the container. The downward zone movement does not guarantee good contact between solid and liquid at the freezing interface because voids or bubbles collect at the upper side of the zone.

3. Conventional apparatus may not withstand even minor changes in heat transfer. This is due to the fact that volume changes in already existing zones may lead to breakage of the container.

B. Specific Features of the Rapid Zone Refiner*

1. The substance to be treated is contained in a vertical Pyrex glass tube subjected to a high-speed rotation which is periodically reversed. The resulting shifting–shearing forces produce intense mixing of the liquid, especially near the freezing interface. Mass transfer is thus promoted to such an extent that zone-travel rates up to 120 cm/hr are permissible without appreciable loss of separation efficiency.

2. Good contact between solid and liquid at the freezing interface is ensured by an *upward* zone movement. Breakage of the container during the formation of a new zone is prevented by a movable Teflon stopper present in the lower side of the tube. The expansion of the substance during the formation of a zone results in an upward movement of the tube and its contents.

3. An increase of zone volumes no longer leads to breakage of the container. Special programming of the zone travel rates and the heater temperatures eliminates this danger; this programming is permissible only because of the high travel rates (*1*).

C. Description of the Apparatus

Figure 21-1 shows the apparatus. Two versions are available. The rapid zone refiner for quantities of 50 or 100 ml is intended primarily for preparative work and for concentrating minor amounts of impurities. The midget rapid zone refiner with a capacity of 0.2–4 ml is excellent for

---

* Manufactured by ENRAF-NONIUS, Delft, the Netherlands.

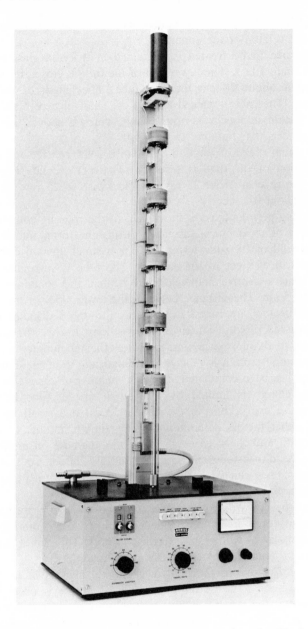

Fig. 21-1. The rapid zone refiner developed by the Institute for Physical Chemistry TNO.

chemical analysis. The experiments described below were performed in the 50-or-100–ml version of the apparatus.

The substance to be treated is contained in a Pyrex glass tube (108 cm long, 9.4 mm I.D.). The lower end of the tube is closed by inserting a Teflon stopper about 20 cm into the tube. The length of the ingot is about 70 cm. The tube is placed around the shaft of a reversible electric motor; the Teflon stopper rests on the shaft, which is about 20 cm long. A coupling connects the container to the shaft.

The maximum speed of rotation of the tube is 25 rev/sec and the direction of rotation of the tube is reversed twice per second. The time required for the reversal from 25 rev/sec clockwise to 25 rev/sec counterclockwise is about 0.2 sec.

The coupling permits upward movement of the rotating container. Thus the expansion of the melting substance during the formation of the zone at the lower end of the tube results only in a small upward displacement of the tube with respect to the stopper. The tube is surrounded by five resistance heaters. Above and below the heaters the container is cooled by compressed air. The distance between the lower sides of the heaters is 14 cm. The heaters are raised by a motor through a distance of 14 cm and then returned rapidly to their initial positions. In this way each heater is transferred to the next zone and the lowest heater initiates a new zone. This reciprocating motion is repeated automatically until the desired number of cycles has been completed. The total number of zones that can pass through the charge is limited by the length of the tube beneath the stopper because every zone in the charge leads to a small upward displacement. Other factors determining the maximum number of zones are the zone length and the percentage of volume increase on melting of the substance. The dimensions of the apparatus are chosen so that in most cases enough zones can be passed through the charge to attain the ultimate distribution.

Of course the upward movement of the tube during the formation of a zone must not result in a displacement of the freezing interfaces of the already-existing zones with respect to their heaters. The rate of zone travel, therefore, is programmed to compensate for this effect.

To prevent fracture of the container due to changes in heat transfer to preexisting zones, the power of the lowest heater is programmed in such a way that the volume of the melted substance decreases just after the formation of the zone. Of course this is accompanied with a change in crystallization speed; this effect is negligible because the usual zone travel rates are of the order of 60–100 cm/hr.

The decrease in the amount of melted substance results in the formation of a void at the upper interface. This void does not hamper the separation but acts as a buffer capable of accounting for small changes in heat transfer or heater travel rate.

The cooling system is provided with shutters in order to allow normal freezing to precede zone melting. During the first five cycles the cooling air is guided in such a way that the molten substance freezes gradually from bottom to top. The zone-melting operation starts immediately after normal freezing; the first zone follows 14 cm behind the freezing interface.

The uppermost end of the container is heated by a sixth heater to ensure that no substance is excluded from the process.

The apparatus is intended for the purification of substances melting up to 250°C. The temperature of the cooling air must be at least 30°C below the melting point. In special cases an inert atmosphere can be employed.

21-3. EXPERIMENTAL

A. Analysis of the Samples

The impurity content of the samples was derived from temperature–heat-content curves covering the melting range (*3, 4, 5*). This general method permits the quantitative determination of the (unknown) impurities as well as their distribution coefficients.

The apparatus used for the determination of the curves was an improved and fully automatic version of the apparatus described by Smit and Kateman (*6*).

B. Purification Experiments

1. Naphthalene (m.p. 80°C)

a. 200 g of technical grade naphthalene (Amsterdamse Chinine Fabriek) was prepurified by normal freezing followed by zone melting. At the start the product contained 0.25 mole% of contaminants with a mean distribution coefficient of 0.2 and <0.02 mole% of contaminants with a distribution coefficient >1.

After 1.5 hr of zone melting (zone-travel rate = 80 cm/hr) the last 10 cm of the ingot was rejected.

The product contained 0.09 mole% of solid soluble impurities with a distribution coefficient of 0.3 and <0.02 mole% of contaminants with a distribution coefficient >1.

b. 100 g was again subjected to normal freezing followed by zone melting. After three hours of operation (zone-travel rate = 40 cm/hr) samples were analyzed by the THC method (see Table 21-1).

TABLE 21-1

Parameters and Purification Data for Zone Melting of Organic Compounds

Exp.	Substance	Melting point (°C)	Starting material Mole % impurity	k^a	Time (hr)	Zone velocity (cm/hr)	Composition of products (ingot length 70 cm) mole % impurity 0–10 cm	10–20 cm	20–30 cm	30–40 cm	40–50 cm	50–60 cm	60–70 cm
1b	Naphthalene	80	0.09	0.3	3	40	nd^b	nd	0.02	0.02	0.04	0.06	>0.4
2	Biphenyl	70	<0.02	>1	5	60	0.06	0.04	0.02	nd	nd	nd	nd
3	Azobenzene	68	0.15	0.3	5	60	0.01	0.02	0.02	0.02	0.03	0.04	>0.9
4	p-Dibromobenzene	87	0.30	0.15	4	60	nd	0.05	0.05	0.05	0.06	0.11	>1.6
5	Dimethylterephthalate	150	0.34	0.2	3	60	0.01	0.02	0.02	0.02	0.03	0.12	>2.0
6	trans-Stilbene	122	0.5	0.3	5	60	nd	nd	nd	0.01	0.05	0.13	>3.3

^{a} k stands for the (mean) distribution coefficient derived from T.H.C. curves; k values of binary systems determined in this way equal the theoretical distribution coefficient.

^{b} nd means "not detectable."

2. Biphenyl (m.p. 70°C)

50 g of biphenyl (British Drug Houses) was used without prepurification. The crude product contained 0.15 mole% of a contaminant with a distribution coefficient of 0.3 and <0.02 mole% of a contaminant with $k > 1$. This substance was subjected to normal freezing followed by zone melting (zone velocity = 60 cm/hr). After five hours of operation samples were analyzed (see Table 21-1).

3. Azobenzene (m.p. 68°C)

50 g of azobenzene (Fluka "purissimum") was used without prepurification. The crude product contained 0.30 mole% of contaminants with a mean distribution coefficient of 0.15. This product was subjected to normal freezing followed by zone melting (zone velocity = 60 cm/hr). After five hours of operation samples were analyzed (see Table 21-1).

4. p-Dibromobenzene (m.p. 87°C)

100 g of p-dibromobenzene (British Drug Houses) was used without prepurification. The crude product contained 0.34 mole% of a contaminant with a mean distribution coefficient of 0.2. This product was subjected to normal freezing followed by zone melting (zone velocity = 60 cm/hr). After four hours of operation samples were analyzed (see Table 21-1).

5. Dimethylterephthalate (m.p. 150°C)

100 g of dimethylterephthalate (old sample of Hercules Powder Co.) was used without prepurification. The crude product contained 0.04 mole% of contaminants with a mean distribution coefficient of 0.1. This product was subjected to normal freezing followed by zone melting (zone velocity = 60 cm/hr). After three hours of operation samples were analyzed (see Table 21-1).

6. trans-Stilbene (m.p. 122°C)

50 g of prepurified trans-stilbene was artificially contaminated with 0.5 mole% of azobenzene. The distribution coefficient is 0.3. This product was subjected to normal freezing followed by zone melting with zone velocity of 60 cm/hr. After five hours of operation samples were analyzed. The azobenzene content of these samples was determined with a Unicam SP 800 B spectrophotometer (see Table 21-1).

21-4. DISCUSSION

The experiments demonstrate that very satisfactory purifications of organic compounds can be obtained by means of the rapid zone refiner within a quite reasonable time and without special effort or skill of the operator.

Mean distribution coefficients are listed in Table 21-1; that is, the crude product contains a complex of impurities. Some of these impurities have distribution coefficients higher than the apparent one. Thus the purification of azobenzene can not be compared with that of stilbene which contains as impurity only one single component.

The zone-travel rates should not be considered as upper limits. Evidence has been obtained that for easily crystallizable substances higher zone-travel rates are permissible without loss of purification efficiency.

21-5. SUMMARY

Crude commercial products containing up to 1% total contaminants can be purified by a novel rapid zone refiner. Quantities up to 100 ml can be processed in four to six hours. The products were analyzed by temperature–heat-content curves.

REFERENCES

1. N. J. G. Bollen, M. J. van Essen, and W. M. Smit, *Anal. Chim. Acta,* **38,** 279 (1967).

2. W. R. Wilcox, R. Friedenberg, and N. Back, *Chem. Rev.,* **64,** 188 (1964).

3. H. F. van Wijk, P. F. J. van der Most, and W. M. Smit, *Anal. Chim. Acta,* **38,** 285 (1967).

4. H. F. van Wijk and W. M. Smit, *Anal. Chim. Acta,* **24,** 45 (1961).

5. W. M. Smit, *Z. Elektrochem.,* **66,** 779 (1962).

6. W. M. Smit and G. Kateman, *Anal. Chim. Acta,* **17,** 161 (1957).

22

INVESTIGATION OF ZONE-MELTING PURIFICATION OF GALLIUM TRICHLORIDE BY A RADIOTRACER METHOD*

Werner Kern

RCA LABORATORIES
RADIO CORPORATION OF AMERICA
PRINCETON, NEW JERSEY

22-1. INTRODUCTION

Radioactive isotopes as analytical tools in zone-melting investigations can yield accurate data on the segregation behavior of impurities present at extremely low concentrations. A nondestructive technique for continuously and automatically measuring the radioactivity in a column is especially useful in systematic investigations involving reactive or expensive materials. The distribution of impurities can be determined by analyzing a sealed column at various stages of zone melting without removing the material

* This work was sponsored by the Manufacturing Technology Laboratory, Aeronautics System Division, Air Force Systems Command, United States Air Force under Contract #AF33(600)-37268.

from its container. The technique is based on the addition of controlled quantities of radioactively tagged inorganic compounds to the material to be purified (*1*). The distribution of the impurities is determined by measuring instrumentally the radiation emitted from the ingot as a function of ingot distance after zone leveling and after various stages of zone refining. The material can then be remixed and used again for studying different zone-melting parameters. Massive lead shields minimize background radiation from the sealed ingot. The radioactivity measurements are conducted by stationary as well as dynamic techniques; the activity profile is recorded continuously and automatically. A variant of this method was described in 1966 by Schildknecht (*2*) for the zone melting of a circular charge of radioactively labelled materials. A shielded radiation-counter tube is fitted over a cool segment for continuously measuring the tracer radioactivity.

A. Applicability of the Method

The technique of measuring the radiation of sealed columns is applicable to the zone melting of many solid materials if the following conditions are satisfied: (a) the impurity element to be traced must be tagged with a radionuclide of the same element; (b) the radionuclide must be in the same chemical state as the impurity element; (c) the emitted radiation must be sufficiently energetic to penetrate through the material in the column without being absorbed to an appreciable extent; and (d) the half-life of the radionuclide should be long enough to allow zone melting and radiation measurements. These requirements restrict the application of the method to radionuclides that emit gamma radiation or hard beta radiation and have half-lives of at least several hours. The method is therefore ideally suited for the tracing of inorganic impurities, whereas the tracing of organic compounds is generally not possible. The available radionuclides for tracing inorganic impurities are plentiful and the proper choice should present no difficulties.

B. Studies with Gallium Trichloride

The method will be exemplified for the specific case of gallium trichloride, a highly reactive, corrosive, and hygroscopic chemical that must be processed in sealed quartz containers. Zone refining of gallium trichloride is an important intermediate purification process in the preparation of high-purity gallium (*3*). During the developmental and production phases of this process, quantitative impurity-segregation data were required to evaluate various types of zone refining. As a nondestructive, sealed-system analysis was particularly desirable, a procedure was developed primarily for this particular objective.

In the present work only one radioactive isotope was used in a zone-melting column. It is possible, however, to add several radioactive tracers and determine simultaneously the concentration of each in a column segment by instrumental analysis. In this technique the static counting is employed and the pulses from the gamma scintillation detector are transmitted to the linear amplifier of a multichannel differential pulse-height analyzer. A gamma-ray spectrum of differential counting rates versus pulse-height energy is automatically recorded, from which the quantity of each tracer can be measured. Radiotracers should be chosen whose characteristic photopeak energies on which the radiation analysis is based are relatively free from spectral interference from the other tracers in the mixture.

22-2. PROCEDURE

A. Preparation of Radioactive Charges of Gallium Trichloride

As shown in Fig. 22-1, flat-bottomed tubes of fused silica (1.2×30 cm) were sealed to a quartz distillation apparatus. A small volume of aqueous solution containing the trace element was introduced in the chemically cleaned tube and evaporated to dryness in vacuo. The solutions contained 0.05–0.5 mCi of radioactivity in the form of either $Fe^{59}Cl_3$, $Zn^{65}Cl_2$, $Mn^{54}Cl_2$, or $Na^{22}Cl$.

The iron deposit was specially prepared to prevent hydrolysis during evaporation. A $Fe^{59}Cl_3$ solution in $6 N$ HCl was extracted with diethyl ether. The ether extracts were chilled in liquid nitrogen, freed from the ice by filtration, introduced into the tube, and finally concentrated by evaporation of the solvent.

Columns for combined spectrographic and radiochemical analyses were prepared with solutions containing 10 ppm of each element in the form of $AlCl_3$, $CuCl_2$, $NiCl_2$, $MgCl_2$, $PbCl_2$, and $MnCl_2$. Controlled quantities of $Mn^{54}Cl_2$ and $Fe^{59}Cl_3$ were added to these solutions as tracers.

The apparatus that contained the zone-melting tube and the dried impurity deposit was evacuated and filled with purified chlorine gas to a pressure of 760 Torr. The break seals were opened, and a predetermined quantity of gallium trichloride was distilled from the storage container into the zone-refining tube, which was then sealed. The contents were dissolved and mixed by repeated melting and rapid freezing so that the impurity solute was uniformly distributed throughout the gallium trichloride charge.

B. Zone-Melting Techniques

Experiments were performed in a Fisher zone refiner designed for automatic upward, downward, and horizontal pass-cycling. Nichrome ribbon

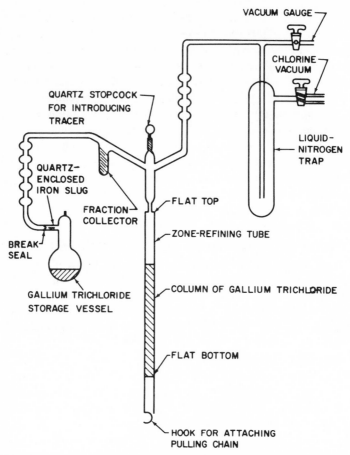

Fig. 22-1. Quartz apparatus for charging zone-melting columns of gallium trichloride with radioactively labelled trace impurities.

looped around the tube and connected to a pair of terminals on a movable
carriage served as the resistance-heating element. No means of stirring the
melted zone was applied other than natural convection in the liquid. The
melted-zone section was quickly resolidified by a blast of room-temper-
ature air from a ring mounted behind the heater. The length of the melted
zone was kept constant at one-tenth the total ingot length by close control
of the heater power supply and the distance between the heater and the air
blast. Zone travel velocities were 0.50, 1.0, and 2.0 in./hr. These travel
rates were regulated by adjusting the movement of the heater with a timer-
controlled variable-speed motor. Radiation measurements were conducted
after each pass. Up to 5 consecutive passes were applied for a given set of

experimental conditions. Transport of the gallium trichloride by the molten horizontal zone was minimized to maintain the uniform charge thickness essential for the subsequent analytical evaluation. Material transport of this type is caused by density changes during melting in horizontal zone refining and can be eliminated by tilting the ingot container slightly (4).

C. Radioactivity Measurements

A thallium-activated sodium iodide crystal built in a 2-in.-thick lead well (Baird Atomic, Model 810) served as the gamma-radiation detector. The photomultiplier pulses were passed to the amplifier of a scaler assembly and to a count-rate meter with four linear ranges. As shown in Fig. 22-2, the radiation detector was shielded from the zone-melting tube by a 6- or 8-in. layer of lead bricks, which were positioned to form a 0.25- or 0.39-in.-wide slit (fixed by spacers) above and across the center of the detector. The lead thickness required to minimize background radiation from the zone-refining column and to maintain a sufficiently high tracer counting rate was determined experimentally from graphs (Fig. 22-3) that measure the radioactivity of standard sources as a function of distance from the slit under various lead-shield thicknesses.

Two types of radiocounting techniques were employed: a dynamic tech-

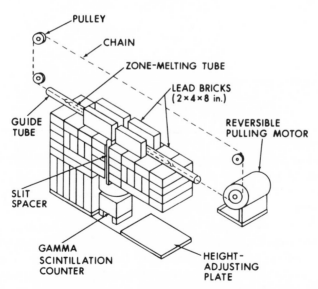

Fig. 22-2. Apparatus for static or dynamic radioactivity measurements of zone-melting columns with 8-in.-thick top shield of lead.

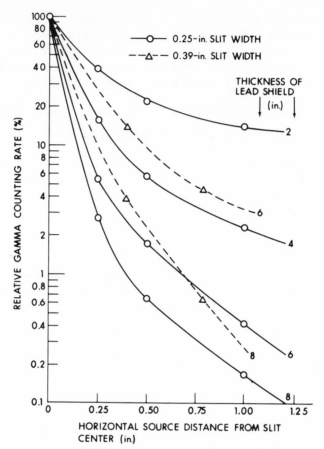

Fig. 22-3. Gamma-radiation counting rates from a Fe⁵⁹ source as a function of
source position and shielding thickness.

nique based on automatic scanning, and a static technique based on section counting.

In the radioscanning analysis, the columns were pulled slowly by a
variable-speed motor across and perpendicular to the slit. A thin-walled
glass tube was used as a guide canal for the column. All columns were
marked with a strip of tape measure to indicate the exact ingot segment
being radiocounted. Ingot profiles of radioactivity as a function of column
distance were obtained by automatic plotting of the counting rates on a
calibrated and synchronized strip-chart recorder. Suitable radioactivity
standards and background scans were included on these charts before and
after scanning of the column. Typical profiles for an ingot after 0, 1, and
3 passes are shown in Fig. 22-4.

The static counting technique was used for accurate analyses and low-level radioactivity measurements. In this technique, the column was positioned so that a single section could be counted until a desired number of counts were collected on the radioscaler; these counting periods depended on the activity level of the section and ranged from 3 to 60 min.

D. Combined Radiochemical and Emission-Spectrographic Analyses

Some radiotracer experiments were complemented by emission spectrographic analyses of the impurity admixtures. After radioscanning of the finished zone-refining columns, single sections of the column were melted and collected in beakers containing purified $6 N$ HCl. The gallium trichloride and the ferric chloride complexes were separated from the other substances by two extractions with isopropyl ether so that emission-

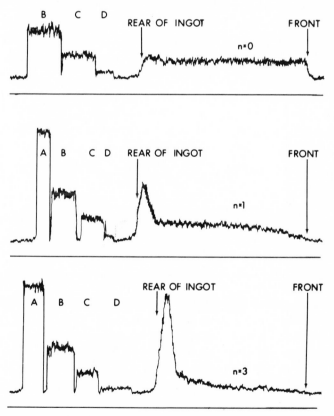

Fig. 22-4. Automatic radioactivity scanning profiles of activity versus ingot distance for an ingot after zone leveling ($n = 0$) and after 1 and 3 zone passes; radioactivity calibration standards (A, B, C, D) are also indicated.

spectrographic analysis of the added net impurities in the acid phases could be made (5). Radioactivity measurements of the solutions provided the concentration data, the acid phases yielding the $Mn^{54}Cl_2$ and the ether phases yielding the $Fe^{59}Cl_3$ concentrations.

E. Radiographic Examination of Ingots

Columns from the vertical zone-refining experiments sometimes contained gas-filled spaces which, if not detected, would lead to errors. A rapid testing technique was designed for checking each column prior to analysis. A source of a few millicuries of a nuclide that emitted low-energy gamma radiation was positioned 1 in. above the slit of the radiation-detector shield. The column was then pulled over the slit as described for the automatic scanning. Any increase in relative radiation transmission was indicated on the chart recorder, which immediately verified the extent and location of voids. Columns with irregularities were excluded from analysis. A radiographic profile of a column with severe defects is shown in Fig. 22-5.

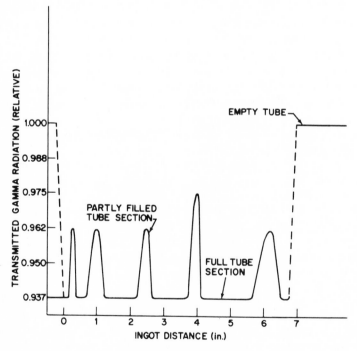

Fig. 22-5. Gamma-radiation transmission profile for an ingot with several voids.

F. Determination of Purification Efficiency

The effectiveness of zone refining for the separation of specific trace impurities under various experimental conditions was evaluated by use of the effective segregation coefficients and the over-all purification factors.

First, the net concentration for each ingot section of the zone-refined column was ascertained. The radioactivity measurement of each section was corrected for normal background activity and for the radiation from the adjacent sections.* The corrected net tracer activity (C) was then proportional to the concentration of the element being traced. The original average tracer activity (C_0) of each ingot section before zone refining was calculated by dividing the sum of all section activities (C) by the number of sections. The ratio values (C/C_0) represented the relative solute concentrations and were plotted for each ingot section as a function of ingot distance. This distance was expressed in terms of the number of zone lengths. Figures 22-6 and -7 show typical semilogarithmic graphs based on experimental and theoretical values.

The effective segregation coefficient (k_e) is an exact mathematical expression of the zone-refining efficiency and is defined as C_s/C_l, the ratio of the impurity concentration of the solid at the interface to the concentration of the liquid beyond the diffusion layer. The value of k_e was normally determined from the interception of the extrapolated C/C_0 segregation curve with the ordinate at zero front-end distance of the ingot. Mathematical solution of the zone-refining equation (4) yielded closely similar results for ingots that followed the theoretical impurity distribution.

In addition to k_e, the purification efficiency was expressed directly by calculation of the mean purification C_0/C that was achieved in the first 80% and the first 90% of the ingot. These values were marked $P_{0.8}$ and $P_{0.9}$, respectively.

G. Accuracy and Precision

The accuracy of the static radioactivity measurements was good. Test results showed that the sum of the corrected radioactivity values from all ingot sections ranged within ±5% of the actual tracer quantity added to the gallium trichloride. The precision of the radiocounting data was statistically dependent on the background activity and the total counts collected. This figure was maintained within ±5% of the true value by choosing suitable lengths of counting period. The accuracy of the dynamic

---

* Radioactivity decay corrections should be introduced at this point if the half-life of the nuclide and the time periods involved should lead to a measurable activity decrease.

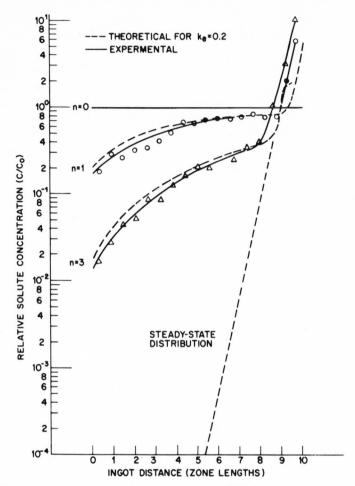

Fig. 22-6. Experimental zone-refining curves for $Fe^{59}Cl_3$ in $GaCl_3$ after 0, 1, and 3 vertical zone passes at 2.0-in./hr velocity; also shown are theoretical curves calculated for 1 and 3 passes, and for the steady-state distribution with a k_e of 0.2. Theoretical curves for $k_e = 0.2$ are dashed lines; experimental curves are solid.

radioactivity measurements was somewhat lower because of statistical reasons of fewer total counts.

The over-all reliability of the results of these experiments was primarily dependent on the reproducibility of various zone-refining parameters, such as zone length, convection, temperature of melt, ingot uniformity, and single-crystal formation. Variations in these factors so reduced accuracy that the resultant effects were far more significant than those caused by any analytical errors. Because the data were obtained from various duplicate experiments, however, the reliability of the results is quite satisfactory.

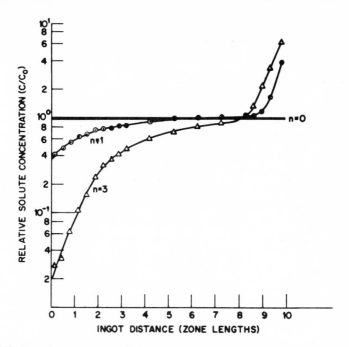

Fig. 22-7. Experimental zone-refining curves for $Fe^{59}Cl_3$ in $GaCl_3$ after 0, 1, and 3 horizontal zone passes at 2.0-in./hr velocity.

22-3. RESULTS

A. Segregation of Iron

Because of practical implications, the zone-refining segregation behavior of iron in gallium trichloride was investigated in greater detail than the other impurities. Table 22-1 presents the essential data and results.

At a zone-travel velocity of 0.50 in./hr, zone refining in vertical downward direction proceeded with an effective segregation coefficient (k_e) of 0.10. At 1.0 in./hr, the k_e attained a value of 0.14, which indicated a slightly lower purification efficiency at double the zone rate. After 4 zone passes, the first 80% of this ingot showed a 20-fold decrease in the mean concentration of iron; the front end of the ingot showed a 500-fold decrease.

At a 2.0 in./hr vertical zone-travel speed, a k_e of 0.17 was attained. Zone-refining curves from this experiment are shown in Fig. 22-6 for 0, 1, and 3 zone passes. Except for some fluctuations in the C/C_0 data because of ingot irregularities, the experimental curves follow nearly ideal zone-refining behavior. For purposes of comparison, Fig. 22-6 also contains theoretical curves based on the zone-refining equation (4) for a k_e

TABLE 22-1

Zone-Refining Results[a,b] for $FeCl_2$ in $GaCl_3$

Zone-refining conditions			Resulting purification			
			Purification factor			
Direction	Velocity (in./hr)	Passes	$P_{0.8}$	$P_{0.9}$	C/C_0 at front end	k_e
v	0.50	1	—	—	0.10	0.10
		2	—	—	0.014	
v	1.0	1	1.8	1.7	0.14	0.14
		2	4.7	3.8	0.050	
		3	7.2	5.3	0.015	
		4	20	10	0.002	
v	2.0	1	1.8	1.7	0.17	0.17
		2	2.5	2.0	0.045	
		3	6.3	3.5	0.014	
h	0.50	1	1.5	1.3	0.38	0.3–0.4
		2	2.3	1.9	0.11	
		3	2.6	2.0	0.05	
h	1.0	1	1.2	1.1	0.38	0.3–0.4
		2	1.4	1.3	0.11	
		3	1.8	1.6	0.02	
h	1.0	1	1.2	1.2	0.3	0.3–0.4
		3	3.0	2.0	0.04	
h	2.0	1	1.2	1.1	0.19	0.3–0.4
		2	1.6	1.4	0.045	
		3	2.6	1.7	0.012	

[a] Experimental data are based on $GaCl_3$ column containing 0.14 ppm iron in form of $FeCl_3$, with $Fe^{59}Cl_3$ as tracer. The charge was remixed and the solute uniformly distributed before each zone refining experiment.

[b] v, Vertical downward; h, horizontal (slightly inclined); $P_{0.8}$, mean purification in first 80% of ingot; $P_{0.9}$, mean purification in first 90% of ingot; C_0, solute concentration before zone refining; C, solute concentration after zone refining; k_e, effective segregation coefficient.

of 0.2 for 1 and 3 passes. The corresponding steady-state distribution is indicated by the steep curve, which represents the ultimate solute distribution achieved at a k_e of 0.2; this maximum segregation is limited by the back-reflection of the solute that accumulates in the last zone lengths.

Calculations for optimum zone-refining conditions require a knowledge of the equilibrium distribution coefficient, k_0. By use of the above data and the Burton–Prim–Slichter equation (4, 6), k_0 is calculated to be 0.08; this figure represents the segregation coefficient obtainable under the most favorable zone-refining conditions. As shown in the experimental data (Table 22-1), the segregation coefficient at a velocity of 0.50 in./hr is 0.10, a value quite close to the theoretical maximum. Calculations also indicate that 8 passes under these conditions should result in a 10^6-fold purification in the first zone length.

Zone refining in horizontally positioned columns, which were slightly inclined to prevent transport of gallium trichloride, resulted in considerably lower segregation effectiveness than vertical zoning. The lower values are caused by the differences in stirring of the molten zone; convectional stirring for a liquid in a horizontal tube is known to be poorer than in a vertical tube (4). As shown in Table 22-1, the k_e values for horizontally positioned columns ranged between 0.3 and 0.4, depending on zoning conditions. Changes in one-travel velocities did not have much effect on the k_e (probably because of the overriding influence of poor stirring). However, because a gas phase is maintained above the ingot in the horizontal zoning techniques, the horizontal technique prevents the formation of gas bubbles in the gallium trichloride charge. As a result, this approach produces considerably more uniform ingots than the vertical technique and reduces the danger of tube breakage. In addition, because multiple-pass horiontal zoning yields ingots of sufficiently high purity, this technique is well suited for production applications. Figure 22-7 shows a typical set of zone-refining curves for these experiments.

B. Segregation of Zinc, Manganese, and Sodium

When $Zn^{65}Cl_2$ was added to gallium trichloride at a concentration of 0.020 ppm (as Zn) followed by vertical zone refining, a 16-fold mean purification ($P_{0.9}$) with a $k_e < 0.06$ resulted. Horizontal zoning is considerably less efficient. The segregation-inhibiting effect caused by water traces was demonstrated experimentally by contaminating a column of gallium trichloride with moisture. The results shown in Table 22-2 indicate a reduction in segregation effectiveness by a factor greater than 10; 4 vertical passes achieved a $P_{0.8}$ of only 3.3. Changes of this sort are to be expected because water readily hydrolizes gallium trichloride.

$Mn^{54}Cl_2$ at Mn concentrations of 0.010 and 0.021 ppm showed excellent segregation with a k_e of 0.02 and 0.03–0.04 for vertical and horizontal zoning directions, respectively. Purification yielded clear, transparent single-crystal gallium trichloride after 1 zone pass. However, the analytical evaluation was complicated because of a small quantity of material that consistently segregated in the front portion of the ingots where manganese depletion was greatest. Gamma-ray spectrometric analysis showed that this radioactivity was definitely caused by Mn^{54} and not by some nuclide impurity. Apparently, this phenomenon was

TABLE 22-2

Zone–Refining Results for $ZnCl_2$, $MnCl_2$, and NaCl in $GaCl_3$

| Impurity added | | | Zone-refining conditions | | | Resulting purification | | |
Compound	Concentration (ppm)	Tracer	Zone direction	Velocity (in./hr)	Passes	Purification factor $P_{0.8}$	$P_{0.9}$	k_e
$ZnCl_2$	0.020	$Zn^{65}Cl_2$	v	1.0	1	16	16	<0.06
$ZnCl_2{}^a$	0.17	$Zn^{65}Cl_2$	h	1.0	1	4.8	3.7	0.04–0.10
			v	1.0	1	1.2	1.2 }	~0.4^b
			h	1.0	4	3.3	1.6 }	
$MnCl_2$	0.021	$Mn^{54}Cl_2$	v	1.0	1	11	8.7	0.02
			h	1.0	1	6.9	6.1	0.03
			h	0.50	1	5.6	4.9	0.04
$MnCl_2$	0.010	$Mn^{54}Cl_2$	h	1.0	1	6.4	6.4	0.07^b
NaCl	37	$Na^{22}Cl$	v	1.0	1	2.6	2.1	~0.1^b
			h	1.0	1	1.3	1.3	~0.4^b
$NaCl^a$	40	$Na^{22}Cl$	h	1.0	1	1.1	1.1	~0.5^b

[a] Contains water and some organic impurities.
[b] Abnormal zone-refining behavior; k_e values were estimated from mean purification.

caused by a small fraction of the manganese in an oxidation state different from that of the major portion of the manganese.

As shown in Table 22-2, segregation for gallium trichloride that contained 37 ppm sodium in the form of $Na^{22}Cl$ proceeded with a $P_{0.8}$ of 2.6 in the vertical direction and 1.3 in the horizontal. This purification did not follow normal zone-refining laws. The first half of the vertically processed ingot showed a 13-fold purification after 1 pass and an apparent $k_e < 0.1$; the concentration in the second half rose abruptly beyond the initial mean concentration. This abnormal behavior was attributed to the high concentration of sodium chloride that was added because of low specific radioactivity. The concentration level in the solvent was apparently beyond the solubility limit of sodium chloride in gallium trichloride. Evidence of incomplete solubility was indicated by the white-colored, polycrystalline appearance of the ingots. Segregation curves of moist gallium trichloride ingots containing sodium chloride were similar to those of the moist column containing zinc chloride in that the center portion of the ingot showed a concentration-leveling effect. A mean k_e of approximately 0.5 was estimated for these ingots.

C. Segregation Effectiveness under Severe Impurity Concentrations

One ingot was prepared with a multiple mixture of elements that were added as chlorides to investigate effective segregation under extreme conditions of impurity concentrations. With the exception of iron, which was added at a concentration of 0.01 ppm, the other six impurities were present at cationic concentrations of 10 ppm each. Mn^{54} was added as a tracer for the manganese. One vertical downward pass was applied at a zone-travel velocity of 1.0 in./hr. Under these conditions, an emission-spectrographic analysis led to the following effective segregation coefficients: 0.11 for aluminum; <0.12 for copper; 0.30 for nickel. Lead and manganese results were not conclusive; iron was not detected.

The radiochemical analysis, however, showed that the segregation of iron was not affected by the high concentrations of added impurities; the k_e of 0.12 checks closely with the values for iron listed in Table 22-1. In the case of manganese, the purification effectiveness at the 10-ppm concentration was about one-half as compared to the values reported in Table 22-2 for 0.02-ppm manganese alone.

On the basis of the data presented in Tables 22-1 and -2, the segregation effectiveness of horizontal zoning at the same impurity concentrations should be lower by a factor of about 2.

22-4. CONCLUSIONS

The radiotracer method described is a valid and accurate method for determinating quantitatively the distribution of impurities in a column of solid material as a function of various zone-melting parameters. One or several radioactively labelled impurities can be traced simultaneously by instrumental methods. The column is analyzed nondestructively by either a static or dynamic technique without removing the material from its container. One charge can therefore be used repeatedly for many zone-melting experiments. The method is ideally suited for investigating zone-melting parameters of inorganic impurities in columns of solid material, and is applicable for measuring impurities at both trace levels and at higher concentrations. In contrast to neutron-activation techniques, which are capable of detecting a range of elements in a given sample, the method described is more limited, as it measures only the added, specific radioisotope(s). However, it is potentially more accurate and sensitive than neutron activation, is nondestructive, and is vastly simpler to perform, as it requires only the measuring of the emitted radiation from the known radioisotope by either instrumental or autoradiographic techniques.

In addition to evaluating zone-refining processes, this technique can be readily used in other applications where the distribution of components needs to be measured, such as in chromatographic and ion-exchange columns, or in rods, ingots, and crystals of uniform thickness.

The method has been exemplified by describing in detail one specific case: the determination of zone-refining parameters for gallium trichloride. The data obtained showed that chlorides of manganese, zinc, and iron, which were added at cationic concentrations of 0.01–10 ppm, had effective segregation coefficients of 0.02–0.4. Similar results were obtained with aluminum, magnesium, copper, and nickel, whose concentrations were determined by emission-spectrographic analyses. Because of its low solubility in gallium trichloride, sodium chloride did not adhere to normal zone-refining laws; however, segregation did occur, and sodium ions collected toward the rear of the ingot. These results show that mutliple-pass zone refining is a highly effective process for the preparation of high-purity gallium trichloride. For purifications on a production scale, horizontal zone refining is considered more efficient than the vertical technique. Although the purification effectiveness in the horiontal direction is less than that in the vertical, horizontal parameters are more easily controlled, and the danger of column breakage is reduced.

REFERENCES

1. W. Kern, *J. Electrochem. Soc.,* **110**, 60 (1963).
2. H. Schildknecht, *Zone Melting,* Academic, New York and London, 1966, p. 131.
3. N. Goldsmith, A. Mayer, and L. Vieland, *J. Less-Common Metals,* **4**, 564 (1962).
4. W. G. Pfann, *Zone Melting,* 2nd ed., Wiley, New York, 1966.
5. E. B. Owens, *Appl. Spectry.*, **13**, 105 (1959).
6. J. A. Burton, A. C. Prim, and W. P. Slichter, *J. Chem. Phys.,* **21**, 1987 (1953).

23

PURIFICATION OF POTASSIUM CHLORIDE BY RADIO-FREQUENCY HEATING

Roger W. Warren

RESEARCH AND DEVELOPMENT CENTER
WESTINGHOUSE ELECTRIC CORPORATION
PITTSBURGH, PENNSYLVANIA

23-1. INTRODUCTION

The floating-zone technique of crystal growth is inherently more difficult than conventional methods that use some kind of container. This technique, therefore, is usually employed only when container problems appear to be insurmountable with high-melting-point materials. In more fortunate circumstances the container problems can be solved, but often only if suitable operating conditions are chosen (e.g., the nature of the ambient gas). In the conventional zone growth of KCl in a quartz boat (*1*), the major container problem is adhesion between the KCl and quartz. In some cases adhesion has been controlled by growth in an ambient of dry HCl. This expedient is not entirely satisfactory, for it results in crystals saturated with HCl and eliminates the possibility of experimenting with different growth environments. In addition, the container problem cannot be solved in this way if other salts such as the iodides or fluorides are to be melted; these materials require ambients of HI or HF, gases that introduce new problems of decomposition and corrosion. Because of these constraints imposed by the container, we have developed techniques (*2*) for the floating-zone growth of KCl that avoid these restrictions and offer additional advantages. These techniques are in some respects novel because KCl is a transparent insulator, a class of material difficult to melt by the usual floating-zone techniques. The techniques described here for the growth of KCl have been used to grow other alkali halides (*2*) and should be applicable to the growth of most other transparent insulators such as those used in solid-state lasers.

The main difficulty encountered with KCl is the heating problem. The

methods we have considered are contact, flame or plasma jet, electron
bombardment, radiation, and induction heating. Contact heating (3), involving a heating element immersed in the molten zone, suffers from most
of the contamination and corrosion problems found in conventional zone
growth. Contamination is also a major problem with flame (4) or plasma
heating (5). Even if the gases used are unobjectionable contaminants,
materials used to confine and direct the hot gases often evaporate or otherwise react so as to ultimately contaminate the melt. Heating by electron
bombardment (6) can also contaminate the melt with evaporated or
sputtered cathode material and, in addition, must contend with the insulating nature of KCl and the high vapor pressure (7) (about 1 Torr)
at its melting point. Radiation heating (8) is difficult to employ with
KCl because of its high transparency. A molten zone at 800°C is completely invisible in a dark room. Such a material can therefore be heated
only in the far infrared or ultraviolet where these salts absorb strongly.
Unfortunately, most radiant-heat sources are very inefficient in these
regions. A possible solution to this problem is the choice of a far-infrared
laser as the radiant-heat source. A CO_2 laser operating at $10.6\ \mu$ could
be used to heat LiF, but light of still longer wavelengths is needed for
KCl and most of the other alkali halides.

Induction heating (9) is normally preferred over the other methods
if the electrical conductivity of the melt is sufficiently high that enough
power can be coupled into the zone to keep it molten. At low temperatures KCl is a very poor conductor, but as the temperature is raised its
electrical conductivity, which is due to ionic motion, increases rapidly,
until at the melting point it jumps by four orders of magnitude to about
2 mho/cm (10). In contrast, typical metals have much higher conductivities, which drop by a factor of 2 at the melting point (11), while
the conductivity of germanium, a typical semiconductor, increases at the
melting point by a factor of 15 to a value of 2×10^4 mho/cm (12). The
low conductivity of KCl obviously makes heating by induction difficult.
Nevertheless, induction heating appears to be the most promising heating
method.

The first of three major problems that have been encountered, the low
conductivity of molten KCl, has been handled by coupling power into
the molten zone at high frequencies (30 MHz) (2). The second problem, the initial melting of the cold, very-low-conductivity salt cannot be
accomplished by induction heating. Two techniques that have been considered are (a) a high purity hydrogen–chlorine torch, which can be
directed on the rod, and (b) an induction-heated platinum or carbon
susceptor in the form of a knife, which can be manipulated so as to cut
through and melt the rod. The knife is preferred because the limited

contamination that the knife contributes to the melt can be removed by the repeated purifying action of the zone.

The third major problem encountered in using induction heating involves the large discontinuity in the conductivity of KCl at its melting point; control of the zone size and position is therefore difficult. To illustrate these related problems, consider a realistic approximation in which solid KCl is assumed to have zero conductivity. Electrical currents can be induced only in the liquid zone; the total heat generated increases with zone size. Unless the heat input is controlled, zones of unstable size will result. A feedback technique for achieving this control is discussed below. When a zone of the right size is established, we must be able to move it through the solid rod. We must heat asymmetrically the zone or the solid rod on each side of the zone. Since the rod cannot be heated and the zone is normally uniformly heated because of strong internal convection currents, the zone cannot be moved unless some new means is found for creating asymmetrical heating or cooling. We have accomplished this by blowing cool gas on the rod above and below the position of the molten zone. If the zone is centered between these cooled positions, the heating and cooling are symmetrical so that if enough power is supplied neither zone boundary moves. If the rod with its zone is moved, the cooling increases at one boundary and decreases at the other so that melting and freezing occur at a rate just sufficient to match the speed of the rod. Additional zone stability is achieved by blowing the gas in such a way that two close-fitting, downward-pointing cones of gas are developed. The zone is imprisoned between these cones so that ordinarily they touch the solid rod in two horizontal circles, one slightly above and one slightly below the zone boundaries. If the crystals grow slightly off the axis of the cones, they touch it along paths tilted toward the axis. This causes the zone boundaries to be similarly tilted, thus changing the shape of the zone with consequent growth back toward the axis. The use of a cooling gas as well as the knife compromises our efforts to eliminate sources of contamination. These devices, however, appear to be essential to the floating-zone melting of transparent insulators.

23-2. APPARATUS AND PROCEDURE

In this discussion we will emphasize the apparatus and procedures when induction heating is employed with KCl and other low-conductivity materials. The work coil that is coupled to the molten zone consists of two 4-cm-diam turns of ¼-in. copper tubing tuned to 30 MHz by two 100-pF vacuum condensers mounted as close to the work coil as possible. This tank circuit (Fig. 23-1) has an unloaded Q of about 1000. It is driven by an ML-6257 vacuum tube operated in the tuned-plate–tuned-

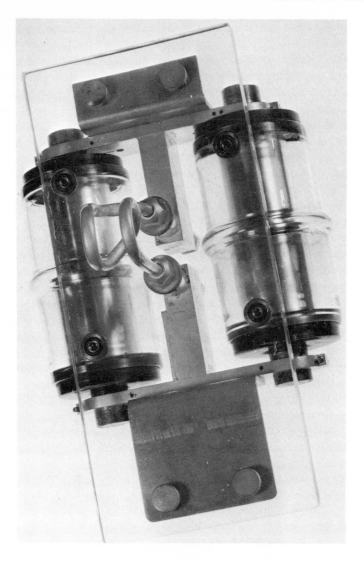

Fig. 23-1. Work coil and condensers resonant at 30 MHz mounted on glass plate.

grid oscillator circuit shown in Fig. 23-2. The oscillator was constructed by modifying a Lepel 3–5-MHz, 2½-kW induction heater,* which contains all of the basic components as well as a power supply. Before conversion, the rf power was adjusted by changing the phase of a 60-Hz signal applied to the grids of thyratrons in the power supply. This affords a convenient place to apply the feedback control needed to stabilize the zone

* Model T-2½-MC, Lepel High Frequency Laboratories, Woodside, New York.

size. The block diagram of Fig. 23-2 indicates the manner of connection. Two signals are derived from the oscillator: V_1 proportional to the plate voltage, V, and V_2 proportional to the plate current, I. These are combined in the Q-control potentiometer, filtered and amplified in a dc amplifier, and then passed through a circuit that adjusts the phase of a 60-Hz signal of constant amplitude so that it is proportional to the amplitude of the input signal. This 60-Hz signal is further amplified and applied to the grids of the power-supply thyratrons. The gain of the apparatus is sufficient so that the power output of the induction heater can be adjusted over its whole range with a very small signal applied to the dc amplifier. Consequently, the particular combination of V_1 and V_2 made in the Q-control potentiometer, and the way in which the feedback is connected, will stabilize the oscillator at a power output such that V/I, the ratio of plate voltage to current, is equal to a constant dependent only on the potentiometer setting. Now, if other losses are neglected, V/I is proportional to the Q of the loaded work coil, which, in turn, is a function of the zone size. Every setting of the Q control potentiometer, therefore, forces the zone to grow to and maintain a unique size.

The change in the Q of the work coil as the zone size is increased from zero to the maximum possible is only a few percent. Therefore, the setting of the Q control potentiometer appropriate for a given zone size is quite dependent on other parameters, such as temperature, which effect the coil Q. It would be an advantage to find a more direct measurement of zone size with which to control the induction heater, but no such means has been found. In spite of these problems, a stationary zone can be maintained all day, and a moving zone can usually be swept all the way through a uni-

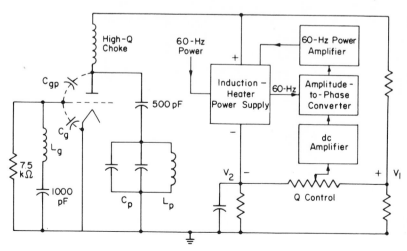

Fig. 23-2. Oscillator and feedback-controlled power supply.

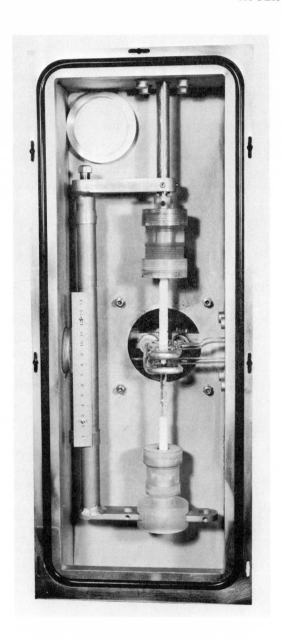

Fig. 23-3. Growing chamber.

form seeded rod without any adjustment of the apparatus. Unseeded crystals grow so randomly that continual adjustments of the Q control must be made until a single crystal forms. This usually occurs within a few centimeters of the start.

A view of the growing chamber is shown in Fig. 23-3. A large dogged door allows easy access to the working parts and provides shielding for the rf. The alkali halide rods are held by nonconducting chucks supported in turn by a motor-driven yoke designed so that its coupling to the work coil is not a strong function of its position. The work-coil leads enter the chamber from the back through a glass plate. Two 4-cm-diam hollow glass rings made of $1/4$-in. glass tubing are pierced with inclined holes to supply the cooling gas, and are sandwiched between the turns of the work coil. A window in the door allows a clear view of this region. A knife mounted on a bellows on the door can be maneuvered from the outside so as to cut and melt the crystal. The gas-circulating system consists of a pump, flow meter, filter, humidity detector, pressure gauges, and valves.

Crystals are grown from 1-cm-diam rods made by extruding a thick paste of water and ground reagent-grade KCl. The grinding results in a distribution of particle sizes that is necessary for a high-density rod. Drying of the paste leads to crystallization of the dissolved salt, which locks the particles together, giving a rod of quite reasonable strength. This technique of rod preparation is an improvement over the use of pressed pellets, for in the latter case contamination is usually introduced from the walls of the die. Unfortunately, the paste technique depends upon a reasonably high solubility of the salt, which excludes the extrusion of strong rods of LiF even when HF is used as a solvent.

To grow crystals of known impurity content, a stock of various doping agents in water solutions is prepared. The solution is sprayed with an artist's air brush in a narrow stripe on the side of a rod as it moves on a constant-speed platform. The resulting impurity concentration can be easily calculated. In another convenient technique, one drop of a concentrated impurity solution is placed on a rod. As the zone sweeps by this point, it absorbs the impurity, which is then slowly released into the growing crystal. Over a few centimeters of such a crystal the impurity concentration may vary by many orders of magnitude; it may reach the solubility limit or be swamped by other background impurities.

To grow a crystal, the knife is first heated by coupling it to the work coil. It is manipulated so as to cut the rod and join the two parts with a molten zone. An auxiliary motor is used to adjust the spacing between the rods during this process. Sometimes this spacing is continually adjusted by an automatic feedback loop during growth to compensate for inequalities in rod density or diameter. Once the zone has been started, the knife is withdrawn and the yoke is then moved until the zone is in the center of the work coil. Now the gas flow is initiated, the Q control is adjusted for the zone size desired, and steady motion of the yoke is initiated. Upon completing a pass of up to 15 cm, the zone is allowed to freeze. If more than one zone pass is desired, a new zone must be created with the knife at the beginning of each pass.

NOTES

Movement of the zone up or down the rod is equally satisfactory. Growth speeds of up to 40 cm/hr are possible before the gas jets must be made so strong that they upset the mechanical stability of the zone. Figure 23-4 shows four typical rods of KCl: a polycrystalline starting rod, a rod seeded at the bottom and grown upward, an unseeded rod grown upward, and an unseeded rod grown downward. Their properties have been investigated by the counting of etch pits, by optical absorption and fluorescence (*13*), as well as by magnetic resonance (*14*) and electrical conductivity measurements (*15*).

All seeded crystals are single crystals; the unseeded ones are single only after the first few centimeters of growth. Because of the nonaxial heat flow due to the gas jets, the dislocation concentration, as shown by etch-pit counts, is usually high. A low dislocation concentration typical of crystals grown by conventional techniques can be achieved by reducing the flow of cooling gas and decreasing zone speed; stability problems, however, become severe.

Most gases are highly soluble in molten salts, less soluble in solid salts. An unfortunate result is that bubbles of the ambient gas form at the freezing interface when the zone is moved too rapidly. On the other hand, this intimate mixing of the growth gas and the melt leads to a reaction, when oxygen or a wet cooling gas is used, causing the removal of some impurities from the melt by precipitation as the oxide. If an oxide is formed in downward zoning, the precipitate settles with the zone to the bottom of the rod. Of approximately forty impurities thus far investigated, all except the alkaline earths can be purged from the melt in this way so that their concentrations are below the limit of detectability. The use of these same gases is found to lead to a strong fluorescence in the O_2^- band (*16*), optical absorption in the OH⁻ and O_2^- bands (*16, 17*), and a magnetic resonance (*18*) due to O_2^-. Growth in dry N_2, H_2, or HCl, on the other hand, essentially eliminates these effects without introducing any new ones.

The extrinsic electrical conductivity of KCl is a very sensitive measure of the presence of most impurities (*15*). By this test the lowest impurity content of crystals grown by these techniques is about 1 ppm. This limit is probably due to contamination introduced by the knife or by the cool-

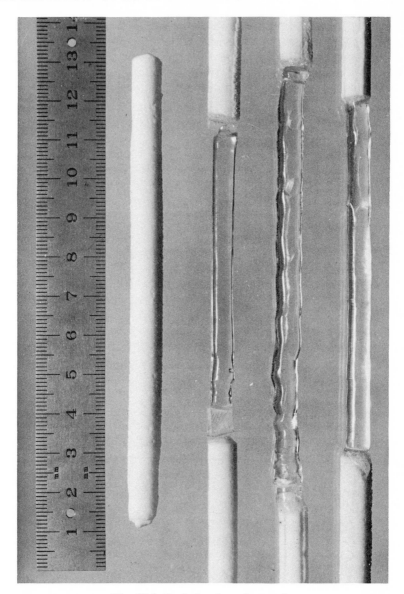

Fig. 23-4. Typical rods and crystals.

ing gas and is not easy to reduce. Thus, the advantage of the floating-zone growth of KCl over conventional techniques is not found in higher purity but in reasonably good purity coupled with speed, convenience, flexibility, and the promise of the extension of the techniques to the growth of other materials that cannot be grown in any other way. In general, almost any ionic solid can be melted by induction heating if an acceptable starting method can be found. Examples are the growth of KCl, KI, KBr, NaCl, LiF, TiO_2 (*19*) and UO_2 (*20*).

REFERENCES

1. R. W. Warren, *Rev. Sci. Instr.*, 36, 731 (1965).

2. R. W. Warren, *Rev. Sci. Instr.*, 33, 1378 (1962).

3. R. G. Seidensticker, A. I. Bennett, and D. R. Hamilton, Westinghouse Research Report 67-9F6-MIOPT-R1, January 23, 1967.

4. M. A. Verneuil, *Ann. Chim. Phys.*, 8, 320 (1904).

5. T. B. Reed, *J. Appl. Phys.*, 32, 2534 (1961).

6. A. Caverley, M. Davis, and R. F. Lever, *J. Sci. Instr.*, 34, 142 (1957).

7. E. W. Washburn, ed., *International Critical Tables,* 1st ed., McGraw-Hill, New York, 1929, Vol. 3, p. 214.

8. R. E. De La Rue and F. A. Halden, *Rev. Sci. Instr.*, 31, 35 (1960).

9. P. H. Keck, W. Van Horne, J. Soled, and A. MacDonald, *Rev. Sci. Instr.*, 25, 331 (1954).

10. E. W. Washburn, ed., *International Critical Tables,* 1st ed., McGraw-Hill, New York, 1929, Vol. 6, p. 149.

11. C. D. Hodgman, ed., *Handbook of Chemistry and Physics,* 40th ed., Chem. Rubber Publ. Co., Cleveland, Ohio, 1948, p. 2590.

12. R. W. Keyes, *Phys. Rev.,* 84, 367 (1951).

13. J. H. Schulman and W. D. Compton, *Color Centers in Solids,* Macmillan, New York, 1962, Chap. V.

14. D. W. Feldman, R. W. Warren, and J. G. Castle, Jr., *Phys. Rev.,* 135, A470 (1964); 136, A1347 (1964).

15. H. Kelting and H. Witt, *Z. Physik.,* 126, 697 (1949).

16. J. Rolfe, F. R. Lipsett, and W. J. King, *Phys. Rev.,* 123, 447 (1961).

17. H. W. Etzel and D. A. Patterson, *Phys. Rev.,* 112, 1112 (1958).

18. W. Känzig and M. H. Cohen, *Phys. Rev. Letters,* 3, 509 (1959).

19. J. Holt, *Brit. J. Appl. Phys.,* 16, 639 (1965).

20. A. T. Chapman and G. W. Clark, *Bull. Am. Ceram. Soc.,* 44, 389 (1965).

24 PURIFICATION OF A METAL BY ELECTRON-BEAM HEATING*

R. E. Reed and J. C. Wilson

SOLID-STATE DIVISION AND
METALS AND CERAMICS DIVISION
OAK RIDGE NATIONAL LABORATORY
OAK RIDGE, TENNESSEE

24-1. INTRODUCTION

Electron-beam float-zone melting (EBFZM) is a process in which the molten zone is floated (i.e., supported) by surface tension between two vertical, solid members of the same material. Heat is produced on the surface of the zone by direct bombardment with electrons. The zone is then moved along the length of the specimen in order to melt a substantial portion of its length.

The principal advantage of electron-beam heating is that the size, location, and power of the beam can be accurately reproduced. Here we shall confine our attention to electron-beam heating in vacuum with a thermionic cathode as the electron source. Recently electron-beam zone melting has become possible at higher pressures (up to 0.5 Torr) by means of a hollow- (cold) cathode gas discharge as the electron source. Although EBFZM is widely used for consolidation of metals, alloying, and crystal

* Research sponsored by the U. S. Atomic Energy Commission under contract with Union Carbide Corporation.

growth (*1*, *2*) we shall restrict our discussion to its use in purification processes.

24-2. ESTIMATION OF FEASIBILITY

A. Zone Refining

Purification by zone refining (*3*) is commonly assumed to take place during zone melting. In the metallurgical literature "electron-beam zone-refined" is a more commonly used term than EBFZM for describing the same process. Purification may be highly selective or not achieved at all. Actually, zone melting can sometimes result in contamination of the material by reaction with residual gases in the vacuum system.

The potential efficacy of zone refining can be estimated from distribution coefficients obtained from constitution diagrams and the composition–distance curves of Pfann (*3*). To approach these calculated distribution coefficients in practice, very slow zoning speeds are required or stirring at the liquid–solid interface is necessary. Inspection of the literature shows that zoning speeds >5 cm/hr are commonly used; these speeds are probably a factor of 10 higher than they should be for zone refining.

B. Other Purification Processes

The molten zone and the solid rod immediately adjacent to the zone are probably protected from any interaction with the residual gases in the vacuum environment by a protective sheath of evaporating metal atoms. Allen (*4*), using the pendant-drop method to measure surface tensions of the refractory metals, found that wide variations in vacuum from 10^{-4} to 10^{-7} Torr as well as leak-rate variations had no measurable effect on the surface-tension determinations. Because of the sensitivity of the surface tension to interstitial impurities, Allen concluded that the vaporizing metal atoms protected the surface from impinging residual gas molecules.

The following purification processes can occur within the molten zone: volatilization of metallic impurities that have higher vapor pressures than that of the host metal at its melting point [Honig (*5*) has the best compilation of vapor pressure data for metals]; reduction of carbon and oxygen by the formation of CO with subsequent evolution of the gas from the molten zone; removal of oxygen, nitrogen, hydrogen, and/or carbon from the molten zone by the formation and subsequent volatilization or floatation of oxides, nitrides, hydrides, and/or carbides of the host metal; and rejection and floatation of insoluble solid materials to the outer surface of the molten zone. In addition, the residual gases in the vacuum environment can interact with the heated solid rod where lower temperatures cause a reduction in the protective sheath of vaporizing metal atoms. These interactions involve attainment of equilibrium concentrations of oxygen, nitrogen, and hydrogen in the heated solid rod and the existence of a carburizing or decarburizing reaction between the vacuum environment and the heated solid rod.

Table 24-1 lists some data that are useful in estimating the effectiveness of these processes on some selected metals. Column 2 lists the ratios of metal monoxide vapor pressure to that of the metal at the melting point of

TABLE 24-1

Table of Parameters Useful in Float-Zone Melting

Element	Oxide volatilization tendency (6)	Carbon deoxidation (6) (ppm)	Vapor pressure at m.p. (5) (Torr)	Maximum zone length, L_m (11) (cm)	Power to melt 1 cm diam (12) (W)
Mo	10^5	1	2×10^{-2}	1.3	1400
Ta	10^4	1	6×10^{-3}	0.96	1800
Hf	10^4	10^5	5×10^{-4}	0.95	750^a
W	10^2	1	3×10^{-2}	0.98	2800
Zr	10^2	10^5	1×10^{-5}	1.3	450^a
Nb (Cb)	10	60	1×10^{-3}	1.4	1800^a
Ti	1	10^5	3×10^{-3}	1.5	—
V	10^{-2}	300	2×10^{-2}	1.5	470
Be	10^{-3}	700	3×10^{-2}	2.6	—
Cr	10^{-4}	70	5	1.25	—
Ni	10^{-7}	1	3×10^{-3}	1.25	220

[a] ORNL data, 1.25-cm-diameter rod.

the metal as calculated by Smith et al. (6). High values of this ratio indicate significant oxygen loss by oxide volatilization. Column 3 gives the residual C and O in parts per million for carbon deoxidation (or oxygen decarburization) calculated for equilibrium with CO at 10^{-5} Torr by Smith (6). High values in this column indicate that it is difficult to remove C and/or O from the metal via the CO reaction. Column 4 lists the vapor pressure of the metal at its melting point as taken from the data of Honig (5).

A consideration of these purification mechanisms leads to the conclusion that it is generally desirable to have as low a total pressure as practicable in the vacuum chamber. However, certain purification processes are made possible by deliberately adding gas to the system. For example, zoning in 10^{-6} Torr of O_2 was effective in removing carbon from low-oxygen niobium at Oak Ridge. In addition, it is desirable to be able to monitor the residual gases in the vacuum chamber to determine their relative partial pressures.

C. Practical Considerations

If the vapor pressure at the melting point of a material exceeds 5×10^{-2} Torr several difficulties arise: a high percentage ($\sim 10\%$) of the material may be evaporated on each pass; condensation of metal on the filament of the electron gun may impair its ability to emit electrons; adjustment of the power is necessary for each pass, if not more often; and the high concentration of evaporated atoms can lead to gaseous arcs.

The maximum height of molten zone that will be mechanically stable has been widely studied (7, 8, 9, 10). The length of a molten zone L_m that can be supported by its own surface tension approaches a limit at large radii; Heywang and Ziegler (9) have shown that no theoretical limit to the maximum diameter of the rod exists, but as the rod diameter increases it becomes difficult to melt through without exceeding L_m. This may be so because the power density is necessarily higher on a large-diameter rod. As a result, superheating and convective stirring of the melt tend to widen the molten zone.

Column 5 of Table 24-1 gives computed values of L_m for several metals. A useful compilation of properties for computing zone heights exists (11). It should be noted that certain impurities markedly lower surface tension (4). On the other hand, a skin of surface oxide may help support the zone. Column 6 of Table 24-1 lists the power needed to melt 1-cm-diam rods as determined by Donald (12).

24-3. EQUIPMENT DESIGN

A. Scanner

Figure 24-1 shows the essential mechanical and electrical components of the evacuated portion (scanner) of a zone melter. The electron gun is mounted on slides so it can be traversed along the specimen by rotating a leadscrew that engages a nut on the crosshead. Usually the gun is traversed rather than the specimen. A variable-speed motor drives the traversing leadscrew. Sliding electrical contacts or long flexible leads carry the current to heat the filament.

The specimen is supported at each end and hung vertically through the center of the gun. It is attached at one end to a movable crosshead (e.g., the lower crosshead in Fig. 24-1) that is manually adjustable from below the base plate. The specimen ends are usually held by springs or clamps in vertically-disposed V blocks. The V blocks must be adjustable in the horizontal plane in order to center specimens in the gun. In addition, a few degrees of tilt about the specimen axis must be provided in order to accommodate distorted specimens and errors in alignment. Three leveling screws will accomplish this purpose. If stirring of the zone is necessary, one end of the specimen must be rotated about its longitudinal axis.

The principal mechanical difficulty in the scanner is friction and seizing of moving parts with minimum or no lubrication. Use of ball bearings, ball bushings, and ball-nut leadscrews (the latter two elements of the re-circulating-ball type) reduces sliding metal-to-metal contact. Sleeve bearings, linear bushings, and ordinary leadscrew–nut combinations have also been successfully used with proper choice of materials. In any moving parts with sliding friction normal clearances should be doubled. Some successful combinations of sliding elements are tinned carbon steel against stainless steel; silver against stainless steel; gold- or silver-plated carbon steel (hardened) against stainless steel, and silver against tantalum. A fine

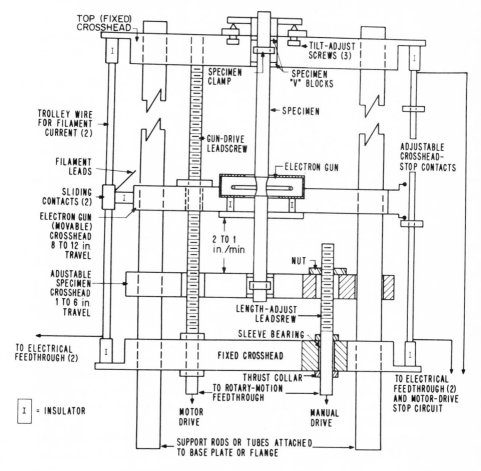

Fig. 24-1. Representative EBFZM apparatus (*in vacuo*).

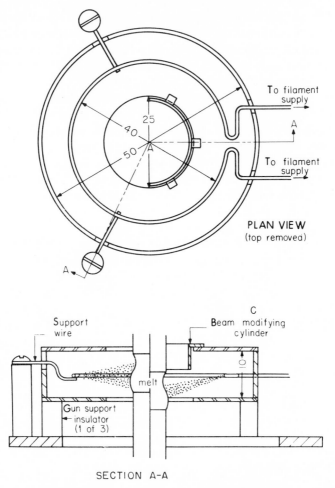

SECTION A-A

Fig. 24-2. Left half, parallel-plate electron gun for EBFZM; right half, same gun modified by addition of cylinder C to narrow and depress the beam. (Dimensions in millimeters.)

machine finish followed by electropolishing of rubbing surfaces appears helpful, even if plating is to follow. Teflon can be used up to 250°C for bearings if the loads are kept low. The new polyimide polymers will probably prove useful also.

Numerous insulators are required in the vacuum system. Glazed porcelain insulators ($\frac{1}{4}$ and $\frac{3}{8}$ in. diam) with both ends threaded for 6-32 screws are available from electronics suppliers. These insulators should be used in compression for maximum strength; care should be exercised in tightening screws. All insulators should be shielded from sources of radiant heat and evaporating metal. A shield of 0.005-in. tantalum sheet spaced ⅛ in. from the insulator is adequate. Machineable ceramics such as Lavite and boron nitride tend to be gassy. In accord with good vacuum practice, all screws in blind, unvented holes, as in the insulators, should be grooved along their length to permit outgassing.

B. Electron Gun

As a number of electron gun designs have been published, more or less exact design is possible for special needs (*13, 14*). Consider the gun in Fig. 24-2 (left side): Electrons will be emitted from the filament (usually tungsten wire) when the temperature is raised to about 1800°C by ohmic heating. When a sufficiently high positive potential is applied to the specimen, the electrons will be drawn from the filament to the specimen. Decreasing the specimen diameter, decreasing the spacing between top and bottom of the gun (often called the "focusing plates"), or increasing the diameter of the filament will tend to narrow the beam (reduce its height) on the specimen, but higher voltages will be required for the same power. Changing dimensions in the opposite direction will have the opposite effect. It is also possible to narrow the beam by applying negative bias to the focusing plates, but again higher potentials are required. To narrow the beam in an existing gun, a cylinder (C) may be inserted in the top plate as shown on the right side of Fig. 24-2. In this case the beam will be directed downward as shown. A gun of the dimensions shown, with a selection of cylinders inserted in top or bottom plates, will enable beam width and direction to be controlled over a wide range.

When materials of high vapor pressure and high melting point, e.g., molybdenum, are float zoned, condensation on the filament may impair emission. In this case, a gun such as that in Fig. 24-3 is useful (*15*). With such "hidden filament" guns deposition of metal on the filament can be minimized, but higher voltages are required (9 kV for the gun shown). Brownsword and Farr (*16*) have described a more compact gun of similar function that employs an auxiliary anode (which they call a grid), shown at A in Fig. 24-3, to reduce the accelerating voltage required.

Tantalum is most frequently used for gun construction because of its fabricability, low vapor pressure, and resistance to acid cleaning solutions. The bottom plate of the gun is usually supported on insulators, and the sides and top, located by aligning pins, are held in place by gravity. The gun parts may be only 0.01 in. thick if cleaned frequently. Condensation of metal on the gun tends to distort it.

The tungsten filament is shaped as in Fig. 24-2 by trial and error so that no hot or cold spots are noted on the periphery of the specimen bar after melting. Intermediate support of the filament by wires as shown in Fig. 24-2 will minimize sagging. Electropolishing of the filament before

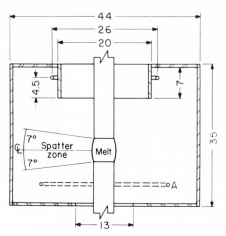

Fig. 24-3. "Hidden-filament" electron gun after Barthel and Scharfenberg (15). (Dimensions in millimeters.)

use in aqueous KOH (17) will remove surface oxides that may otherwise evaporate onto the specimen. A 0.025-in.-diam filament will require a heating current of about 25 A, the potential drop per cm of length will be 0.65 V, and the electron emission will be on the order of 130 mA per centimeter of length. For 0.015- and 0.020-in.-diam wire the appropriate values will be, respectively, 12 and 18 A, 0.7 and 0.8 V/cm, and 50 and 100 mA/cm.

C. Vacuum System

The primary purpose of the vacuum system is to keep the pressure below 10^{-4} Torr so that the electron gun will operate without interruption by gaseous arcs. The pressure necessary during zoning depends upon the need for gas removal and the need for preventing contamination from residual gases. Purification of a large molybdenum bar, for example, might be adequate at 10^{-4} Torr, while a small bar of titanium might be seriously contaminated by multiple passes at 10^{-9} Torr.

Study of some excellent books on vacuum technology (18, 19, 20) will be helpful. The pressure of most systems is not limited by the pump but by outgassing, which the operator can control by proper design and operation. For example, a square foot of stainless steel surface, after vacuum pumping 10 hr at room temperature, will outgas at the rate of 2×10^{-5} Torr-liters/sec (18). Therefore 20 liters/sec of pumping speed will maintain a pressure of 1×10^{-6} Torr. Baking this square foot of stainless steel surface at temperatures from 200–300°C can lower the outgassing rate by factors of 10 to 1000 in practical systems (21). Thus the same pumping speed will attain lower pressures. During zoning, additional outgassing can be expected from the specimen and other heated areas in the chamber. This can increase the pressure in the chamber by orders of magnitude.

The following examples will illustrate the range of pressures attainable in zone-melting systems. A modern 6-in. diffusion pump using silicone oils can be expected to reach pressures from 10^{-7} to 10^{-9} Torr (cold) with elastomeric seals (preferably Viton "A") in a standard 12-in. bell jar. The lower pressures would require good vacuum practice, baking to 150°C would speed pumpdown and lower the base pressure. The residual gases in the system would contain relatively large amounts of water and probably measurable pump oil. During zoning, pressures from 10^{-6} to 10^{-8} Torr can be reached.

Addition of an efficient liquid–nitrogen trap would greatly speed pumpdown and lower the percentage of water and pump oil in the residual gas. A stainless-steel chamber with copper-gasketed seals would enable baking to higher temperatures, e.g., 250–400°C. After baking, the blank-off pressure on such a system can be about 10^{-10} Torr. After the first one or two outgassing passes it should be possible to zone in the 10^{-9}-Torr range. A 2- or 4-in. booster (diffusion) pump between the 6-in. pump and mechanical pump is effective in keeping vapors from the mechanical pump out of the system.

To achieve even lower pressures ion pumps are commonly used. These pumps are very expensive, but oil contamination is practically eliminated if roughing is done by an adsorption pump. A water-cooled stainless-steel enclosure with a 140-liter/sec ion pump supplemented by a titanium evaporator (getter pump) will make possible zoning in the 10^{-11}-Torr range after baking at 250–400°C.

A number of ports in the vacuum chamber are required. Two rotary-motion ports (three if stirring is contemplated) are needed to operate the leadscrews. Double pumped O-ring seals can be used down to 10^{-8} Torr. At lower pressures, or for bakeability, magnetically coupled feedthroughs are best. As these units operate with tight clearances, the operator must avoid foreign contamination. They also will slip above certain torque values, so they may help protect the apparatus in case of seizing. Bellows-type rotary feedthroughs are also satisfactory.

High-voltage ports to carry currents up to 50 A at 12 kV are widely available to carry the high potential and current to the filament. Low-voltage electrical ports (with a few spare pins) are needed to carry current to limit switches and to the filament if the specimen is at high potential.

With metal enclosures, at least one viewing window is needed to observe the full range of gun travel. An oblique window near the bar axis is often useful. It should be possible to cover the inside of the windows at will by using a sheet of iron inside the vacuum, held by a magnet outside, or by using a shutter on yet another rotary feedthrough.

The contacts on the gun crosshead in Fig. 24-1 may be used to operate relay circuits to stop, reverse, or shut off the scanner and power supply. Another safety feature, incorporated in one of the commercially built zoners, is a pressure switch that shuts off the high-voltage supply when the chamber is at atmospheric pressure so that the user will not be subjected to shock hazard.

The vacuum chamber should be provided with at least three extra blanked-off ports for future use. Such devices as residual-gas analyzers, gas inlet or flushing valves, or spare ion gauges can be added to these ports as needed.

D. Power Supply

The power supply heats the filament for the production of thermionic emission, furnishes dc power for the electron beam, and exercises one of several possible control functions. In the simplest and usual case, the dc voltage is kept constant and beam current is controlled at some constant value by varying the voltage to (and thus the temperature and thermionic emission of) the filament. The power in watts = volts × amperes (or kilovolts × milliamperes).

Figure 24-4 shows a typical circuit. The voltage drop across the resistor R is proportional to the beam current. This voltage is compared to a reference voltage, supplied in this case by a battery. The difference voltage is then applied to the emission-control circuit. Schadler (2) has discussed three different types of emission-control circuits.

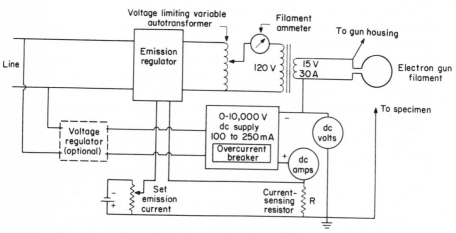

Fig. 24-4. Power supply essentials for EBFZM (specimen at ground potential).

The filament transformer, if used as shown with the specimen grounded, operates at high potential with respect to ground and must be insulated for voltages higher than produced by the dc supply. The variable auto-transformer on the line side limits the maximum current to the filament, even when another device is used to set or control the filament voltage. An ammeter in the primary of the transformer is useful as a rough indication of filament temperature and the state of contamination of the filament.

The dc supply should furnish 30% excess power above that needed for melting the work at hand. The supply should be sufficiently rugged to withstand occasional short circuits without damage. An adjustable dc over-current trip circuit should be provided. For versatility the output polarity should be reversible. High-voltage power supplies normally have one side grounded. "Positive output" means the high potential lead is $+$, the ground is $-$ or *vice versa*. A 10,000-V supply with enough current capacity to supply the maximum power is recommended. While much EBFZM has been done at 3000 V or below, the higher voltages give flexibility in gun design. Voltages above 10,000 V become expensive, require more care with insulation, and may give rise to hazardous x-rays.

Large, accurate meters for dc current and voltage are desirable. If a wide range of powers will be used, multiscale meters are recommended. The load regulation (change in output voltage with change in load current) and the ripple (ac modulation of the output) are not critical: 30% is allowable in both cases. The line regulation (change in output voltage with change in line voltage) should be on the order of 2–5%. Regulation of this order is usually obtained with a separate line-voltage regulator ahead of the power supply.

More sophisticated circuitry may be necessary when gassy materials are routinely zoned. If the pressure in the gun rises to about 10^{-4} Torr, a self-sustaining gaseous arc may start. The current will rise sharply because the voltage required to sustain the arc is relatively low. The usual result is that overload circuit breakers will trip. Ideally the power supply would be current limited; that is, the voltage would drop (and so, then, would the power) as the current tried to increase above the set value until the arc was extinguished. Power supplies of this type were originally developed for commercial production-scale electron-beam melters (6), and now units suitable for zone refining are available. Internal reactance in ordinary power supplies, or a resistor in series with the high-voltage output, may help to some extent. Sell and Grimes (22) also described a constant-current, variable-voltage circuit.

It is not possible to state what sort of power regulation is necessary for zone melting. Most operators don't really know because their meters cannot read any closer than 10% (in power). Control to $\pm2\%$ is probably adequate for most purposes. In very large bars only a 5% difference may exist between the power to melt through the bar and the power at which the zone is unstable. According to Barthel and Scharfenberg (23) power fluctuations can cause uneven distributions of impurities in a zone-melted bar.

24-4. PRACTICAL OPERATION

Cleanliness is very important for over-all success in the operation of a float-zone system. Vacuum-chamber components must be handled with thin cotton or plastic gloves rather than by bare hands. Oils or greases for lubrication or vacuum seals in the electron gun chamber should be avoided. The electron-gun cage and the screws and slides on the scanner must be free from excessive metallic deposits. A regular cleaning schedule is recommended for removal of metallic films on all insulators in the chamber.

The specimen rod should be loaded in two pieces, one in each grip. The two pieces should be centered and lined up vertically in the electron gun. A gap should be left between the ends of the rod prior to heating to allow for thermal expansion. If the specimen is under high voltage, the high-voltage connection should be made to both grips to assure even heating of both specimen ends. After the formation of a molten zone, moving one rod with respect to the other demonstrates that the zone is molten throughout. This can be accomplished by moving the bottom specimen grip slightly up and down or by inducing a sidewise vibration by jarring the equipment carefully.

In general, inexperienced operators encounter zone-stability problems by keeping the molten zone too hot. It is better to approach the melting point of the specimen slowly and to allow the rods, grips, and other parts to reach thermal equilibrium before melting. If zone stability is still a problem, reversing the zoning direction may help. However, the possibility of zone failures, when molten metal spills from the specimen, must be considered in designing and operating this equipment.

At the completion of a zoning pass, the gun power should be reduced enough to solidify the last zone length; the electron gun should then be returned to the start at this lower power level. This simple step keeps the specimen hot and prevents large strains from thermal-expansion effects in case the specimen rod has welded to the grips. The power level is then increased until the molten zone is gradually reformed at the starting position. At the end of the last pass the molten zone on the rod should be pulled apart by moving the specimen-grip crosshead in order to prevent thermal strains in the rod upon cooling. Multipasses will generally result in a necked-down region at the finish for upward zoning and at the start for downward zoning. The extent of the neckdown will increase with subsequent passes, the heat loss (by conduction) will change near the bar ends, and the molten zone may become unstable unless the bar diameter is filled out by adjustment of the lower crosshead. Gross bulges or necks in the specimen rod can be smoothed during zoning by careful manipulation of the movable specimen grip. However, electron-gun power adjustments or grip movement will generally result in a noticeable ridge on a smooth rod surface. If the zoning is proceeding smoothly, don't alter the settings.

REFERENCES

1. A. Lawley, in *Introduction to Electron Beam Technology* (R. Bakish, ed.), Wiley, New York, 1962, Chap. 8.

2. H. W. Schadler, in *The Art and Science of Growing Crystals* (J. J. Gilman, ed.), Wiley, New York, 1963, Chap. 17.

3. W. G. Pfann, *Zone Melting,* 2nd ed., Wiley, New York, 1966.

4. B. C. Allen, *Trans. AIME,* **227,** 1175 (1963).

5. R. E. Honig, *RCA Rev.,* **23,** 567 (1962).

6. H. R. Smith, C. de'A. Hunt, and C. W. Hanks, in *Reactive Metals* (W. R. Clough, ed.), Wiley (Interscience), New York, 1959, p. 131.

7. P. H. Keck, M. Green, and M. L. Polk, *J. Appl. Phys.,* **24,** 1479 (1953).

8. W. Heywang, *Z. Naturforsch.,* **11A,** 238 (1956).

9. W. Heywang and G. Ziegler, *Z. Naturforsch.,* **9A,** 561 (1954).

10. R. E. Green, Jr., *J. Appl. Phys.,* **35,** 1297 (1964).

11. M. S. Brooks, E. Owen Fisk, and B. Rubin, *Semicond. Prod. Solid State Technol.,* **8**(12), 34 (1965).

12. D. K. Donald, *Rev. Sci. Instr.,* **32,** 811 (1961).

13. K. R. Spangenberg, *Vacuum Tubes,* McGraw-Hill, New York, 1948.

14. L. H. Leonard, in *Introduction to Electron Beam Technology* (R. Bakish, ed.), Wiley, New York, 1962, Chap. 3.

15. J. Barthel and R. Scharfenberg, ORNL translation No. 1403, Scientific Translation Service, Ann Arbor, Mich.

16. R. Brownsword and J. F. G. Farr, *J. Sci. Instr.,* **41,** 350 (1964).

17. W. J. McG. Tegart, *Electrolytic and Chemical Polishing of Metals,* 2nd ed., Pergamon, New York, 1959.

18. C. M. Van Atta, *Vacuum Science and Engineering,* McGraw-Hill, New York, 1965.

19. A. Guthrie, *Vacuum Technology,* Wiley, New York, 1963.

20. W. F. Brunner, Jr., and T. H. Batzer, *Practical Vacuum Techniques,* Reinhold, New York, 1965.

21. D. J. Santeler, D. W. Jones, D. H. Holkeboer, and F. Pangano, *Vacuum Technology and Space Simulation,* NASA Report SP-105, 1966.

22. H. G. Sell and W. M. Grimes, *Rev. Sci. Instr.,* **35,** 64 (1964).

23. J. Barthel and R. Scharfenberg, in *Crystal Growth* (H. S. Peiser, ed.), Pergamon, New York, 1967, p. 133.

25
HEATING BY HOLLOW-CATHODE GAS DISCHARGE

Walter Class

MATERIALS RESEARCH CORPORATION
ORANGEBURG, NEW YORK

25-1. INTRODUCTION

The different methods of float-zone refinement differ in the manner by which the floating zone is created. Thus, radio-frequency, electron-beam, radiation, and optical methods can be employed to provide the highly localized heating needed to form a molten zone sufficiently short to be supported by its own surface tension. Of the above mentioned methods, electron-beam and radio-frequency methods are by far the most popular means of accomplishing float-zone refinement. The other methods are frequently difficult to apply and also require rather cumbersome equipment.

A new and rather simple method of accomplishing float-zone refinement will be described here. This method is inherently very stable, is applicable to both electrical conductors and dielectrics, and is amenable to a high degree of control. It is therefore applicable to the processing of a wide variety of materials that presently cannot be processed by any other float-zone technique. This method makes use of a hollow-cathode gas discharge to accomplish the highly localized heating required to form the molten zone.

25-2. THEORY OF OPERATION

When a relatively large direct voltage is applied to a gas at a reduced pressure, the gas "breaks down" and conducts electricity with an accompanying glow within the gas. Consider the typical plane cathode dis-

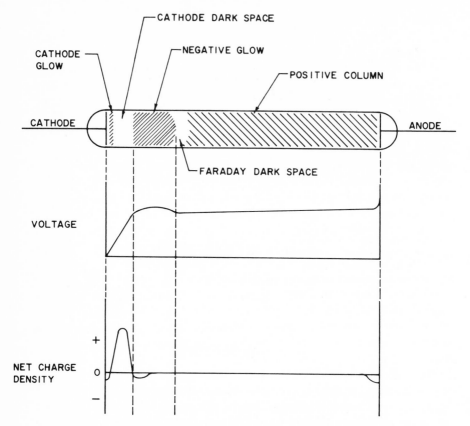

Fig. 25-1. Illustration of discharge parameters.

charge represented in Fig. 25-1 along with some pertinent operating characteristics. It is immediately apparent that the glow associated with an ordinary discharge is far from uniform, being instead distributed into various luminous regions separated by dark spaces. It is further evident that the voltage drops across a typical discharge are far from linear across the anode–cathode space. Instead, a very large voltage drop exists across a relatively small dark space immediately adjacent to the cathode. This so-called cathode dark space or cathode fall region is essential to the manner by which the gas-ion and electron-current carriers are created, thereby making the discharge self-sustaining.

The negative glow region of Fig. 25-1 contains a very large density of positive gas ions that are attracted to the cathode by the large cathode voltage fall. Upon bombarding the cathode, these ions liberate electrons, which are repelled from the cathode and, upon travelling through a discharge gas, create further ions by electron–gas-atom collisions, thereby maintaining the ion density needed to continue this electron–ion regeneration cycle. Any barrier to this regeneration cycle will extinguish the discharge.

The voltage and the same self-sustaining mechanism exist within the hollow cathode, but are significantly more efficient by virtue of the fact that electrons can be trapped and made to oscillate across the hollow, thereby generating a much greater number of gas ions.

When the current density of a plane-cathode system increases, the discharge impedance, and therefore the cathode fall voltage, increases, giving rise to the condition where the electrons emanating from the cathode begin to experience an accelerating voltage in excess of 1 kV. Furthermore, because the collision probability of an electron decreases with increasing electron energy, many electrons are able to travel rather long distances through the discharge without losing any energy. Consequently, when the discharge is made to operate at a high voltage and current density, a stream of electrons emanates from the cathode that has many of the characteristics of an electron beam.

Similarly, within the hollow cathode, a beam of electrons emanates from the cathode walls and tends to converge at the center of the hollow. These electrons are called runaway electrons and are responsible for the heating within the hollow cathode discharge. It is important to note that the energy and the path of the runaway electrons are determined by the electric field of the cathode dark space. The anode position is important only in determining the path of the electrons after their energy is dissipated in collision processes. Because of this, the cathode acts not only as a source of high-energy electrons, but further determines their trajectory by influencing the shape of the dark-space electric field. Therefore, if a cathode is shaped into the form of a spherical hollow, the energetic runaway electrons can be made to converge upon the center of the sphere and accomplish the heating and localized melting of any material placed at this focal point.

This is the manner by which molten zones are formed within the hollow cathode. Note that the electron-bombardment heating is accomplished within the hollow cathode glow, which, being a plasma, can effectively neutralize any space charge that would ordinarily build up upon the surface of a dielectric material subjected to this type of heating. Hollow-cathode heating consequently can be applied to any material, conductor or dielectric.

25-3. SCANNING AND SHIELDING

Application of the hollow-cathode discharge to float-zone purification requires that a means be provided for execution of the required mechanical motions within a reduced-pressure atmosphere of a controlled composi-

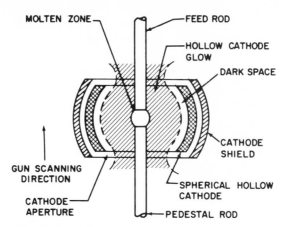

Fig. 25-2. Hollow-cathode zone-refining geometry.

tion. Thus, the scanning of the molten zone is accomplished within a vacuum chamber equipped with a controlled leak valve to allow dynamic maintenance of the proper operating pressure required for the discharge, typically between 0.1 and 2 mm Hg. Molten-zone scanning is accomplished by means of an assembly located within the chamber. This scanning assembly permits controlled vertical travel of a hollow-cathode gun wherein the discharge and heating take place. This assembly also permits

Fig. 25-3. Hollow-cathode zone refiner (MRC Model PBZ-98).

vertical alignment of the pedestal (purified material) and feed (impure material) rods so that the rod axes are located at the focal point of the runaway-electron beam.

The hollow-cathode gun used in this operation consists of a shielded, water-cooled stainless-steel cathode having a truncated spherical hollow geometry as shown in Fig. 25-2. The shielding suppresses the formation of a discharge at all surfaces of the cathode external to the hollow. It consists of a stainless-steel shell electrically isolated from the cathode and located within ⅛ in. of all the cathode surfaces requiring discharge suppression. This small separation causes the shield to act as a barrier to the discharge-regeneration mechanism mentioned previously. A typical example of a hollow-cathode float-zone apparatus may be seen in Fig. 25-3. This instrument is available from Materials Research Corporation, Orangeburg, New York (MRC Model PBZ-98).

25-4. SPECIMEN PREPARATION

The application of float-zone refining to a particular material requires that this material first be put into the form of a long, slender rod (feed rod). This does not pose any problem for many metallic materials readily available in rod form. However, many other materials can be purchased only in the form of powders or irregular shapes, and the process of converting these into a rod can be difficult.

The easiest method of preparing feed rods is by the use of isostatic pressing. This method consists of immersing the powders contained within a sealed rubber bag into a chamber filled with a hydraulic fluid. The application of pressure to this fluid then results in the very uniform application of pressure to powders contained within the rubber bag. Isostatic-pressing equipment is available from several manufacturers.*

The preparation of a long, slender rod by isostatic pressing requires some care if a straight and uniformly compacted rod is to be achieved. First, a bag-holding jig is required to ensure that the rubber bag remains straight during the application of pressure. If this is eliminated, the bag will flex during loading, and upon subsequent unloading will yield either a curved rod or one that is broken up into several small pieces. The required degree of bag holding can be achieved by means of the fixture shown in Fig. 25-4. This consists of nothing more than a perforated stainless-steel tube having tapered end fittings. The rubber bag is then held to the tapered end fitting by a similarly tapered bag clamp, which has an end plug through which the bag is loaded and unloaded. When properly

* This author has used a Loomis Hydraulic Isostatic Chamber, Model 220E-1-60,000 psi in conjunction with a Loomis Model 341-30S Hydraulic Press, with some success.

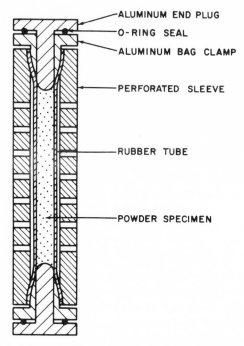

ALUMINUM END PLUG

O-RING SEAL

ALUMINUM BAG CLAMP

PERFORATED SLEEVE

RUBBER TUBE

POWDER SPECIMEN

Fig. 25-4. Schematic illustration of the isostatic tooling fixture.

mounted, the rubber bag (which frequently consists of a piece of thin-walled rubber tubing) is held in tension between the clamps, thus ensuring that it remains straight throughout the entire pressing cycle. The entire fixture is immersed in the hydraulic fluid during the pressing operation.

The achievement of good rods also requires that some care be exercised regarding the selection of the powder particle sizes selected for the pressing operation. The best results are achieved with a graded distribution of particle sizes ranging from 150 to —325 mesh. Such a graded distribution is much more easily loaded into the bag and yields a more uniform and higher level of as-pressed density. With a graded particle-size distribution, excellent quality feed rods can be obtained using pressures of between 10,000 and 20,000 psi for the pressing operation. Finally, many materials will press more easily if a small percentage of moisture (1–3%) and a binder, such as dextrin or polyvinyl alcohol, are added to the pressing mixture. The use of a binder must be exercised with caution, however, since it may result in contamination.

Good rod strength requires that the as-pressed rod be sintered subsequent to pressing. Sintering is relatively simple because the as-pressed rods are quite strong and easy to handle. The selection of sintering time and temperature is dependent upon the material. This author has found temperatures up to 1500°C to be adequate for most of the oxide and metallic materials studied. More refractory materials, such as the carbides, borides, and nitrides, would most probably require higher temperatures.

The objective of this preparatory procedure is *not* to achieve rods that are fully dense. Instead, rods that are between 70 and 80% of full density prove to be superior for float-zone operations. Such rods yield molten zones that are more stable than those of fully dense rods, thereby making control of the refining operation simpler.

25-5. OPERATION OF A HOLLOW-CATHODE FLOAT-ZONE REFINER

A. Specimen Setup

Upward scanning is most commonly employed with the hollow-cathode technique. Thus, an experimental setup would consist of a feed rod held in the upper grip of a float-zone apparatus, a pedestal rod set in the lower grip, and the hollow-cathode gun mounted on a scanning assembly positioned such that it is initially at the junction between the pedestal and feed rods. The grips in which the feed rods are held should permit feed- and pedestal-rod alignment in order to accommodate the slight curvature of most rod specimens. Furthermore, the grips should permit the opposite sense rotation of the pedestal and feed rods. Typical rotation rates vary between 5 and 60 rpm for both the pedestal and feed rods.

The most critical feature is the proper positioning of the hollow-cathode gun. It is of utmost importance that the pedestal and feed rods be at the focusing center of the hollow-cathode gun. If this is not achieved, then the heating will not be uniform and control of the molten zone will become difficult. If the feed and pedestal rods are improperly positioned, then a hot spot will be observed on one side of the feed rod. This is the side of the feed rod closest to the center of the gun, and the rod must be moved accordingly. Figure 25-5 shows an improper alignment as seen from the top. The indicated feed-rod repositioning is shown.

B. Commencement of a Purification Operation

Once the proper experimental setup has been achieved, the system should be evacuated and then the desired operating gas introduced into the system. This is accomplished through a bleed valve. Table 25-1 gives some typical operating-pressure ranges for the various gases this author has investigated. These results apply for a cathode having the truncated

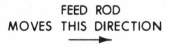

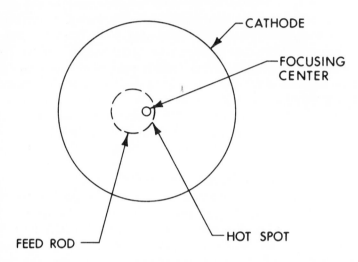

Fig. 25-5. Schematic representation of improper gun alignment.

spherical hollow geometry in which the sphere diameter is 1¾ in. Larger sphere sizes will operate at lower pressures.

The best manner for achieving the appropriate gas pressure is to use the discharge impedance as measured from the voltage–current settings of the high-voltage supply used to operate the discharge. Thus, this supply should be equipped with the required votage and current meters. It is desirabe to adjust the gas pressure such that the voltage remains between 1 and 2½ kV. The current used may vary between 100 and 1500 mA, depending upon the size specimen studied and its melting point. For a gun having the above-described hollow-cathode geometry, the largest feed

TABLE 25-1

Typical Operating-Pressure Ranges for Various Gases

Gas	Pressure (mm Hg)
Nitrogen	0.1–0.6
Oxygen	0.1–0.6
Argon	0.3–0.8
Helium	1.0–3.0 (approximate)
Hydrogen	1.0–3.0 (approximate)
Methane	0.2–0.5

rod that can be conveniently processed would have a diameter of $5/16$ in. Larger feed-rod sizes would require a correspondingly larger hollow-cathode size.

A typical refinement procedure is initiated by mounting the pedestal and feed rods, evacuating the system and introducing the appropriate pressure of the operating gas, and applying a negative dc voltage of approximately 500 V to the cathode; the glow is then observed. More power is then slowly applied to the cathode, and the pressure is adjusted until the proper gun-operating characteristics are achieved. This procedure is continued until the end of the feed rod is seen to melt. At this point, the feed and pedestal rods should be welded together, After welding there may be a change in the gun-operating characteristics, requiring some further small adjustment of the operating pressure. When this has been accomplished, the power should be raised still further until the zone is fully molten. At this point rod rotation and upward scanning can be initiated.

No further changes in operating pressure shoud be made subsequent to initiation of the scanning motion. Any adjustments in molten-zone temperature are made by means of the power supply. The initial inch of scan is generally critical and requires a good deal of operator experience and observation. If the molten zone is too hot, then the material that recrystallizes upon the pedestal rod will slowly increase in diameter and render the molten zone unstable. Thus, if this condition is observed, the power of the gun must be slowly decreased while scanning is continued until it is observed that the diameter of the recrystallized rod becomes stable. At this point the rod diameter will probably be smaller than the feed-rod diameter if a low-density feed rod was employed. Once a stable rod diameter is achieved, very little attention is required throughout the remainder of the refining operation.

C. Choice of Operating Gas

The hollow-cathode gun may be operated in any gaseous environment, provided that a suitable pressure is provided. If the pressure is too low, then a stable glow discharge will not ignite. If the pressure is too high, then a gas breakdown to the gun shield will occur. This is visible as a general glow located about the entire gun shield. Within these limits the choice of gas is subject to the discretion of the operator. Thus, a gas may be chosen that may help to stabilize the compound or element to be subjected to the refining operation. Therefore, oxide materials may be run in oxygen, nitrides in nitrogen, carbides in hydrogen–methane gas mixtures, and so on. In this manner, the operating gas can aid in stabilizing a compound. However, it must be emphasized that this stabilization can be effected only within the pressure range required for gun operation.

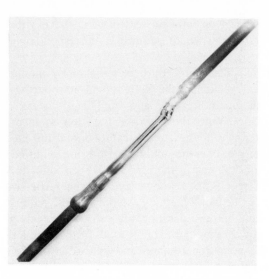

Fig. 25-6. Hollow-cathode zone-refined iron.

Similarly, a gas of a reactive nature may be selected to chemically assist in the purification operation. For example, the purification of a metal such as iron may be accomplished with hydrogen as the discharge gas. Figure 25-6 shows a sample of iron that was subjected to three molten-zone passes in hydrogen gas. The interstitial contamination was significantly reduced as may be seen from the results in Table 25-2. The

TABLE 25-2

Reduction of Interstitial Contamination in Iron

Contaminant	Concentration in starting material (ppm)	Concentration in refined material (ppm)
Oxygen	115	16
Nitrogen	117	7
Carbon	32	4
Hydrogen	0.8	0.5

interstitial elements of carbon, nitrogen, and oxygen were efficiently removed, whereas the hydrogen level remained unchanged within the limits of the analytical error. This result compares very favorably with electron-beam float-zone refined material and is further significant because the amount of material lost through evaporation was considerably suppressed in comparison with electron-beam methods.

25-6. CONTROL OF CATHODE SPUTTERING

The question of specimen contamination is worthy of further consideration because contamination can occur from the relatively cold cathode
used in this operation. This arises because the cathode is subject to ion
bombardment and will therefore undergo a certain degree of sputtering.

There are many ways in which the effects of sputtering can be completely eliminated. First, the cathode can be "aged" by using it to process
a given material. A similar state can be achieved by fabricating the cathode
of the same material as that to be processed.

Finally, if these two techniques cannot be applied, the simple process
of inserting tubular shields into the cathode aperture can very effectively
eliminate sputtering. These sputtering shields should be placed coaxial
with the feed and pedestal rods and should surround the rods in the region
about the cathode aperture. The last method proved very effective in the
growth of garnet crystals, which required gun scanning speeds as low as
$\frac{1}{8}$ in./hr.

26

CONTINUOUS ZONE REFINING OF BENZOIC ACID

J. K. Kennedy and G. H. Moates

AIR FORCE CAMBRIDGE RESEARCH LABORATORIES
BEDFORD, MASSACHUSETTS

26-1. INTRODUCTION

The technique of continuous zone refining has not been widely employed, although at least six systems have been described (*1–11*). Perhaps the reluctance to use this technique has been based on an aversion to complex apparatus. Certainly the inherent advantage of a constant, predictable, low limiting concentration should be desirable both in the laboratory and in industry. The apparatus employed in this study is quite simple and has eliminated the danger of column rupture.

The essential features of any continuous zone-refining apparatus include provision for feed of raw material and separation of refined solvent from solute-enriched solvent. Thus the apparatus is generally divided into feed, enriching, and stripping sections respectively. As the design of the system used in this study precluded the need for a stripping section, the stripping column was eliminated; thus the problem of mixing stripped solute and enriched solvent in the feed section in order to maintain an invariant solute concentration in the feed was avoided. Furthermore, the only molten zone that is required to travel through a completely enclosed solid is associated with the feed-enriching junction. The first zone length of this solid that is melted each cycle causes the increased volume of the melted material to be transferred by the matter-transport phenomenon to the main enriching column. As a consequence of this lateral material transfer, mechanical stress on the container wall is prevented and structural integrity is assured.

An often ignored but obvious experimental pitfall confronted in both batch and continuous zone refining is the deviation from calculated results because of the inclusion of extraneous components in a system. In the extreme case it is conceivable that the equilibrium value of k_0 may be different in a polynary system from that in a binary system. Little can be done to avoid this effect of additional soluble impurities except to start with the best available material. On the other hand, insoluble extraneous material on either a macroscopic or microscopic scale may be included in the system as a result of contamination by transfer or by deterioration of a part of the solute–solvent system. This insoluble impurity may be of a density greater or less than that of the solvent. Impurity solute may either be adsorbed by this extra component or occluded within it. Then, regardless of the efficiency of the zoning process, included solute may be carried along in the recrystallized solvent. The system employed in this study minimized such contamination because extraneous impurities less dense than the solvent cannot move down the feed column into the refiner. Extraneous impurities more dense than the solvent are likely to be removed at the drain tube prior to entry into the refiner. The vertical matter-transport system (5, 12) completely eliminates this danger, but problems of structural integrity are more acute for that apparatus. Thus it is seen that the choice of a continuous zone-refining apparatus is based on chemical and physical properties of the system being refined.

26-2. MATERIALS

Benzoic acid containing 1% iodine was employed as the solute–solvent system for one experiment. In the other experiment benzoic acid containing 0.25% by weight Oil Red was used to demonstrate that the vapor pressure of the solute was not a significant factor in the segregation. The benzoic acid was Fisher reagent grade. The iodine was Baker and Adamson resublimed reagent grade. The Oil Red was produced by E. I. du Pont de Nemours and Company.

For the benzoic-acid–iodine system and the benzoic-acid–oil-red system the continuous horizontal zone-refining apparatus is satisfactory. Rough melting–freezing experiments visually indicate that the solute is more soluble in the liquid phase than in the solid, i.e., $k < 1$. The density of the solid is approximately 10% greater than that of the liquid. The melting points of the systems are approximately 120°C. Both systems are chemically stable well above 120°C, although at high concentrations there is a tendency for some of the iodine to sublime.

26-3. DESCRIPTION OF APPARATUS

The apparatus used for continuous zone refining in this study is described in detail elsewhere (9). The essential features of the apparatus are found in Fig. 26-1.

The apparatus was filled in the following manner: All moving heaters and auxiliary heaters except auxiliary heaters #1 and #5 were turned on. Molten feed material was then slowly added in small quantities until a solid plug formed at the restriction in the waste exit. Molten feed material was then added rapidly until the enriching section, mid-feed section, and feed section were filled to a height such that molten material just started to flow over into the product receiver. Auxiliary heaters #2 and #3 were then turned off and, after all the material in the mid-feed section had solidified, the feed hopper was filled with molten feed material. With all the moving heaters still on, the auxiliary heaters were set on their programmed timers, the drive system for the moving heaters was started, and the first pass was begun.

The molten zones created by the moving heaters were caused to move through the material in the enriching section from the product exit to the waste outlet. Continuous operation resulted from the reciprocating action of the heaters (13). Solvent movement toward the product exit resulted from the matter-transport phenomenon (5, 12). At the start of every pass auxiliary heater #5 turns on and, in every pass except the first, the moving heater closest to the product exit melts the material of mass h immediately adjacent to the product exit. Because $D_l < D_s$ (D_l = density of liquid; D_s = density of solid) the mass of material h expands on melt-

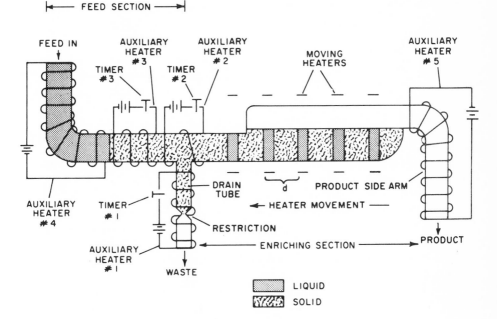

Fig. 26-1. Continuous zone-refining apparatus.

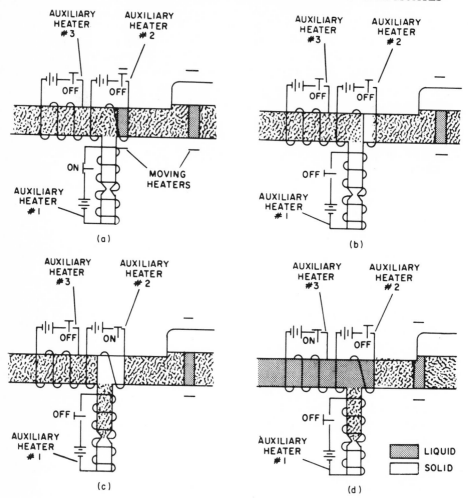

Fig. 26-2. Matter-transport continuous zone refining (see text).

ing, causing refined product to overflow into the product collector. As the drive system causes the moving heaters to move toward the waste outlet, the material that freezes out behind the moving heaters freezes at the level of the product sidearm. When the liquid zone reaches the drain tube, the entire zone drains into the waste container, the heaters reciprocate to start a new pass, and the empty spaces generated by draining the liquid zone are filled in. The steps in this operation can be visualized with the aid of Fig. 26-2.

In Fig. 26-2(a) the molten zone is about to melt the last bit of solid that prevents it from draining through the drain tube. Auxiliary heater

#1 has already been turned on by its automatic timer and the solid in the drain tube has melted and flowed into the waste container. In (b) the molten zone has drained into the waste container through the drain tube and the moving heaters have reciprocated to start a new pass. Auxiliary heater #3 has been shut off by the programmed timer. In (c) auxiliary heater #2 has melted some of the solid material in the feed tube and this material has flowed into the drain tube, creating a solid plug. In (d) auxiliary heater #3 has melted the solid material within its province, filling in the empty spaces. Auxiliary heater #3 then turns off and a solid block again forms between the feed and the drain tube. In this system the moving heaters were evenly spaced 10 cm apart and moved at a rate of 5 cm/hr. Thus, the 2-cm-long molten zones cause product collection and move from the product exit to the waste exit while becoming enriched in solute $(k < 1)$. After discharge of the solute-enriched solvent, feed material of concentration c_f is introduced into the system as described.

The glass apparatus in this system was made of Pyrex. The enriching section consisted of a 22-mm O.D. tube 43 cm long joined to a 17-mm O.D. tube 8.9 cm long. The feed tube was a continuation of the 17-mm O.D. section of the enriching section. Auxiliary heater #4 kept the feed material in its province in the molten state at all times. The 10-mm O.D. drain tube that extended from the 17-mm O.D. tubing to the restriction was 8.9 cm long. The restriction in the drain tube was approximately 3 mm I.D.

The moving heaters were made of nichrome wire. They were wired in parallel and were capable of individual control. The auxiliary heaters were individually controlled and programmed by means of a Zenith three-circuit program clock.

In order to maintain equal volumes in the zones contained in the 17-mm and 22-mm O.D. tubing, a 43-cm-long sealed tube of 9 mm O.D. was placed at the bottom of the 22-mm O.D. tube.

26-4. COMPUTED BOUNDARY CONDITIONS AND DIMENSIONS

The restrictions normally placed on the physical dimensions of most continuous zone refining systems, because of the need to balance the solute concentration in the feed section, were eliminated in this system by eliminating the stripping section. The difficulties normally encountered in attaining material and solute balance were also greatly reduced.

In this system the material balance is given by

$$F = W + P \qquad (26\text{-}1)$$

where F is the weight of feed added to the system per pass, W is the weight of waste removed from the system per pass, and P is the weight of product collected per pass. In this system P is given by

$$P = (D_s - D_l)v \qquad (26\text{-}2)$$

where v is the volume of a molten zone. The solute balance of the system is expressed by

$$FC_f = PC_p + WC_w \qquad (26\text{-}3)$$

where C_f, C_p, and C_w are the solute concentrations in the feed, product, and waste respectively.

The steady-state equations for this system have been derived elsewhere (9, 14) and are as follows:

$$L_e = (0.434B_e)^{-1} \log\left(\left[\frac{w(P + l) + l}{\alpha k\,(P + l)}\right] - w\right) \qquad (26\text{-}4)$$

Here l is the weight of molten material of density D_l that is maintained molten and caused to travel by a moving heater; k is the effective distribution coefficient; L_e is the weight of material in the column from the product exit to the point where the solute concentration is C_f; α is the purification factor for the system ($\alpha = C_p/C_f$); and B_e and w are given by

$$e^{B_e(P+l)} = \left(B_e\frac{l}{k}\right) + 1 \qquad (26\text{-}5)$$

and

$$w = -\frac{P}{(P + l)(1 - k)}$$

The actual length of the enriching section needed to give a desired α is expressed by

$$L = \frac{L_e + h}{D_s}$$

where h is the weight of solid of density D_s that is melted by a moving heater.

The limits of α for this system depend on k in such a way that for effective purification k must be greater than $l/(P + l)$.

26-5. ANALYSIS AND RESULTS

Once started, the system was operated for 24 hours a day. For 48 passes product was removed from the benzoic-acid–iodine run and discarded as forerun. In the case of the benzoic acid–Oil Red, the first 39 passes were discarded. For each cut, a clean product flask was substituted as the product receiver. Approximately 0.65 g of purified product was collected in each pass. A sample of each product cut was weighed, dissolved in $CHCl_3$, and analyzed colorimetrically. Iodine could be detected to 2 ppm, Oil Red to 0.04 ppm.

Table 26-1 shows that the purified material for both runs was below the limit of detectability of the colorimetric procedure. For the iodine experiment the purification factor α^{-1} was $>5 \times 10^3$, and for the Oil Red experiment α^{-1} was $>6 \times 10^4$.

TABLE 26-1

Iodine–Benzoic-Acid and Oil-Red–Benzoic-Acid Runs

Product cut	Passes	Amount of iodine detected
Forerun	1–24	Not analyzed
1	24–47	N.D.
2	47–59	N.D.
3	59–71	N.D.
4	71–84	N.D.
		Amount of Oil Red detected
Forerun	1–39	Not analyzed
1	39–54	N.D.
2	54–66	N.D.
3	66–78	N.D.
4	78–88	N.D.
5	88–123	N.D.

REFERENCES

1. W. G. Pfann, *J. Metals,* **7,** 297 (1955).
2. W. G. Pfann, U. S. Pat. 2,739,045 (1956).
3. W. G. Pfann, U. S. Pat. 2,852,351 (1958).
4. W. G. Pfann, U. S. Pat. 2,926,075 (1960).
5. J. K. Kennedy, *Rev. Sci. Instr.,* **35,** 25 (1964).
6. K. M. Rozin, V. N. Vigdorovich, and A. N. Krestovnikov, *Akad. Nauk SSSR, Otd. Tekhn. Nauk, Izv. Met. Topliv.,* **6,** 56 (1961).
7. V. N. Vigdorovich and I. F. Chernomordin, USSR Pat. 161,488, 1964.
8. G. H. Moates, in *Solid State Physics in Electronics and Telecommunications,* Vol. 1 (M. Désirant and J. L. Michiels, eds.), Academic, New York, 1960, pp. 1–8.
9. J. K. Kennedy and G. H. Moates, *Rev. Sci. Instr.,* **37,** 11 (1966).
10. W. G. Pfann, *Zone Melting,* Wiley, New York, 1965.

11. M. Zief and W. Wilcox, *Fractional Solidification,* Vol. 1, Dekker, New York, 1967.

12. G. H. Moates, W. J. Jackson, and J. K. Kennedy, U. S. Pat. Appl. 81,203 (1961).

13. W. J. Jackson, U. S. Pat. 2,952,722 (1960).

14. J. K. Kennedy and N. G. Parke III, *J. Appl. Phys.,* **35,** 2248 (1964).

27
PURIFICATION OF NAPHTHALENE IN A CENTRIFUGAL FIELD

E. L. Anderson

IRON AND STEEL INDUSTRIAL
CORPORATION, LTD.
PRETORIA, SOUTH AFRICA

27-1. INTRODUCTION

The zone refining of organic compounds can be considerably speeded up by carrying out the process in a centrifugal field (*1*). Various forms of apparatus for zone melting in rotating equipment are shown in Figs. 27-1 to -8. It is assumed in all cases that pure material will concentrate at the head, i.e., the end from which the molten zones move, and impure material at the other end, the tail. In all cases the containers are rotating fairly rapidly and are partially filled with material to allow expansion to take place safely into the free space behind the material thrown to the outer walls.

In Fig. 27-1 two straight tubes are rotated about an axis parallel to their lengths. The heating elements need not rotate with the tubes, but have to be moved either up or down as in a conventional vertical zone-melting apparatus. The axis of rotation may be horizontal or at any angle, but the best results are obtained if it is vertical.

In Fig. 27-2 the arrangement is similar to that of Fig. 27-1 except that the tubes have been replaced by an annular container. The inner walls may be dispensed with; i.e., an ordinary closed tube may be used.

The spiral tube arrangement shown in Fig. 27-3 is somewhat more complicated. The molten zones that form under the vertical heaters are shown by the darker shading. The heaters rotate with the spiral container, but at a slightly different speed. In the case of the left-handed helix shown,

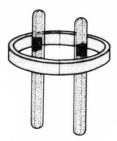

Fig. 27-1. Using straight tubes.

if the relative movement of the heaters with respect to the helix is clockwise when viewed from above, the zones will move upward, and vice versa. The helical form of container permits relatively long column lengths to be used.

As the molten zones extend from top to bottom in Figs. 27-4, -5, and -6, the container must be tapered to the angle the free surface of a liquid would assume at the given speed of rotation. Radiant heating is required in Fig. 27-4 because of the vertical barrier. Pure material may be removed from each side of the barrier when feed is introduced at the top. In Fig. 27-5 radiant or immersion heaters can be employed. Circumferential and vertical components during zone melting concentrate purer material at the top and impure material at the bottom; the feed and sampling points are indicated.

In Fig. 27-6(a) the rotating annular container has a spiral immersion heater that rotates slowly with respect to the container. If the heating element rotates clockwise with respect to the container when viewed from above, the molten zone [darker shading in (b)] will move downward.

In Fig. 27-7 the spiral element is coiled in one plane like a watch spring and is immersed in the material confined between two disks. Depending on whether the spiral is gaining or losing on the rotation of the container, zone melting will be inward or outward. Since the molten canal (darker shading) extends all the way along the heating element to the free surface near the axis of rotation as shown, any expansion or contraction during a

Fig. 27-2. Using annular container.

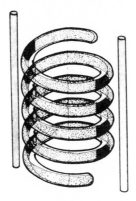

Fig. 27-3. Helical tube form.

melting–freezing cycle will be taken up by the liquid in this canal. The spiral element, of course, must be stiffened to prevent "unwinding" by the centrifugal field. This problem becomes greater as the length of the heater is increased. In Figs. 27-4 to -7 there is a danger of back-diffusion of concentrated impurities from one end of a molten canal to the other.

In all of the above arrangements, heat must be removed from the material for freezing to take place. This occurs by conduction through solidified material as well as the walls of the container and by convection in the molten zones. Because of the low thermal conductivities of organic materials (e.g., the values for naphthalene are 263 and 680 μcal/sec-cm-°C for liquid and solid respectively) the material in the center of a 100-mm-diam tube will take hours to freeze. Radiant or simple immersion heating, therefore, is not practical for large quantities of organic compounds.

FEED

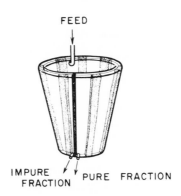

IMPURE FRACTION   PURE FRACTION

Fig. 27-4. Tapered container using straight molten zones.

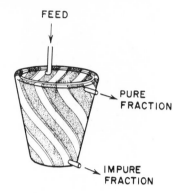

Fig. 27-5. Tapered container using spiral molten zones.

An arrangement of heat-exchanger tubes (Fig. 27-8) may be used for tonnage quantities. The distributor valve [Fig. 27-8(c)] consists of two parts, one containing the curved slots and the other the six holes. Fluid is fed from the slots into the holes; at any stage three of the holes will be receiving hot fluid and three cold fluid. The heat exchanger to which these holes are connected will generate molten and solid zones [dark and light shading in Fig. 27-8(a)]. The centers of the zones will be around the heat

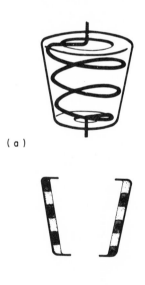

(a)

(b)

Fig. 27-6. (a) Tapered container with spiral immersion heater; (b) section through scheme shown in (a).

Fig. 27-7. Flat-disk container with spiral heater.

exchangers receiving the maximum flow of fluid. It can be seen that as relative motion between the two parts of the valve occurs, the pattern of distribution will change, so that after a movement of 60° the maximum fluid flow will have advanced to the next hole, resulting in the centers of the molten and solid zones having shifted to the adjacent sets of heat-exchanger tubes. The six feed pipes are shown in the center and the outlets at the circumference in Fig. 27-8(b). The baffles near the center of the vessel shown in Fig. 27-8(a) take up the expansion of the organic material on melting to prevent overflowing down the center of the container.

27-2. EXPERIMENTAL

A. Apparatus

The various parts of the apparatus [Figs. 27-9(a) and (b)] are the following:

1. Glass Column

The column consists of a helix (diameter, 200 mm; pitch, 17 mm) wound from borosilicate glass tubing of 10-mm bore and 2-mm wall thickness. A convenient length of column is 10½ turns, which gives an effective length for zone melting of about 680 cm (Note 1). This column has short lengths of narrow-bore glass tubing sealed at its ends for sampling. There are three small holes, each about 3 mm diam, on the inside of the coils at the ends and half a turn from the upper end as shown. The latter hole is for feeding naphthalene into the column from the container shown. The other holes may be used for thermistor probes or for adding small amounts of materials.

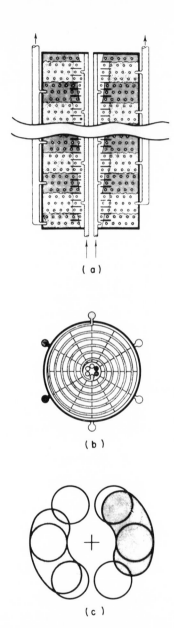

Fig. 27-8. Apparatus using heat-exchanger elements. (a) Section through rotating vessel. Dark areas are molten zones, lighter areas are solid. Arrows indicate flow of heat-exchanger fluids. (b) Plan of heat-exchanger element. (c) Differential valve showing ports for hot and cold fluid (dark and light areas, respectively).

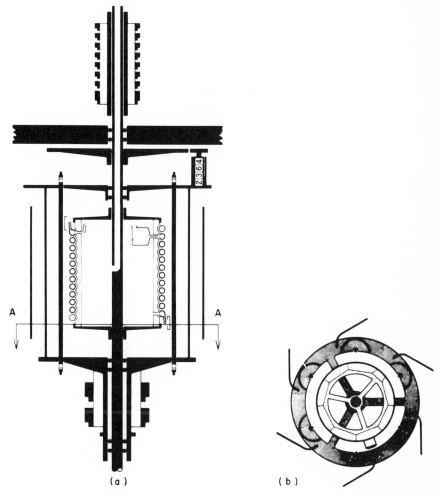

Fig. 27-9. Apparatus for zone melting of naphthalene in helical glass column. (a) Section through apparatus without gear system. (b) Section A-A. The sample-collecting cup is shown at "5 o'clock" position. For clarity, the relative positions of the two sets of platforms are different in the two views.

2. Column Support

The glass helix is supported by the segments (Note 2) immediately behind it. They fit together to form a grooved cylinder, being held in position by the narrow tapered key piece, shown at "2 o'clock" in Fig. 27-9(b). With the "antisublimation" heating system in position [the dots immediately behind the column in Fig. 27-9(a)] the column fits the support exactly. The helix is driven directly from the main shaft.

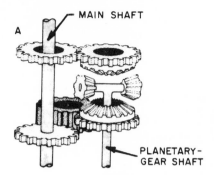

Fig. 27-10. Gear system for achieving differential rotation.

3. "Antisublimation" Heaters

"Antisublimation" heaters are necessary for naphthalene, which tends to sublime onto the back surface of the column. If allowed, this sublimation will eventually build up enough solid to fill the space behind the material being zone melted, defeating the object of the rotating system. By keeping the back surface at a temperature above the melting point of naphthalene, any material condensing here will remain liquid and be immediately centrifuged back into the main bulk of the material.

4. Reflectors

Provision is made for six semicylindrical reflectors, which are mounted on the larger platforms as shown. They focus the heat from Calrod heating rods (Note 3) onto the material in the spiral. Because the reflectors have to move at a slightly different speed from the helix, the platforms supporting them are mounted on the main shaft by ball or roller bearings. The cylindrical shaft of the lower reflector platform is coupled directly to the gear A of Fig. 27-10.

5. Differential Gearbox

The small difference in speed between the two sets of platforms is controlled by the gear system shown in Fig. 27-10. This system is easily built up from automobile gear wheels. Differential motion is achieved by rotating the planetary gears at half the required relative speed. The mechanical arrangement shown in Fig. 27-11 has been used, but any system with a separate slow-speed motor for driving the planetary-gear shaft is applicable. However, the somewhat heavy arrangement of motor, clutch, worm boxes, and so on shown in Fig. 27-11 has definite advantages. It makes a very steady base for the apparatus with very little vibration during rotation; this system thus can be left running with a minimum of attention for days and nights on end.

In this system a 3½-hp 3-phase motor drives the gears through a centrifugal clutch (Note 4) and heavy flywheel. The flywheel ensures rotation for about 4 minutes after a power failure. This provides solidification of the molten zones by the time the column comes to rest. Also, the wiring is so arranged that upon motor failure, heating will be automatically terminated to prevent melting while the apparatus is stationary. Motor speed of 1425 rpm is reduced to 274 rpm for the main shaft of the apparatus by a 5.2:1-ratio worm reducer (Note 5). In the secondary drive to the planetary-gear shaft, the speed is first reduced from 1425 rpm to 937.5 rpm by a chain drive from a toothed wheel of 25 teeth to one with 38 teeth. After passing through the "Kopp variator" (Note 6) this speed is further reduced by the series of worm boxes to 1 revolution every 12 hr for the planetary-gear shaft. (Worm-box ratios are 25:, 15:, 30:, and 60:1). The differential speed between the spiral and the reflectors is therefore 1 revolution every 6 hr. This can be either increased or decreased by the "Kopp variator" by a factor of 3.

6. Revolution Counter

The relative motion between the two sets of platforms can be measured by a toothed wheel actuating a revolution counter fixed to the top of the upper reflector platform [Fig. 27-9(a)]. One hundred teeth on this wheel enable a relative movement of 0.01 revolutions between the spiral and the reflectors to be measured.

7. Slip Rings

One set of slip rings at the top of the main shaft feeds the various heating systems of the mounted spiral through wires passing down the

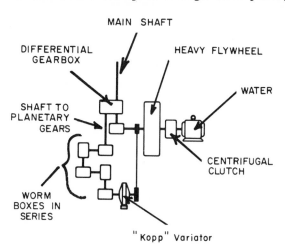

Fig. 27-11. Drive system for rotating helical apparatus.

hollow main shaft. Spring-loaded carbon brushes, which make contact with these slip-rings, are fixed to the stationary cross-member supporting the shaft near the top of the apparatus. The large slip rings on the lower reflector platform feed the Calrod heaters through spring-loaded carbon brushes fixed to the main platform separating the actual zone-melting portion of the apparatus from the gear system.

8. Stroboscopic Viewing

A cam, shown just below the large slip rings at the bottom of the apparatus in Fig. 27-9(a), actuates an automobile "make-and-break" points system to work a flash gun (Note 7). This enables readings to be taken on the revolution counter and for examination of the column during zone melting. To eliminate unwanted reflections, the backs of the reflectors and the cooling vanes may be painted with a nonreflective black paint.

9. Sleeve Heaters

Situated at the ends of the column [shading with concentric circles in Fig. 27-9(a)], they are of the same shape and size as a single coil of the column. They compensate for heat losses from the end coils of the helix, thereby helping to achieve uniformly wide molten zones throughout the column.

10. Sampling System

Small heaters enclose the short side tubes at the ends of the column to melt out solid plugs in the side tubes. For samples that contain very little oil, the cup shown at the top of the column may be used; for samples that do not solidify completely, the type of cup shown at the lower end of the column prevents oil from the sample running out when the apparatus comes to a standstill after sampling. The cups are designed to be interchangeable and for easy clipping into position on the apparatus.

11. Feed Bottles

The feed bottles melt naphthalene into the column while the system is rotating. The capacity of the larger bottle need be only about 30 ml, since filling is best carried out in stages (Note 8). Rapid melting of the solid plug in the side tube is achieved if the heating wire (No. 40 S.W.G. nichrome) wound around the bottle is also passed down the capillary of this tube. The smaller container shown at the top left of the spiral is for adding eluants or mixtures to be separated by zone-melting chromatography.

B. Procedure

1. Filling of Column

Powdered material is placed in the column with a vibrator to obtain uniform packing. Naphthalene can be crushed to contain about 40–50% voids. It will melt into place to fill about half the cross section of the column uniformly along its length. However, oily materials such as crude hot-pressed coke-oven naphthalene (Note 9) are packed into a column with difficulty. They must therefore be added in molten form to the rotating spiral for partial filling uniformly along the length of the column. Moreover, this latter technique has the advantage that the column may be partially filled to any desired extent.

The apparatus is started without the cooling vanes but with the anti-sublimation heater, and sleeve heaters and reflectors switched on at above-normal settings. In addition the differential rotation is set at an above-normal rate. In this way the entire column is heated to a temperature above the melting point of the naphthalene. When the spiral has been sufficiently warmed up, the apparatus is quickly brought to rest and 25 g of molten naphthalene are added quickly to the feed bottle (Note 10). The apparatus is quickly started again with the bottle heater switched on. The molten material will be discharged steadily into the column and will run down to the bottom two coils. The apparatus is again stopped while the bottom two coils are screened from the radiant heat with aluminum foil (Note 11); another batch of molten naphthalene (30 g) is added. The apparatus is rotated until the bottle is emptied. The molten material will run down to the bottom again, but will solidify just beyond the screening so that the next coil or two above the foil screen will be charged partially with naphthalene. The apparatus is stopped, another two coils screened off, and the process is repeated. This is continued until the whole column has been partially filled more or less uniformly to the top with with about 145 g of naphthalene. This uniform distribution of material in the column is important for obtaining uniformly wide molten zones throughout the column. No zone melting takes place during this filling operation because the molten naphthalene solidifies all at once in each coil. Some segregation may take place behind the screening when the naphthalene solidifies here while the rest of the batch is still molten, but this is considered negligible. When all of the naphthalene has been added, the aluminum foil is removed and the spiral is ready for zone melting.

2. Zone Melting

With the packed column and the cooling vanes in position, rotation is initiated; the heated backing and the sleeve heaters at the ends of the column are switched on to suitable voltages. The Variac feeding the Calrod heaters of the reflectors is adjusted to maximum heat and the differential movement is set to its slowest speed. The spiral is viewed under the flashing light. When molten zones are established under the heaters, the reflectors are adjusted to a voltage that gives a minimum width of molten zones as well as a molten zone in every coil under a reflector (Note 12). The differential gear system is adjusted to give the required zone speed, about 15 cm/hr in a clockwise direction (Note 13); the reading is noted on the revolution counter. Because naphthalene expands on melting, it tends to build up toward the head (Note 14); this effect is used to counteract the natural draining toward the bottom by moving the molten zones downward. If the process has to be interrupted for any reason, the revolution counter reading can be noted, the differential movement set to its lowest speed, and the apparatus switched off. On start-up the differential speed can be set temporarily to maximum to bring the reflectors nearly to such a position that when they are switched on the molten zones will be formed in exactly the same position as when zone melting was interrupted; i.e., the heaters are advanced in relative position by 60°. The differential setting is then returned to the value used before the run was stopped (Note 15).

With relatively impure naphthalene the molten zones can be easily distinguished from the solid zones, which are opaque because of the small crystal size. However, as the naphthalene in the column becomes purer, it becomes difficult to distinguish molten material from crystal-clear, glassy solid. Generally this highly pure solid remains clear and glass-like. The noise of ensuing cracking may be heard for several minutes after this apparatus has been switched off. However, with experience one is able to distinguish molten and solid forms of highly purified naphthalene under the stroboscopic light.

3. Sampling

The amount of material collected may be varied by switching on the heater at different stages in the life of a molten zone at the end of the column. A minimum will be collected at the head when the tip is just beginning to melt, and at the tail just before the last portion of the molten zone solidifies. A maximum sample will, of course, be collected when the molten zones are fully formed at the ends. Any sample will be contaminated by the small amount of material making up the solid plug. This is generally material from the previous sample unless the side tube is specially filled with pure naphthalene after sampling. However, as the volume of material in the side tube is of the order of 0.02 cm^3 compared with the 2 or 3 cm^3 of the sample, its effect can be ignored for our purposes (Note 16). The cup used for collection [Fig. 27-9(a)] may be lined with degreased aluminum foil for easier removal of sample.

4. Elution of Column

Eluting agents are generally introduced at the head of the column. With liquids such as ethylene glycol, toluene, methyl naphthalenes, piperidine, and so on, small quantities are injected into the side tube by means of a hypodermic syringe. The side tube can then be sealed again with pure naphthalene to prevent overflow of liquid. Solid eluants may be added as solutions or dispersions in pure naphthalene.

5. Handling of Samples

Most of the oil may be separated from an impure sample by centrifugation at about 2000 rpm in special Erlenmeyer flasks (2). The solid and the liquid are then examined separately.

The zone-refined naphthalene was not handled in any special way, since our interest was the removal of major impurities in coke-oven naphthalene to barely detectable levels, not the preparation of ultrapure naphthalene. Attention was also focused on the concentrated impurities from the tail of the column.

6. Analysis

Melting point has been found to be the simplest and best criterion of purity. In the case of the starting material the melting point may be determined by a standard method (3) which requires at least 20 grams of sample. In the case of small samples from the column, the melting point may be carried out in sealed capillary tubes under carefully controlled conditions. The impurities in small samples are also determined by gas–liquid chromatography (Note 17).

C. Application

Zone refining in a centrifugal field may be employed for rapid preparation of purified material; it may make possible the purification of compounds that have been reported to give difficulties in normal zone refining (4). Since higher zoning speeds may be tolerated in rotating equipment, the refining of bulk chemicals such as naphthalene, p-xylene, phthalic anhydride, dimethyl terephthalate, and so on may be economically feasible in the equipment characterized by Fig. 27-8. Centrifugal zone melting may also be more efficient than normal zone melting in concentrating various solutes from dilute solutions; it may be possible to make concentrates from such materials as fruit juices, coffee extracts, and so on, or for the concentration of heavy water from ordinary water (5).

Finally, the field of zone-melting chromatography remains to be explored by centrifugally accelerated zone melting. In this technique, the mixture to be separated is introduced at the head of the column and zone melted into pure solid solvent (6). The technique is uniquely suited to the separation of high-molecular-weight mixtures that are not amenable to separation by gas–liquid chromatography. Furthermore, it appears that this form of chromatography will be easier to scale up for large-scale separations than ordinary adsorption or partition chromatography.

Naphthalene offers possibilities as a solid solvent, since it is relatively low-melting, has good solvent power, and is sufficiently volatile for easy removal from high-molecular-weight solutes. The helical column should be well suited for zone-melting chromatography because of the long lengths possible. The mixture to be separated, if liquid, may be injected directly into the head of the column through the sampling side tube with a hypodermic syringe. Alternatively, or if solid, the mixture may be dissolved in pure naphthalene and melted into a molten zone at the head of the column from the small heated container. Samples taken from the other end of the column may be freed of naphthalene by sublimation before examination.

An unexpected advantage of a centrifugal field was found in zone chromatography of a coal-tar pitch resin fraction in naphthalene. A 17% w/w solution of this resin in zone refined naphthalene exhibited the peculiarity that upon solidification all the crystallizing solid crept up the walls of the beaker. In the centrifugal field of the rotating apparatus creeping was suppressed.

NOTES

1. This is the length of material that would be thrown against the outer wall of the column, i.e., based on a diameter of 210 mm. The factor limiting the length of column is the time for a molten zone to traverse the column. A 40-turn helix of the above coil diameter, for example, would have a length of about 2590 cm; even with the relatively high zone speed of 40 cm/hr, a molten zone would take about 65 hr to travel through the column.

2. This backing must be dismantleable to enable the spiral to be mounted on or removed from the apparatus. Compressed asbestos has been used, but steel or aluminum is suitable when insulated thermally and electrically from the antisublimation backing of the spiral.

3. Calrod heating elements, 0.32-in. diameter, manufactured by S. A. General Electric Co. (Pty.), Ltd., P. O. Box 1905, Johannesburg, South Africa.

4. Size CS 73H, Maximum bore 2 in., 1450 rpm, 5 h.p., supplied by Edward L. Bateman Ltd., P. O. Box 1671, Johannesburg, South Africa.

5. "Radicon" Worm Reducers, supplied by David Brown Precision Equipment (Pty.), Ltd., P. O. Box 540, Benoni, South Africa.

6. Kopp Variator, Type 16 F.S., 1½ hp at 1440 rpm, supplied by J. H. Vivian and Co., Ltd., P. O. Box 301, Johannesburg, South Africa.

7. Model B 37 "Powerflash" Automobile Timing Light, manufactured by Crypton Equipment Ltd., Bridgewater, England.

8. If each coil is filled to a depth of 3 mm, the surface of the molten material will be at a 7° angle at 274 rpm. Only 1 coil, or at most 1½ coils, can be filled at a time; each coil will take about 12 cm^3 (13.7 g) of naphthalene if 3 mm deep.

The crude, hot-pressed, coke-oven naphthalene is freed from insoluble impurities by filtering through fluted filter paper in an oven maintained at about 90°C. For convenience, the filtrate may be cast into degreased aluminum-foil cups of approximately 100 ml capacity. The solidified cakes can be sealed by wrapping with additional aluminum foil for storage.

9. Our starting material was 97.5% pure, based on the melting point (78.99°C) (*3*). This material is refined satisfactorily but tends to form traces of dark, insoluble material toward the tail of the column in very long runs. This discoloration persists after all the soluble impurities have been removed, even when the melting point indicates that the material has reached a very high state of purity.

10. The molten naphthalene will immediately solidify in the narrow-bore side tube, while the bulk of the material will remain molten for several minutes. The bottle must never be filled completely with liquid, as overflow will then occur upon rotation.

11. Care must be taken to avoid short circuits in the various heating systems on the mounted spiral when the aluminum foil is positioned.

12. With relatively impure starting materials the molten zones will tend to become broader toward the bottom as impurities lower the melting point. Similarly, the melting point becomes higher toward the head as the material there becomes purer. If uneven distribution of naphthalene exists in the column, uniformly wide molten zones will not be obtained. Molten zones may merge because of insufficient material.

13. Most of our work has been carried out at a zone speed of 12–16 cm/hr (differential speed between spiral and heaters of 1 revolution every 5.5 and 4 hr respectively), but subsequent work in a straight-tube apparatus [see Fig. 1 in Reference (*1*)] showed satisfactory zone refining under forced cooling at zone speeds of up to 40 cm/hr with naphthalene. As the zone speed is increased in the helical column, the molten zones may

become so broad that they tend to merge into each other, especially at zone speeds above 16 cm/hr in warm weather. Under these conditions only three of the available six heaters are used.

14. This transfer of material toward the head can become a problem in very long runs if one starts with the column about 50% full. From time to time, therefore, the head of the column should be inspected; if material threatens to overflow, bleed off a portion through the sampling system.

15. It is very difficult to adjust the differential speed to the exact setting, but generally the error in restoring the setting to its previous value is not more than the normal fluctuations in the differential speed caused by variations in the voltage.

16. This volume of the side tube can be made even smaller by filling with glass beads. The beads in the upper sampling tube may be cemented in with pure naphthalene to prevent their falling out when the apparatus is stationary.

17. Components were separated in a Perkin-Elmer Fractometer, Model 116E, with a Golay column (0.01 in.) at 125°C, nitrogen as a carrier gas at 1.8 kg/cm^2 inlet pressure, and a flame-ionization detector.

REFERENCES

1. E. L. Anderson, *Chem. & Ind.* (*London*), **1966**, 1615.
2. E. L. Anderson, *Analyst,* **85**, 228 (1960).
3. *Standard Methods for Testing Tar and its Products,* 6th ed., Standardization of Tar Products Committee, Gomersal, Yorkshire, England, 1967, p. 380.
4. W. R. Wilcox, R. Friedenberg, and N. Back, *Chem. Rev.,* **64**(2), 215 (1964).
5. H. Schildknecht, *Zone Melting,* Verlag Chemie, Weinheim, and Academic, New York and London, 1966, p. 197.
6. W. G. Pfann, *Zone Melting,* 2nd ed., Wiley, New York, 1966, p. 58.

28

ZONE-MELTING CHROMATOGRAPHY OF ORGANIC MIXTURES*

H. Plancher, T. E. Cogswell, and D. R. Latham

LARAMIE PETROLEUM RESEARCH CENTER
BUREAU OF MINES
U. S. DEPARTMENT OF THE INTERIOR
LARAMIE, WYOMING

28-1. INTRODUCTION

Zone-melting chromatography involves placing a sample at some point in a solidified column of purified solvent and then distributing the sample through the solid solvent by repeated passes of the molten zone. Several workers (1, 2) have used this technique to study the molecular-weight distribution of polystyrene. Their results indicated that a molecular-weight distribution of the polymer had occurred within the solvent column after repeated passes of the molten zone and that the highest-molecular-weight material was at the top of the column.

* This investigation was performed as a part of the work of American Petroleum Institute Research Project 60 on the Characterization of the Heavy Ends of Petroleum, carried out by the Bureau of Mines at Laramie, Wyoming, and Bartlesville, Oklahoma. Work was done under cooperative agreements between the Bureau of Mines, U. S. Department of the Interior; the American Petroleum Institute; and the University of Wyoming. Reference to specific commercial materials or models of equipment in this report is made to facilitate understanding and does not imply endorsement by the Bureau of Mines.

Pfann (3) has discussed some of the elementary theory necessary for the successful application of zone-melting chromatography. The parameters discussed included distribution coefficients, zone length, zone speed, and zone stirring. Although he referred to this technique as zone chromatography, we believe that zone-melting chromatography (ZMC) is a more descriptive and less ambiguous term.

One of the most important requirements for efficient ZMC is constant, low-volume molten zones. The development of ZMC as a separation tool for organic mixtures has been handicapped by the inability to produce the necessary constant, low-volume molten zones. The electrical-resistance heaters usually employed for zone melting in organic systems are incapable of producing such zones. Induction heating, common in zone melting of metals, has not heretofore been considered applicable to organic systems because these materials are nonconductors.

An induction-heating system for the zone melting of organic systems was recently developed; a metallic conductor served as the susceptor (4). The advantages of induction heating (internal heating, efficient mixing, and short zones) formerly available only with metals are now applicable to organic systems, making ZMC of organic materials feasible. The application of this separation technique to a mixture of polycondensed aromatic materials is described in this chapter.

28-2. APPARATUS

A photograph of the assembled apparatus is shown in Fig. 28-1.

A. Induction Generator

The induction generator, designed for continuous zone-melting processes, has an output of 2.5 kW and a nominal power-output frequency of 450 kHz. It is equipped with a constant-voltage filament transformer, a heavy-duty plate transformer, a vernier power control, a primary saturable-core reactor, and silicon-diode rectifiers. This generator is capable of operating simultaneously as many as ten load coils connected in series.

B. Load Coils

Plate-type coils are used because they concentrate the radio frequency into a shallow horizontal plane. The two-turn, planar spiral coil is made from $3/16$ in. copper tubing, and the inner turn of the spiral is silver-soldered to the $1/8$ in. copper sheet.

C. Susceptors

The susceptors are flat, circular disks of 18-mesh, galvanized wire screen whose cross linkages are soldered to ensure rigidity. The disks are cut

0.015 in. smaller than the diameter of the tube, using a punch and die set. Each susceptor is matched to the tube in which it is used by selecting only those disks that consistently remained horizontal as they sank through the tube containing a viscous oil. The selected disks are then gold plated to prevent contamination of the sample.

D. Tubes

Precision-bore glass tubes, ½ in. I.D. × 20½ in. long, are used.

E. Tube-Raising Mechanism

Tubes are raised vertically through the load coils at 47.4 mm/hr, using a windlass and pulley system.

F. Tube Holders

Tube holders consist of male Swagelok connectors fastened to brass weights attached to the ends of the tube-raising cables. This type of fitting, with Teflon ferrules, permits rapid attachment or removal of the sample tubes.

G. Low-Temperature Cabinet

A household refrigerator, extensively modified to maintain temperatures as low as −30°C, is equipped with a horizontal five-unit load coil as-

Fig. 28-1. Zone-melting chromatography apparatus.

sembly, installed inside the cabinet. A separate cooling system circulates an antifreeze solution through the coil assembly.

H. Gas–Liquid Chromatograph (GLC)

A Perkin–Elmer Model 880 chromatograph equipped with a flame-ionization detector and a $\frac{1}{8}$ in. $\times$ 15 ft. silanized column of 5% SE-30 on 28–40 mesh acid–base washed Chromosorb P is used.

28-3. EXPERIMENTAL

The solvent column is prepared by adding 40 ml of purified benzene to a precision-bore glass tube stoppered at one end. The solvent column is partly degassed and frozen by slowly lowering the tube into a freezing bath. A vibrator is attached to the tube to increase the efficiency of the degassing procedure.

When the solvent column has solidified, 4.7 mg of the aromatic mixture (36% benzo[ghi]perylene, 60% coronene, and 4% materials of unknown structure) is dissolved in 5 ml of purified benzene and added to the top of the column. An additional 3 ml of benzene is added to the top of the solidified mixture to allow materials with $K > 1$ to migrate upward. With the tube inverted, the stopper is removed and the void area is filled with benzene, which is then solidified. A polyethylene cap is press fitted over the bottom of the tube as a receiver or sample cup.

A susceptor is placed horizontally on top of the solidified column by means of a magnet. The tube is suspended vertically through the center of the load coil inside the refrigerated cabinet ($-30°C$) at a level that places the susceptor about 2.5 cm below the plane of the coil. The tube is raised through the energized coil by the tube-raising mechanism. As the susceptor, supported by the solidified column, is drawn upward near the high-energy field of the coil, it is heated by the induced current and melts the top of the solvent column. The susceptor sinks through the molten material, remaining below the coil at a distance at which the susceptor receives just sufficient energy to melt the sample. When the molten zone (about 1 mm long) reaches the bottom of the tube, the molten material and susceptor drop into the sample cup. The "eluted" fraction is recovered by evaporating the benzene (about 0.05 ml), and the susceptor is used for the next pass of the molten zone. To avoid shortening the column, pure solvent is added to the bottom of the column after each pass to replace the eluted material. Forty fractions were obtained in this manner.

Selected fractions, average weight 0.1 mg, were analyzed by GLC under the following conditions; detector 310°C, inlet 440°C, and column 290°C with a helium flow of 70 ml per minute.

28-4. RESULTS AND DISCUSSION

Figure 28-2 shows the composition of the charge material and of selected fractions obtained during the ZMC runs. Benzo[ghi]perylene was
concentrated in the early fractions but decreased to a minimum of 10%
in fractions 35–40. Also, the 4% materials of unknown structures were
eluted in the early fractions and were completely removed after 15 passes.
The coronene concentration increased with increasing fraction number and
reached a maximum of 90%.

Ultraviolet irradiation of the column after 40 passes showed the presence of fluorescent materials in the lower 3 in. of the column. This residue,
6.3% of the charge material, was recovered by evaporating the entire
solvent column. The composition of the residue was similar to that of
fraction 40.

The most important and attractive feature of induction heating in the
ZMC process is the ability to maintain a constant, low-volume molten
zone. The generator vernier is set for maximum power output. The susceptor will approach or fall away from the high-energy plane of the coil as
the melting point varies. Thus, the zone length remains constant. An
additional attractive feature of induction heating is that mixing within the
molten zone is produced by vibrations of the susceptor within the energized coil. These vibrations, caused by electromagnetic inducton, contribute to the efficiency of the process.

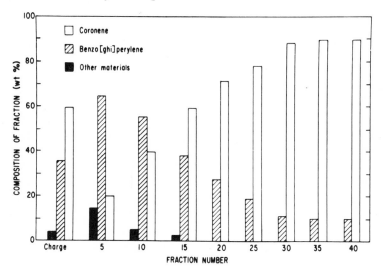

Fig. 28-2. Composition of selected fractions from ZMC separation.

28-5. CONCLUSIONS

Induction heating via internal susceptors can be applied to the zone melting of organic materials. This technique produces constant, low-volume molten zones necessary for making ZMC separations of poly-condensed aromatic materials of similar structures. The technique is attractive for separating a variety of materials in appropriate solvents.

REFERENCES

1. F. W. Peaker and J. C. Robb, *Nature,* 182, 1591 (1958).
2. J. D. Loconti and J. W. Cahill, *J. Polymer Sci.,* A1, 3163 (1963).
3. W. G. Pfann, *Anal. Chem.,* 36, 2231 (1964).
4. H. Plancher, J. C. Morris, and W. E. Haines, Preprints, Am. Chem. Soc., *Div. of Petrol. Chem.,* 11(1), 57 (1966).

29

THE CONCENTRATION OF FLAVORS AT LOW TEMPERATURE

M. T. Huckle

UNILEVER RESEARCH LABORATORY
SHARNBROOK, BEDFORD, ENGLAND

29-1. INTRODUCTION

The standard methods for the production of flavor concentrates for analytical purposes involve solvent extraction of either the foodstuff concerned or its steam distillate. Fractionation of this dilute extract usually entails at least one distillation. Serious losses of the more volatile constituents occur and thermally labile substances decompose to produce "off flavors." The flavor of the concentrate, therefore, does not resemble that of the original foodstuff but is usually associated with cooked or processed food.

Concentration of a solvent extract by zone melting minimizes flavor loss and thermal decomposition. Very pure solvents necessary for the extraction stage can also be produced by the zone-melting technique. This chapter describes an extraction procedure followed by a three-stage concentration by zone melting.

29-2. APPARATUS

The apparatus employed for the solvent purification as well as the concentration stages (Fig. 29-1) has double the number of tubes previously reported (*1*). The zone-melting assembly is contained within a vertical display deep-freezer (Fogel VM-25-IC). The cabinet, which is provided with a glass door for the observation of molten zones, can be operated at $-20°C$ without frosting the apparatus. A circulating fan minimizes the temperature gradient within the cabinet.

Each of the six charge-tubes (A), 72 cm $\times$ 1.75 cm (O.D.) thick-

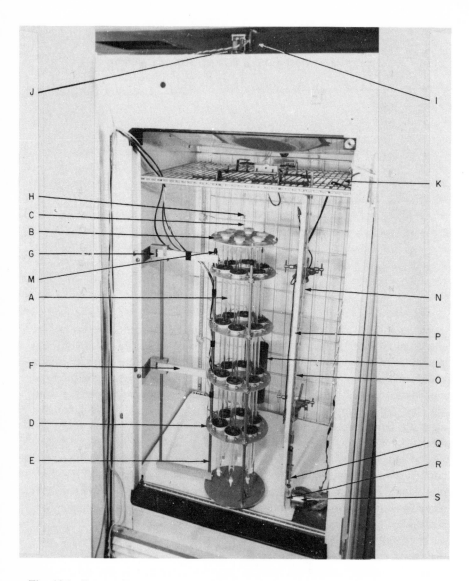

Fig. 29-1. Zone-melting assembly. Large-scale apparatus: A, charge-tube; B, charge-tube support; C, release hook; D, heater plate with six heaters; E, heater frame; F, support rod; G, hinge with locking bar; H, support wire connecting C to I; I, pulley wheel; J, heavy-duty clock motor; K, refrigerator shelf holding six pulley wheels with string connecting B to L; L, counterpoise; M, rubber contact foot. Small-scale apparatus: N, sample tube; O, heater; P, heater support; Q, push rod; R, Archimedean cam; S, motor.

walled (2 mm) Pyrex tubing, has a capacity of 100 ml. The upper and lower ends of each tube are closed by means of B14 and B7 stoppers respectively. B7 stoppers with Teflon sleeves are bound into the lower ends with Teflon tape to provide leak-free seals without contamination from grease. The tubes are circularly arranged and held in a movable aluminum tube support (B). The support holes do not allow the lips on the B14 stoppers to pass through. A three-point wire suspension connects the support rim to a release hook (C) and ensures that the plate remains in a horizontal plane during its upward movement. Four equally spaced, cloth covered, 11-W heaters surround each charge tube and form molten zones approximately 5 cm long. The heating elements consist of spirals of oxidized nichrome wire (5.3 Ω/meter) positioned in grooves in circular formers. Adjacent turns are sufficiently separated to prevent electrical contact. Six heaters are connected in series; each group of six is plugged into holes in four circular aluminum plates (D). The plates are held in fixed positions by means of a light frame (E) and are concentrically aligned with the charge-tube support. The frame is held in position by means of three support rods (F) attached to hinges (G) on the cabinet door frame. A flexible support wire (H) passes through a hole in the refrigerator roof and connects the charge-tube assembly, via the release hook, to the pulley-wheel rim (I) of a device for producing zone movement (2). A gear wheel, with several missing teeth, is driven by a heavy duty clock motor (J) geared to $\frac{1}{4}$ rev/hr and is in mesh with another gear wheel on the pulley spindle. For a short time during each revolution the gear wheels are out of mesh and the tubes fall under gravity until the pulley is arrested by a stop. The pulley-wheel circumference (20 cm) is equal to the distance between heaters; thus the zone from the heater above is passed to the one below and a continuous downward traverse of the charge, at a speed of 5 cm/hr, is maintained. A string over six ball-race pulleys, suitably arranged on the upper refrigerator shelf (K), connects two diametrically opposite points on the charge-tube support to a counter-poise (L). The clock motor lifts a weight slightly greater than the resistance to motion. The tension on the support wire is reduced to zero, after each gravitational fall, by means of three rubber feet (M) on the heater frame, which contact the charge-tube support immediately before the wire becomes taut.

The final concentration stage is performed in the small-scale apparatus shown on the right-hand side of Fig. 29-1. The charge-tube (N) consists of a Pyrex tube, 80 cm $\times$ 0.7 cm (O.D.), with 20-ml capacity. The 16 heaters (O), equally spaced on support (P), each consist of two turns of wire (14.1 Ω/meter) wound in series; each fits the charge-tube closely. The tube is pushed up through the heaters by means of a rod (Q) in contact with an Archimedean cam (R) on a motor spindle (S) (*3*). The motor speed is 1 rev/hr and the cam step allows a heater spacing of 5 cm.

29-3. PROCEDURE

The freezing and solvent properties of benzene make it a suitable solvent for this technique. Prior to extraction the benzene (B.D.H. grade; m.p. > 5.4°C) is purified by zone-melting with 0.1% methyl red as a visual indicator. After 2 days the pure upper portion of the charge is melted out at room temperature while the impure fraction is kept frozen. Gas–liquid chromatography has shown the pure section to consist of one component, and a melting-point determination (5.538°C ± 0.002° by Beckman thermometer) has indicated purity comparable to that used as a reference standard (*4*). The chosen fruit is cold pressed at 6000 psi; the filtered juice is immediately saturated with salt and mechanically shaken with pure benzene. The benzene layer is separated as a foam and centrifuged in glass bottles at 2000 rpm. The benzene extract is again separated and dried with granular anhydrous sodium sulfate. The large-scale tubes are filled with the dilute extract and stage 1 of the zone-melting concentration is carried out for 16 hr. The tubes are removed from the cabinet and the charge immediately above the concentrate is kept frozen, with powdered solid carbon dioxide in a cloth, while the concentrate is melted out with a heater. During the course of a week four such concentrations can be performed, yielding 24 concentrates at stage 1. These can be bulked into one or more large-scale tubes and stage 2 of the concentration is performed over a week end. Some indication of the degree of concentration can be obtained from the band spreading at the bottom of the tubes. This can be observed visually as some traces of colored compound have been extracted with all materials that have so far been treated. At this juncture the concentrate is usually ready for stage 3, which takes place in the small-scale apparatus and is continued until the ultimate distribution is reached (5 days). In this way the original extract can be concentrated 1000–3000-fold, depending upon the nature and concentration of the components and also their behavior in benzene at higher concentrations. The final concentrate is collected by cutting the tube into sections and is stored in sealed ampoules at −20°C. Analysis can be performed by a combination of chromatographic and spectroscopic techniques. On a gas chromatogram the benzene peak masks a small region near the injection point. If this region is important the process must be performed in a solvent of longer retention time. The odor of the benzene concentrate, on evaporation of solvent, is very similar to that of the fresh parent material. This similarity is not necessarily expected even with total concentration without decomposition, as the relative amounts of components extracted depend upon their distribution coefficients between water and benzene.

29-4. ADVANTAGES OF THE METHOD

1. The extraction of fresh, cold-pressed juice minimizes enzyme action and hydrolysis.

2. The use of solvent purified by zone-melting eliminates ambiguities that can arise from concentration of solvent impurities; furthermore, this solvent is continually regenerated in the concentration process.

3. The flavor molecules are entrapped within the solid benzene lattice during concentration and cannot escape to the atmosphere.

4. The distribution coefficients of the flavor molecules between liquid and solid benzene are much in favor of the liquid, thus making zone melting an efficient concentration procedure with the minimum of fractionation. This, combined with point 3, reduces the amount of parent material required.

5. Artifact formation is minimized throughout the concentration owing to the low temperature employed in the zone-melting process.

6. The large-volume, multiple-zone, multiple-pass system used is a valid method for automatic concentration.

NOTES

1. Maximum capacity is obtained by minimizing the heat output within the cabinet. This is achieved by disconnecting the thermostat, internal lighting, defrost and antimist door heaters. Room lighting is adequate for observation of the equilibrium; frosting of the door and compressor does not occur in the sealed system used.

2. Open heaters cannot be used in the presence of convection currents from the fan. The top and bottom of each heater is covered by a piece of cloth containing a hole just large enough to admit a charge tube. These radiant heaters are efficient for melting a section of sample. The cloth is sufficiently flexible for the tubes to fall smoothly under gravity and simultaneously minimize convection inside the heaters. Series connection of heaters, in a horizontal plane, allows the voltage across the lower batches to be reduced to allow for zone elongation as the concentration proceeds.

3. During a zone-melting experiment solid carbon dioxide is placed within the cabinet to provide an inert atmosphere in case of tube fracture, a possibility in the event of an electrical failure.

4. Tube fracture, due to expansion on melting, can occur if molten zones are formed from the solid phase. Thus the heaters are switched on and the tubes put into motion when the benzene has only partially solidified. Contraction to the solid/liquid equilibrium now occurs and four un-

strained molten zones are formed simultaneously in each tube. After the first pass the danger of tube fracture is remote owing to the buffer effect of air bubbles that form within the charge.

5. The heater frame is connected by means of two side arms to hinges on the cabinet door frame. A quick-release hook, between the charge-tube support and the support wire, allows the heater-and-tube assembly to be removed from the cabinet for insertion of tubes. The tension in the counterpoise string should also be released to facilitate this process. A locking bar ensures that the heater assembly is correctly aligned with respect to the suspension system on reintroduction into the cabinet.

REFERENCES

1. M. T. Huckle, *Chem. Ind.* (*London*), 1966, 1490.
2. W. G. Wilman, *Chem. Ind.* (*London*), 1961, 1825.
3. J. H. Beynon and R. A. Saunders, *Brit. J. Appl. Phys.,* 11, 128 (1960).
4. A. R. Glasgow, E. T. Murphy, C. B. Willingham, and F. O. Rossini, *J. Res. Natl. Bur. Std.,* 37, 141 (1946).

PART **III**
CONTAINMENT

30 CONTAINERS FOR PURE SUBSTANCES

E. C. Kuehner and D. H. Freeman

NATIONAL BUREAU OF STANDARDS
GAITHERSBURG, MARYLAND

30-1. INTRODUCTION

In contrast with the rapid advances in the measurement and control of modern purification processes, the art of effective sample storage has improved slowly. It is obvious that efforts to achieve extreme purification are easily wasted if the container allows degradation, decomposition, permeation, or similar processes to occur. The definition of the container system is often regarded as the device which is used for storage. Many instances require a much broader definition in order to guarantee minimal deterioration of a sample. A container is frequently selected without full consideration of the possible harmful qualities that a chosen container may contribute. When scrupulous attention to containment is a necessity, no systematic approach is available to aid the selection process. The purpose of this chapter is to provide a point of departure for evaluating the various major container categories.

30-2. CONTAINER MATERIALS

A model concept of a high performance container is instructive. In view of the many limitations of working with real materials, the absence of any container may be considered to be the best system, even though certain practical problems are thus implied. The next best container may involve the storage of a purified material in itself. An outstanding example is afforded by the floating zone refining of silicon (*1*) in which the material being purified, the apparatus for performing the purification, and the storage vessel are identical.

The materials commonly used in the manufacture of various containers are glass, quartz, platinum, stainless steel, graphite, and synthetic polymers such as polyfluorocarbons, polyethylene, polypropylene, polyvinyl chloride, polystyrene, and polycarbonate. None of these storage materials has universal applicability. Some of the important properties and features to be considered in selecting the container material are as follows:

1. Composition and impurities.
2. Chemical and heat resistance.
3. Sorption properties.
4. Permeability of gas, vapors, and liquids.

In some cases, container purity is a primary consideration. However, it is seldom realistic to ignore the interaction between container and contents or between storage requirements and storage conditions. This duality is a basic aspect of container technology: container materials are evaluated in terms of their intrinsic physical properties; their use depends upon these properties and the effect caused by the addition of the sample into the container.

A. Container Impurities

Any statement of container impurities tends to be technically complex because impurities may be incorporated according to none, any, or all of the rules for forming chemical mixtures. The mixture may involve surface adherence phenomena, particle inclusion, solid solution, or molecular bonding. Furthermore, the attempt to clean a container, or otherwise prepare it for use, may shift the quantitative aspects of contamination either by improvement or by introduction of a new contaminant or a new contamination problem. The following illustrates known or typical contamination profiles of the common container materials.

The composition of natural quartz is approximately 99.6% silicon dioxide. The impurities in high purity quartz are shown in Appendix I for comparison with impurities in borosilicate (2, 3), graphite carbon (4), polyethylene (2, 4, 5), polyvinylchloride (2), and tetrafluoroethane (2). High purity quartz has been prepared with less Al, B, Ca, Cu, Fe, Mn^+, Na, than polyethylene, while borosilicate contains relatively large amounts of the above elements. The catalyst used for the polymerization process may introduce metal ions and other contaminants into plastic. For example, metal alkyls and Ziegler catalyst (6, 7) consisting of organic-metal halides and hydrides of Al, Ga, B, and In are used in the polymerization of hydrocarbons of the olefin series in the manufacture of polyethylene and polypropylene. Styrene polymerization is sometimes initiated by organolithium compounds.

The fabrication process may contaminate the container material. Our microscopic examination of various samples of polyfluorocarbon and polyethylene showed the presence of fine particles (0.5 mm or smaller) distributed throughout the material. Furthermore, our laser probe spectroscopic analysis of such particles has revealed Fe, Mg, Si, Zn, and Al as the major constituents and Ni, Cu, and Mn as minor constituents.

B. Chemical Durability

There are many possible causes for the failure of a container to provide suitable protection to its contents. The use of borosilicate glass tends to be particularly well suited for the storage of organic chemicals. Such glass is not totally inert, however, as is known from chemical instability exhibited during the melting point measurement of certain organic compounds (in those cases, quartz can be used). Some inorganic reagents are quite corrosive so that glass or quartz is entirely unsuitable for the storage of hydrofluoric acid, or various caustic or alkaline solutions; with slower but measurable rates, soft glass or borosilicate glass is attacked by fluoride ion, and by all aqueous mineral acids including phosphoric acid (8–14).

In general, polyethylene, polypropylene, polystyrene, polycarbonate, and polyvinylchloride are examples of polymeric organic substances that tend to be swollen by, or dissolved by, organic solvents such as hydrocarbons, esters, ethers, and ketones (7, 15–17). Polycarbonate and polyvinylchloride are attacked by organic acids, organic or inorganic bases, alcohols, glycols, and dimethylsulfoxide. To a lesser extent, similar difficulties occur with polystyrene.

Polyfluorocarbons have provided an extremely important inertness to the storage of most organic solvents, acids, bases, and a number of other highly corrosive liquids (18). At high temperatures, the material is eventually prone to attack by fluorine or by molten alkali metals. In this, as in other polymeric organic materials, we have previously noted a tendency toward contamination by particulate inorganic matter.

Various durability criteria are available to alert the user of a container to check chemical resistance charts and information obtainable from manufacturers of the container products. A summary of the chemical resistance of common container material is included in Appendix II. The letter "Y" indicates that the container material has been claimed to be resistant to the chemical it intercepts on the chart upon exposure for a year at room temperature, but it does not assure that the chemical will not be contaminated by the container material. The letter "C" cautions the use of the container material for only short periods of less than a day and the probability of contamination to the purified chemical or container damage is much greater than a "Y" rating while a container material is not recommended for the chemical where its intercept is denoted by a letter "N."

The thermal stability of a container, another technically complex quality, is usually stated in terms of the nature of the container material. It is obvious that one must also consider the possible mechanisms for attack of the container by the sample; in general these are accelerated by elevated temperatures. It is a matter of common practice at the National Bureau of Standards to store highly purified corrosive reagents at temperatures below $-30°$ regardless of the container. In cases of uncertainty, the shipment of a chemical requires refrigeration provided by solid carbon dioxide in a well-insulated container.

C. Sorption Properties

When new containers are used directly, the original purity of the container material is the primary concern. This is not always practical for the entire techniques of containment. When a container is used for an ultrapure chemical that was previously used for another material, the sorption properties and history of the container have to be considered. There are numerous examples in the literature in which molecules and ions of chemical compounds are retained or absorbed on the surface of containers and cause erratic analytical (3, 11, 17, 19–21) results or changes in standardized solutions. The absorbed molecules and ions are sometimes retained on the surface of the container after considerable washing and rinsing and would gradually be desorbed into an ultrapure chemical that may come in contact with the used container. This has been confirmed by measurements using radioactive isotopes of chromium, phosphate, cesium, barium, lanthanum, and strontium ions (22–26). Glass and quartz may be stained by iron (27).

D. Permeability

The diffusion of gases through a container may present problems. Diffusion can easily involve a pathway for the loss of a volatile substance or for the entry of a volatile contaminant such as oxygen or water from the air. This is especially the case when volatile substances are stored in organic polymer materials. A comparison of the permeability of various plastic materials to water vapor and other gases, and the permeability of Teflon (28) and polyethylene (7) for a variety of solvents are given in Appendix II.

APPENDIX I

Comparison of Trace Element Concentration in Container Materials (Parts Per Million)

Elements	Quartz (4)	Borosilicate		Polyethylene			Polyfluoro-carbon (2)	Polyvinyl chloride (2)	Graphite (4)
		(2)	(3)	(4)	(5)	(2)			
Ag		<0.000001		0.02	<0.01	<0.001	0.0003	<0.005	<0.01
Al	<0.02		10,000	0.3	0.08				<0.1
As	<0.0002								<2
Au				0.09	0.001				<0.1
B	<0.01		50,000						3
Ba									0.05
Be									<0.01
Bi									<0.1
Br					0.03				
Ca	<0.1		1,000	0.2					0.5
Cd									<0.01
Cl					1.5				
Co		0.081			0.005	0.00007	0.0017	0.045	<0.2
Cr				0.3	0.015	0.076	<0.03	0.002	<0.1
Cs		<0.1				<0.00005	<0.00001	<0.001	
Cu	<0.0002		3,000	0.004	0.03	0.0066	0.022	0.630	0.01
Fe	<0.1	280	3,000	0.6		10.4	0.035	270	0.03
Ga	<0.004								0.05
Hf	<0.005	0.597				<0.0005			
K	<0.005		3,000	0.08					<10
Mg	<0.001		600						0.02
Mn			1,000		0.01				<0.01
Na	<0.04		30,000	0.17					<0.5
Sb	<0.0001	2.9			0.005	0.00018	0.0004	2.69	
Sc		0.106				0.000008	<0.000004	0.0045	
Zn		0.73	10		0.09	0.028	0.093	7.12	

APPENDIX II

Properties of Container Materials[a]

	Quartz	Boro-silicate	PFC	PE	PP	PvC	PS	PC
Transparency[b]	P	P	L	L	L	P	P	P
Heat resistance[c]	1100°	800°	205°	L110° C80	135°	70°	80°	130°
Autoclavability[d]	Y	Y	Y	N	Y	N	N	Y
Chemical resistance[e] and permeability[f] of the following chemicals:								
Organic acids	Y	Y	Y	C	Y	C	C	N
Acetic anhydride			Y	N 5	Y			N
Acetic acid (glacial)			Y 4	Y 5	Y			N
Formic acid			Y	Y 4	Y			N
Phenol (97%)			Y	C 4	N			N
Alcohols	Y	Y	Y	Y	Y	C	C	C
Allyl alcohol			Y	4				
Amyl alcohol			Y	C	N			Y
Benzyl alcohol			Y	Y	Y			N
Butyl alcohol			Y	Y 5	Y			Y
Cyclohexanol			Y	N	C			N
Ethyl alcohol			Y 1	Y	Y			Y
Isopropyl alcohol			Y	C				Y
Methyl alcohol			Y	C 5	C			N
Octyl alcohol			Y	4				
Esters	Y	Y	Y	C	C	N	N	N
Amyl acetate			Y	N	N			N
Butly acetate			Y	Y 6	C			Y
Dimethyl phthalate			Y	N 3				
Ethyl acetate			Y	C 6	Y			N
Ethyl acetoacetate			Y	5				
Ethers	Y	Y	Y	C	C	N	N	C
Dibutyl ether			Y	7				
Diethyl ether			Y	C 7	C			N
Glycols	Y	Y	Y	C	Y	N	C	C
Ethylene glycol			Y	Y 3	Y			C
Glycerine			Y	Y	Y			Y
Aldehydes	Y	Y	Y	C	C	N	N	N
Acetaldehyde			Y	C	C			N
Benzaldehyde			Y	N	C			N
Formaldehyde (40%)			Y	Y	Y			Y
Propionaldehyde			Y	6				

APPENDIX II (*continued*)

	Quartz	Boro-silicate	PFC	PE	PP	PVC	PS	PC
Ketones	Y	Y	Y	C	N	N	N	N
Acetone			Y	C 5	N		N	N
Acetophenone			Y	C	N			N
Cyclohexanone			Y	N	N			N
Methyl ethyl ketone			Y	N 6	N			N
Amines	Y	Y	Y	C	C	N	C	N
Aniline			Y	C 5	N			
Dimethylaniline			Y	6				
Pyridine			Y	6				
Nitrates			Y					
2-Nitro-1-butanol			Y	3				
Nitroethane			Y	5				
Nitrobenzene			Y	N 5	N			N
Aliphatic hydrocarbons	Y	Y	Y	C	C	C	N	N
Cyclohexane			Y					
Heptane			Y					
Hexane			Y 4	6				
Styrene			Y	7				
Aromatic hydrocarbons	Y	Y	Y	C	C	N	N	N
Benzene			Y 4	N 7	N			N
Xylene			Y	N 7	N			N
Toluene			Y	C 7	C			N
Halogenated hydrocarbons	Y	Y	Y	N	N	N	N	N
Amyl chloride			Y	N	N			
Benzoyl chloride			Y		N			
Acetyl chloride			Y	6	N			
Carbon tetrachloride			Y 4	N 7	N			N
Chloroform			Y	N	N			N
Chlorobenzene			Y	N 6	N			N
Ethylene chloride			Y	N 6	N			N
Ethylene chlorohydrin			Y	N 4	N			N
Methylene chloride			Y	N	N			N
Trichloroethylene			Y	N	N			N
Dioxane			Y	N 6				
Dimethyl sulfoxide	Y	Y	Y	Y	Y	N	N	N
Water	Y	Y	Y 4	Y 5	Y	Y 5	Y 5	Y 5
Hydrogen peroxide (30%)	Y	Y	Y	C	C			Y
Inorganic acids								
Aqua regia	C	C	Y		N			N
Hydrochloric (36%)	C	C	Y	Y	C			N
Hydrochloric (10%)	Y	C	Y	Y	Y			Y
Hydrofluoric (10%)	N	N	Y	Y	Y			C

APPENDIX II (*continued*)

	Quartz	Boro-silicate	PFC	PE	PP	PVC	PS	PC
Hydrofluoric (50%)	N	N	Y	Y	Y			N
Nitric (69%)	C	C	Y	N	N			
Nitric (10%)	Y	C	Y	C	Y			
Sulfuric conc.			Y	N	Y			
Sulfuric (10%)	Y	C	Y	Y	Y			
Chromic (30%)	C	C	Y	C	C			
Sulfurous				C	Y			
Phosphoric conc.	N	N		C	N			
Phosphoric (10%)	C	C		Y	Y			
Perchloric (70%)			Y	Y	Y			
Chlorosulfonic				N	N			
Hydroxides								
Ammonium hydroxide	C	N	Y	Y	Y			
Sodium hydroxide	N	N	Y	C	N			
Neutral salts	Y	Y	Y	Y	Y	Y	Y	Y
Acid salts	Y	Y						
Basic salts	C	C						
Bromine	Y	Y	Y					
Chlorine	Y	Y	Y	N	C			
Oxygen			5	4	4	4	4	4
Nitrogen			4	4	4	4	4	4
Carbon dioxide			5	5	5	5	5	5
Hydrogen			4	4	4	3		4
Fluorine	N	N	C					

[a] PFC = polyfluorocarbons;   PE = polyethylene;   PP = polypropylene;   PVC = polyvinyl chloride; PS = polystyrene; PC = polycarbonate.

[b] Transparency: P = transparent; L = translucent.

[c] Heat resistance in °C: L = linear; C = conventional.

[d] Autoclaveability: Y = yes; N = no.

[e] Chemical resistance: Y = Resistant to container at room temperature for a year; C = Caution, only for exposure of less than 24 hours; N = Not recommended.

[f] Permeability: In g/24 hr/100 in.²/mil at room temperature and atmospheric pressure. The numbers which follow the chemical resistance letters indicate the following: (1) None or negligible; (2) Less than 0.01; (3) 0.01 to 0.1; (4) 0.1 to 1.0; (5) 1.0 to 10.0; (6) 10 to 100; (7) >100.

Glasses are slightly permeable to some gases, especially at high temperature. Although quartz appears to be most permeable, ony helium diffuses somewhat readily (8). No indication of permeability to hydrogen or oxygen was found at atmospheric pressures in the case of borosilicate or quartz, but diffusion was found below atmospheric pressures (29).

E. Cleaning of Containers

Since absorbed chromium on container surfaces, especially glass, cannot be readily removed, the use of chromic acid cleaning solutions is not always recommended (24, 26). The use of acid cleaning, however, is often quite useful. Thiers (3) recommends a one-to-one mixture of concentrated sulfuric acid and nitric acid, and he presents useful techniques in the use of this mixture. Stronger leaching agents for glass containers, such as dilute solutions of HF and ammonia, may sometimes be necessary. Hot hydrochloric acid has also been used (30). Glassware has been rinsed consecutively with 0.5 M HCl, alkaline 0.01 M EDTA, and deionized water (31, 32). The amount of contamination on containers may often be lowered by subjecting the container to a prolonged steaming process. The use of EDTA for cleaning plastic materials may lead to difficulty. We have observed that ashed polyethylene shows an excessive sodium content in spite of thorough rinsing with water. Concentrated acid mixtures may be used for brief cleaning of polyethylene; ethanol is also considered effective (3). Treating polyethylene with hot water, dilute acid, or aqueous or alcoholic alkali solution may remove, to a large extent, metal alkyls and Ziegler catalyst that may have been used in the polymerization process of polyethylene and polypropylene (7).

Finally, the modern concern for contamination by particulate matter should be noted. Soft plastics, such as polyethylene, are readily abraded during cleaning so that scrubbing or brushing is apt to introduce particulate contamination. The removal of particulate matter is often approached with the use of ultrasonic baths containing various possible cleansing agents, and with the use of high velocity rinse streams that are made up of carefully filtered solvents.

REFERENCES

1. W. G. Pfann, Zone Melting, 2nd ed., Wiley, New York, 1966, p. 107.
2. D. E. Robertson, Anal. Chem., 40, 1067 (1968).
3. R. E. Thiers, Methods of Biochemical Analysis, Vol. 5, Wiley (Interscience), New York, 1957.
4. H. J. M. Bowen and D. Gibbons, Radioactivation Analysis, Clarendon Press, Oxford, 1963.
5. H. Sorantin and P. Patek, Z. Anal. Chem., 211, 99 (1965).
6. J. Boar, Jr., J. Polymer Sci. C, Polymer Symposia, No. 1, 237 (1963).
7. R. A. V. Raff and J. B. Allison, Polyethylene High Polymers, Vol. II, Wiley (Interscience), New York, 1956.
8. G. W. Morey, The Properties of Glass, Reinhold, New York, 1938.
9. F. Mylius and A. Meusser, Z. Anorg. Chem., 44, 221 (1905).
10. F. C. Raggon and F. R. Bacon, Bull. Am. Ceram. Soc., 33, 267 (1954).

11. E. B. Shand, *Glass Engineering Handbook,* Corning Glass Works, Corning, N. Y., 1955.
12. R. D. Smith and P. E. Corbin, *J. Am. Ceram. Soc.,* 32, 196 (1949).
13. W. A. Weyl and E C. Marhol, *The Constitution of Glass,* Vol. 2, Pt. 2, Wiley (Interscience), New York, 1967.
14. E. Wickers, A. N. Tinn, and W. S. Clabaugh, Natl. Bur. Stds. Research Paper, *R.P. 1394,* (1941).
15. W. F. Christopher and D W. Fox, *Polycarbonates,* Reinhold, New York, 1962.
16. *Modern Plastics Encyclopedia,* Hildreth Press, Bristol, Conn., 1968.
17. C. E. Schildknecht, *Vinyl and Related Polymers,* Wiley, New York, 1952.
18. M. M. Renfrew and E. E. Lewis, *Ind. Eng. Chem.,* 38, 870 (1946).
19. H. M. Hershenson and L. B. Rogers, *Anal. Chem.,* 24, 219 (1952).
20. I. C. Schoonover, *J. Res. Natl. Bur. Stds.,* 15, 377 (1935).
21. I. E. Starik, "Principles of Radiochemistry," *A.E.C.-tr-6314,* 1959.
22. F. B. Butler and W. H. Johnston, *Science,* 120, 543 (1954).
23. G. G. Eichholz, A. E. Nagel, and R. B. Hughes, *Anal. Chem.,* 37, 863 (1965).
24. R. J. Henry and E. C. Smith, *Science,* 104, 426 (1946).
25. J. W. Hensley, *J. Am. Ceram. Soc.,* 34, 188 (1951).
26. E. P. Lang, *Ind. Eng. Chem, Anal. Ed.,* 6, 111 (1934).
27. E. C. Marhol and W. A. Weyl, *J. Am. Ceram. Soc.,* 30, 320 (1947).
28. Dupont Company Publication, *Teflon, Tetrafluoroethylene Resin,* E. I. Dupont Co., Wilmington, Del.
29. E. C. Mayer, *Phys. Rev.,* 6, 283 (1915).
30. G. Brandshaw and J. Rands, *Analyst,* 85, 76 (1960).
31. E. Häberli, *Z. Anal. Chem.,* 160, 15 (1958).
32. D. W. Margerum and R. K. Steinhaus, *Anal. Chem.,* 37, 222 (1965).

AUTHOR INDEX

Numbers in parentheses are reference numbers and indicate that an author's work is referred to although his name is not cited in the text. Numbers in italics show the page on which the complete reference is listed.

SUBJECT INDEX

A

Acetylacetonato metal chelates, zone melting, 183–188
Alkaline iodides, purification, 177–181
    analytical methods, 179–180
    apparatus, 177–178
    procedure, 179
Aluminum purification, 139–145
    controls, 143–144
    flow diagram, 140
    operation, 144
    production data, 141
    safety, 144–145
    thermal design, 140–143
Amines, aromatic, purification, 121–124
Analysis of ultrapure materials, 1–9
Aniline purification, 123
Anthracene, large-crystal purification and growth, 157–168
    crystal growth, 162
    procedure, 158–162
    purification step, 158–160
    sublimation, 160–161
    zone refining, 161–162
Anthracene-phenanthrene phase diagram, by DTA and DSC, 98
Atomic-absorption spectroscopy, 39–46
    analytical parameter for quantitative analysis, 43–45
    analytical potential, 40
    analytical procedures, 45–46
    calibration curves, 43–44
    compared to emission spectrography, 39–40
    detector, 41–42
    determination of, elements, 46
    equipment, 40–42
    flame composition, 44–45
    flame position, 45
    interferences, 44, 45
    modulation, 42
    monochromator, 41
    optical slit system, 42
    radiation source, 41
    solvent, 45
    spectrometer diagram, 41
Azobenzene, rapid purification, 206, 207

B

Benzene, cyclohexane reduction in, 107–119
Benzoic acid, continuous zone refining, 261–268
    analysis and results, 266–267
    apparatus, 262–265
    computed boundary conditions and dimensions, 265–266
    materials, 262
    purification of kilogram quantities, 195–199
    purity determination by DTA, 87–88
Benzoic acid–naphthalene phase diagram, by DTA and DSC, 95
Benzophenone, purity determination by DTA, 87
Benzoylacetone metal chelates, zone melting, 183–188
Biphenyl, rapid purification, 206, 207
Boiling point determination by DTA, 93

C

Centrifugal field, naphthalene purification in, 269–284
Cesium iodide, purification, 177–181
Chelates of metals, see Metal chelates
Chromatography, zone-melting type, see Zone-melting chromatography
Columns for gas-liquid chromatography, 63–66
Containers for pure substances, 297–306
    container materials, 297–304
    cleaning, 305
    properties, 297–304
Continuous zone refining of benzoic acid, 261–268